INTRODUCTION
TO
NUMBER
THEORY

James E. Shockley
Virginia Polytechnic Institute

HOLT, RINEHART AND WINSTON, INC.
New York · Chicago · San Francisco · Toronto · London

Dedicated to my friend and teacher
Alfred T. Brauer

Library of Congress Catalog Card Number: 67-10267
ISBN 0-03-059760-9
Printed in the United States of America

56   038   987654

PREFACE

Two principles have guided me during the writing of this book: (1) It should be written for mathematics majors at the Sophomore-Junior level; (2) it should still be adaptable enough for courses at different levels. It contains more expository material than the usual text; and the proofs of the theorems are presented in a gradual style, rather than being condensed to a set of terse statements.

In order to make the book suitable for various courses, I have tried to include most of the number theory topics that are of interest to either undergraduate mathematics majors or to high school teachers of mathematics. Because some instructors require a course in modern algebra as a prerequisite to the number theory course, several topics (including all of Chapter 7) are included that can be best appreciated by students with that background. Without exception these topics may be omitted with no loss of continuity.

In Chapter 7 algebraic concepts are used in the treatment of arithmetic functions. This approach has several advantages over the usual method of presentation, not the least being that all mystery is removed from the role played by the Möbius function in the inversion of certain sums. Although no technical results from modern algebra are used in the presentation, it probably would be best to omit this chapter unless the students have successfully completed a course in that subject.

Of necessity Chapter 8 (on the distribution of prime numbers) is mainly expository. A few of the very elementary results are proved while, in Section 8.4, a number of the more advanced results are stated without proof.

Most of the sections contain sets of exercises or problems. Many of the exercises are of a computational nature and are designed to illuminate the developed theory. Most of the problems, on the other hand, require some degree of originality on the part of the student and many of them are suitable for class discussion. With a few exceptions the text is independent of the exercises and problems.

A star in the title of a section indicates that it is optional. Several of these sections are expository, containing historical information or statements of additional results, and should be assigned to be read. Others contain either special techniques or technical results.

For a three-hour course at the Sophomore-Junior level my personal choice would be Chapters 1, 2, 3, 4, 6, 8, 9, 10, 11 (not necessarily in that order). For a class composed of prospective high school teachers, I prefer Chapters 1, 2, 3, 4, 5, 6, 8, 11, including the appendices to Chapters 1, 3, and 4.

James E. Shockley

BLACKSBURG, VIRGINIA
JANUARY 1967

CONTENTS

* *Optional*

LOGICAL INTERDEPENDENCE OF CHAPTERS

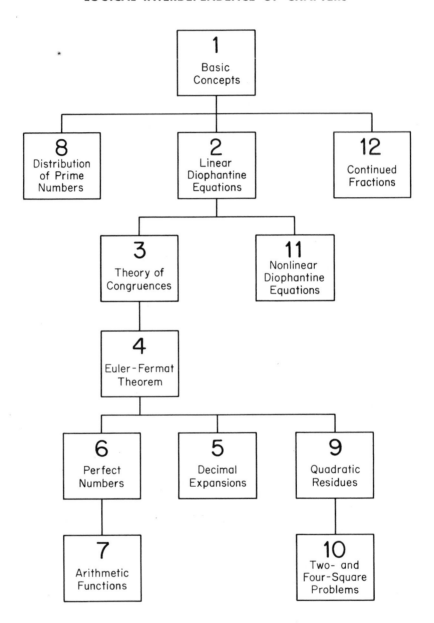

BASIC CONCEPTS / 1

1.1 / INTRODUCTION

In the elementary branches of the theory of numbers we are concerned with the study of the integers—the numbers $\{\cdots, -2, -1, 0, 1, 2, \cdots\}$—and with the problem of obtaining integral solutions to equations.

This study is ancient, having, to some extent, arisen out of the pseudo-science of numerology. For example, the followers of Pythogaras (sixth century B.C.) classified the positive integers according to both arithmetical and magical properties and discovered a number of important relationships. By the time of Euclid (third century B.C.) a fairly extensive body of knowledge had been compiled, much of which was later lost to the western world. The Hindus in the fifth to eighth centuries A.D. made important advances in the theory, in some ways showing greater sophistication than their predecessors.

The modern revival of the study began in the seventeenth century and is due primarily to the great French mathematician Pierre Fermat (1601–1665). Fermat, a lawyer who considered mathematics his avocation, had great insight into the properties of numbers. Although he did not publish his results, his correspondence with other mathematicians stimulated much research in this realm. His work was continued by two of the greatest mathematicians of all times, Leonhard Euler (1707–1783) and Carl F. Gauss (1777–1855), and by many other famous mathematicians. To these men we owe most of the theory that will be developed in this book.

There are a few prerequisites to the study. In addition to the arithmetic properties of the number system, the reader should be familiar with the order properties of the integers (the "greater-than" and "less-than" relations) and with the absolute value function. In a few places in the text, a knowledge of elementary analytic geometry is presupposed; and in Chapters 5 and 12, the basic limit theorems from calculus are used.

1.2 / THE PRINCIPLES OF WELL-ORDERING AND MATHEMATICAL INDUCTION

The most important subset of the integers is the set of *positive integers* (*natural numbers, counting numbers*): the numbers $\{1, 2, 3, \cdots\}$. In this section we discuss two important properties of these numbers: The *well-ordering principle* and the *principle of mathematical induction*. Either of these can be proved as a theorem if the other is assumed. (They are said to be equivalent because of this.) The well-ordering principle is the simplest of the two and, in this book, will be used more often than the principle of mathematical induction.

■ WELL-ORDERING PRINCIPLE / *Any nonvoid set of positive integers has a smallest member.*

Using the well-ordering principle it is easy to prove a similar well-ordering principle for nonnegative integers. Hereafter, we will use either of these.

Example I.

Prove a well-ordering principle for nonnegative integers.

SOLUTION: Let S be a nonvoid set of nonnegative integers. We must prove that S has a smallest member. Two cases arise. If the number zero is in S, then it is less than any positive member of S and is thus the smallest member. If zero is not in S, then S consists entirely of positive integers and, from the well-ordering principle, it follows that S has a smallest member. In either case, we have shown that S has a smallest member.

■ PRINCIPLE OF MATHEMATICAL INDUCTION / *If P is a set of positive integers that has the following two properties, then P is the set of all positive integers:*
Property I. 1 is in P.
Property II. If the integer k is in P, the integer $(k + 1)$ must also be in P.

Many readers will have seen the following modified form of the principle of mathematical induction:
A proposition about positive integers that has the following two properties is true for all positive integers:
Property I'. The proposition is true for the integer 1.

Property II′. If the proposition is true for the integer k, it must also be true for the integer (k + 1).

The fact that the two forms are equivalent should be obvious after reflection on the part of the reader.

Example 2.

Prove that 1 is the smallest positive integer.

SOLUTION I: (Based on Principle of Mathematical Induction.) Let S be the set of all positive integers greater than or equal to 1. It is trivial that 1 is in S. If the integer k is in S, $k \geq 1$. Therefore,

$$k + 1 > k \geq 1$$

and so the integer $k + 1$ is in S. It follows from the principle of mathematical induction that S is the set of all positive integers. Therefore, each positive integer is greater than or equal to 1.

SOLUTION II: (Based on Well-Ordering Principle.) It follows from the well-ordering principle that there is a smallest positive integer, which we call s. Assume that $s < 1$. We multiply the inequality

$$0 < s < 1$$

by s, obtaining

$$0 < s^2 < s$$

which implies that s is not the smallest positive integer. Because our assumption led to a contradiction, it is false. Therefore, 1 is the smallest positive integer.

Example 3.

Prove the formula for the sum of the first n terms in an arithmetic progression:

$$a + (a + d) + (a + 2d) + \cdots + [a + (n - 1)d] = na + \frac{n(n - 1)}{2} d$$

SOLUTION: The formula is obviously correct for the special case $n = 1$, because the left- and right-hand sides of the equation are equal to a. Assume the formula holds for the positive integer k; that is, assume

$$a + (a + d) + (a + 2d) + \cdots + [a + (k - 1)d] = ka + \frac{k(k - 1)}{2} d \qquad (1.1)$$

By adding $a + kd$ to both sides of (1.1), we obtain

$$a + (a + d) + \cdots + [a + (k - 1)d] + (a + kd)$$

$$= ka + \frac{k(k - 1)}{2} d + (a + kd) = (k + 1) a + \frac{(k + 1)k}{2} \cdot d$$

Thus, if the formula holds for the integer k, it must also hold for the integer $k + 1$. It follows from the principle of mathematical induction that the formula holds for each positive integer n.

Example 4.

Let a and n be positive integers. Prove that a positive integer m exists such that $am > n$.

SOLUTION: The proposition is obviously true when $n = 1$, for $2a > 1$.
Suppose the proposition is true for the case $n = k$; that is, an integer m_k exists such that $am_k > k$. Then

$$a(m_k + 1) = am_k + a > k + a \geq k + 1$$

so that the proposition is also true for the case $n = k + 1$. It follows from the principle of mathematical induction that the proposition is true for each positive integer n.

EXERCISES

1. Prove the formula for the sum of the first n terms in a geometric progression:

$$a + ar + ar^2 + \cdots + ar^{n-1} = \frac{a(r^n - 1)}{r - 1} \quad (r \neq 1)$$

2. Prove that if n is a positive integer, then

$$1^3 + 2^3 + \cdots + n^3 = (1 + 2 + \cdots + n)^2$$

The following problem was devised by E. Lucas, a prominent nineteenth-century French mathematician:

3. In a temple in India stand three upright posts. At the beginning of time (for our purposes we shall assumed this was 10,000 B.C.), 64 concentric disks were placed on one of the posts; the largest disk at the bottom, the next largest resting on it, and so on. Priests have been engaged in shifting the disks to other posts, subject to the following laws:
1. Only one disk may be moved at a time.
2. A disk may never be placed over a smaller disk.
When all 64 disks have been moved to one of the other posts the world will come to an end.
Assume that the priests have been working in shifts, moving 1 disk per second for 24 hours a day, and have never made a mistake. How much

longer will the world exist? [*Hint:* Use mathematical induction to obtain a formula for the minimum number of moves needed to shift the first m disks to one of the other posts.]

PROBLEMS

1. Use the well-ordering principle to prove that a nonvoid bounded set of integers must contain a largest element. [*Hint:* Suppose that each element in the set is less than n. Consider the set of all numbers of form $n - s$, where s is in the original set.]

2. Let n be a positive integer and let k be an integer in the range $0 \leq k \leq n$. Define the binomial coefficient $\binom{n}{k}$ by

$$\binom{n}{k} = \frac{n!}{k!(n-k)!}$$

Prove that $\binom{n}{k}$ is always an integer. [*Hint:* Prove first that if $0 \leq k < n$, then

$$\binom{n}{k} + \binom{n}{k+1} = \binom{n+1}{k+1}]$$

3. *The Binomial Theorem.* Let α and β be numbers. Let n be a positive integer. Prove by mathematical induction that

$$(\alpha + \beta)^n = \binom{n}{0}\alpha^n + \binom{n}{1}\alpha^{n-1}\beta + \cdots + \binom{n}{k}\alpha^{n-k}\beta^k + \cdots + \binom{n}{n}\beta^n$$

1.3* / EQUIVALENCE OF THE PRINCIPLES OF MATHEMATICAL INDUCTION AND WELL-ORDERING

In this section, we will establish that either the principle of mathematical induction or the well-ordering principle can be proved as a theorem, given the other principle and the arithmetic properties of the integers.

The following result is needed in the proof of the theorem. The proof is left as an exercise.

■ **LEMMA** / If k is an integer, there is no integer between k and $k + 1$ (exclusive).

■ **THEOREM 1** / The principles of mathematical induction and well-ordering are equivalent.

PROOF: (Part I) Assume that the well-ordering principle holds for the positive integers. Let S be a set of positive integers with the properties:

(1) 1 is in S.

(2) If k is in S, $k + 1$ is also in S.

We must prove that S is the set of all positive integers.

Let T be the set of all positive integers not in S. If T is nonvoid, it follows from the well-ordering principle that T has a smallest member, t. Since 1 is in S and 1 is the smallest positive integer (established in Solution II of Example 2, Section 1.2, using the well-ordering principle), then $t > 1$. Therefore, $t - 1$ is a positive integer that must be in S since $t - 1 < t$. The second property of S insures that t, equal to $(t - 1) + 1$, is also in S—a contradiction. Because our assumption that T is nonvoid leads to a contradiction, it is false. Therefore, T is void and S is the set of all positive integers.

(Part II) Assume that the principle of mathematical induction holds for the positive integers. Assume also that there exists a nonvoid set of positive integers, S, that does not have a smallest member. Because 1 is the smallest positive integer (established in Solution I of Example 2, Section 1.2, using the principle of mathematical induction), then 1 is not in S and is smaller than all of the elements of S.

Let T be the set of all positive integers that are less than all of the elements of S. We have established that 1 is in T. Suppose the integer k is in T. If $k + 1$ is in S, then, because there is no integer between k and $k + 1$ (by the lemma), $k + 1$ is the smallest element of S—a contradiction to our assumption about S. Therefore, if k is in T, $k + 1$ must also be in T. It follows from the principle of mathematical induction that T contains all the positive integers and, consequently, S is void. This is a contradiction to our original assumption that S is nonvoid. Therefore, if S is a nonvoid set of positive integers, then S has a smallest element.

There is a variation on the principle of mathematical induction that, in some cases, is easier to apply: the *second principle of mathematical induction.*

■ SECOND PRINCIPLE OF MATHEMATICAL INDUCTION / *If S is a set of positive integers that has the following two properties, then S is the set of all positive integers:*
Property I. 1 is in S.
Property II. If all the positive integers less than k are in S, k must also be in S.

The proof that the second principle of mathematical induction is equivalent to the principle of mathematical induction and to the well-ordering principle is left for the reader (Problem 1).

EXERCISE

1. Prove the lemma. [*Hint:* Assume there is an integer n such that $k < n < k + 1$, and consider the integer $n - k$.]

PROBLEM

1. Prove that the second principle of mathematical induction is equivalent to both the principle of mathematical induction and the well-ordering principle.

1.4 / DIVISIBILITY OF INTEGERS

■ DEFINITION / Let a and b be integers. If an integer m exists such that $b = ma$, we say that a *divides* b and that b *is a multiple of* a. We denote this fact by writing "$a|b$."

For example, $2|4$, $7|21$, $0|0$, $3|0$.

The symbol $a|b$ should not be confused with the rational number a/b.

Some of the basic properties of the divisibility relationship are established in the next theorem.

■ THEOREM 2 / (*a*) If $a|b$ and $b|c$, then $a|c$,

(*b*) If $a|b$ and $a|c$ and if m and n are integers, then $a|(mb + nc)$,

(*c*) If $a|b$ and $b \neq 0$, then $0 < |a| \leq |b|$,

(*d*) If $a|b$ and $b|a$, then $a = \pm b$.

PROOF: (*a*) If $a|b$ and $b|c$, there exist integers m and n such that $b = ma$, $c = nb$. Substituting, we obtain

$$c = nma$$

Since nm is an integer, this means that $a|c$.

(*b*) If $a|b$ and $a|c$, there exist integers x and y such that $b = ax$, $c = ay$. Thus,

$$mb + nc = max + nay = a(mx + ny)$$

Since $mx + ny$ is an integer, $a|(mb + nc)$.

(*c*) If $a|b$, there exists an integer m such that $b = ma$. Since $b \neq 0$, neither a nor m is zero, so that $1 \leq |a|$ and $1 \leq |m|$. Therefore,

$$|b| = |am| = |a| \cdot |m| \geq |a| \cdot 1 > 0$$

(*d*) Suppose that $a|b$ and $b|a$. If $b = 0$, then obviously $a = 0$ and so $a = \pm b$. If $b \neq 0$, it follows from (*c*) that $|a| = |b|$, which is only possible if $a = \pm b$.

THE DIVISION ALGORITHM

The next theorem asserts that "long division is possible." This is a fundamental result and will be used many times in the remainder of this book.

■ **THEOREM** 3 / (The Division Algorithm.) Let a and b be integers, $b \neq 0$. There exist unique integers q and r, $0 \leq r < |b|$ such that

$$a = bq + r$$

(The numbers q and r are called the *quotient* and *remainder* when a is divided by b.)

PROOF: Let S be the set of all integers of form $a + kb$ where k ranges over the integers, that is,

$$S = \{\cdots, a - 2b, a - b, a, a + b, a + 2b, \cdots\}$$

Observe that the integer

$$a + (|a| + 1)|b|$$

is nonnegative and is in S. It follows from the well-ordering principle for nonnegative integers that S contains a smallest nonnegative integer r. Then $r - a$ is a multiple of b; therefore, we may write

$$a = bq + r$$

If $r \geq |b|$, the integer $r - |b|$ is a nonnegative element of S, smaller than r, which is impossible. Therefore,

$$0 \leq r < |b|$$

To show that q and r are unique, suppose we can also write

$$a = bq_1 + r_1 \qquad 0 \leq r_1 < |b|$$

where q_1 and r_1 are integers. Then

$$b(q_1 - q) = r - r_1$$

so that $$b|(r - r_1)$$

It follows from Theorem 2(*c*) that if $r \neq r_1$, then $|r - r_1| \geq |b|$. But this is impossible, because

$$-b < r - r_1 < b$$

Therefore, $r = r_1$. Since $b(q_1 - q) = r - r_1 = 0$ and $b \neq 0$, then $q_1 - q = 0$. Therefore, $q = q_1$.

The division algorithm is frequently used in classifying the integers. For example, if $a = 2q + 1$, we say that a is *odd*, and if $a = 2q + 0$ that a is *even*. Similar classifications may be made with respect to division by 3, 4, and so on.

EXERCISES

1. Discuss the expression "$a|b$" when a and/or b is zero.

2. Write a in the form $a = bq + r$, $0 \leq r < |b|$:
   (a) $a = -17$, $b = 5$;
   (b) $a = -39$, $b = -8$.

3. Prove that the integer $a + (|a| + 1)|b|$, mentioned in the proof of Theorem 2, is in the set S and is nonnegative.

4. Prove that:
   (a) The sum of two even integers is even.
   (b) The sum of two odd integers is even.
   (c) The product of two even integers is even.
   (d) The product of two odd integers is odd.

5. Show that an odd integer is of form $4n + 1$ or $4n + 3$.

6. If a is an odd integer, prove that a^2 leaves a remainder of 1 when divided by 8.

1.5 / THE GREATEST COMMON DIVISOR

It is obvious that if a and b are not both zero, there is a largest positive integer that divides both a and b. (See also Problem 1.)

■ DEFINITION / Let a and b be integers, not both equal to zero. The largest positive integer that divides both a and b is called the *greatest common divisor* (g. c. d.) of a and b. This number is denoted by the symbol (a, b).

For example, $(3, 9) = 3$, $(-7, 21) = 7$, $(0, -5) = 5$.

In a similar way we define the greatest common divisor of a finite set of integers $a_1, a_2, \cdots, a_n$ (not all zero) to be the largest positive integer that divides all of the numbers. This number is denoted by the symbol $(a_1, a_2, \cdots, a_n)$.

■ DEFINITION / Two integers are said to be *relatively prime* if their greatest common divisor is 1.

A number of the properties of the greatest common divisor can be established directly from the definition. Our work will be expedited, however, if we first prove a fundamental characterization of the greatest common divisor.

■ THEOREM 4 / The greatest common divisor of $a_1, a_2, \cdots, a_n$ is the smallest positive integer that can be written as a sum of multiples of $a_1, a_2, \cdots, a_n$.

PROOF: Because at least one of the given integers, say a_j, must be nonzero (in order to have the greatest common divisor defined), then obviously at least one positive integer can be written as a sum of multiples of $a_1, a_2, \cdots, a_n$; namely,

$$|a_j| = 0 \cdot a_1 + \cdots + (\pm 1)a_j + \cdots + 0 \cdot a_n$$

It follows from the well-ordering principle that a smallest such positive integer exists, which we will call s. We will prove that

$$s = (a_1, a_2, \cdots, a_n)$$

Since s is a sum of multiples of $a_1, a_2, \cdots, a_n$ we can write

$$s = m_1a_1 + m_2a_2 + \cdots m_na_n \tag{1.2}$$

If we divide a_1 by s, obtaining

$$a_1 = sq + r \qquad 0 \le r < s$$

and substitute into Equation (1.2), we obtain

$$r = a_1 - sq = a_1(1 - m_1q) + a_2(-m_2q) + \cdots + a_m(-m_nq)$$

so that the nonnegative integer r is also a sum of multiples of $a_1, a_2, \cdots, a_n$. Because $r < s$, this implies that $r = 0$. Therefore, $s|a_1$. In a similar way, it follows that s is a common divisor of $a_1, a_2, \cdots, a_n$.

Suppose now that $d = (a_1, a_2, \cdots, a_n)$. Since s is a common divisor, then s is not greater than d, the greatest common divisor. On the other hand, because d divides each a_j, it follows from Equation (1.2) that $d|s$, so that [by Theorem 2(c)] $d \le s$. Therefore,

$$s = d = (a_1, a_2, \cdots, a_n)$$

The following corollary states a basic property of the greatest common divisor.

■ COROLLARY 4.1 / If d is a common divisor of $a_1, a_2, \cdots, a_n$, then d divides $(a_1, a_2, \cdots, a_n)$.

PROOF: If d divides $a_1, a_2, \cdots, a_n$, then d divides any sum of multiples of $a_1, a_2, \cdots, a_n$; in particular, d divides the greatest common divisor of these numbers.

We will next show that the greatest common divisor of a set of integers can be found by a series of steps, each involving the greatest common divisor of two integers.

■ COROLLARY 4.2 / If $a_1, a_2, \cdots, a_n$ are nonzero integers, then

$$(a_1, a_2, \cdots, a_n) = ((a_1, a_2, \cdots, a_{n-1}), a_n).$$

PROOF: Let $d = (a_1, a_2, \cdots, a_n)$. Then d divides each a_i ($i = 1, 2, \cdots, n - 1$); therefore by Corollary 4.1, $d | (a_1, \cdots, a_{n-1})$. Since d also divides a_n, we may apply Corollary 4.1 again; we find that

$$d | ((a_1, \cdots, a_{n-1}), a_n)$$

On the other hand, the integer $((a_1, \cdots, a_{n-1}), a_n)$ is a common divisor of $(a_1, \cdots, a_{n-1})$ and a_n, implying that it divides $a_1, a_2, \cdots, a_n$. Therefore, by Corollary 4.1,

$$((a_1, \cdots, a_{n-1}), a_n) | d$$

Because $((a_1, \cdots, a_{n-1}), a_n)$ and d are positive, it follows from Theorem 2(d) that

$$d = (a_1, a_2, \cdots, a_n) = ((a_1, \cdots, a_{n-1}), a_n)$$

In Section 1.7 we will devise a method to calculate the greatest common divisor of two integers. Assuming that this can be done, we work the following example:

Example.

Calculate (1029, 1911, 9177).

SOLUTION: Because $(1029, 1911) = 91$,

$$(1029, 1911, 9177) = ((1029, 1911), 9177) = (91, 9177) = 7$$

■ COROLLARY 4.3 / If $d = (a, b)$, the integers a/d and b/d are relatively prime.

PROOF: It is obvious that a/d and b/d are integers. From Theorem 4 it follows that

$$d = ma + nb$$

where m and n are integers. Therefore,

$$1 = ma/d + nb/d$$

so that 1 is obviously the smallest positive sum of multiples of a/d and b/d. Therefore, by Theorem 4, a/d and b/d are relatively prime.

■ **COROLLARY 4.4** / Let a and b be relatively prime integers. If $a|bc$, then $a|c$.

PROOF: Since a and b are relatively prime, we may write

$$1 = ma + nb$$

Because $a|bc$, there is an integer k such that $bc = ak$. If we multiply the above equation by c, we obtain

$$c = mac + nbc = mac + nak = a(mc + nk)$$

so that $a|c$.

This result can be extended to more than two factors. The proof is left for the reader.

■ **COROLLARY 4.5** / If $a|b_1 b_2 \cdots b_n$, and a is relatively prime to b_j ($j = 1, 2, \cdots, n - 1$), then $a|b_n$.

In Section 1.7, we will need the following corollary:

■ **COROLLARY 4.6** / If $a = bq + r$ and $b \neq 0$, then $(a, b) = (b, r)$.

PROOF: Obviously, any sum of multiples of a and b can also be written as a sum of multiples of b and r, and conversely. Thus, it follows from Theorem 4 that the greatest common divisor of a and b is equal to the greatest common divisor of b and r.

EXERCISES

1. Use Corollary 4.2 to calculate $(381, -216, 48, 918)$.

2. Discuss the symbol "(a, b)" if a and/or b is zero.

3. Prove that two consecutive integers are relatively prime.

4. Prove that if $(a, b) = 1$, then $(a - b, a + b) = 1$ or 2. [*Hint:* Use Theorem 2(*b*).]

PROBLEMS

1. Use Problem 1 of Section 1.2 and Theorem 2(*c*) to prove that if $a_1, a_2, \cdots, a_n$ are not all zero, there is a largest positive integer that divides these integers.

2. *Prove:* If a, b, and m are nonzero integers, $m > 0$, then

$$(ma, mb) = m(a, b)$$

3. Use Theorem 4 to prove: If $(a, b) = (a, c) = 1$, then

$$(a, bc) = 1$$

4. Prove Corollary 4.2 without using Theorem 4 or Corollary 4.1.

1.6 / THE LEAST COMMON MULTIPLE

It follows from the well-ordering principle that if a and b are nonzero integers, there is a smallest positive integer that is a multiple of both a and b. This integer is called the *least common multiple* (l. c. m.) of a and b and is denoted by the symbol $[a, b]$. The least common multiple of a finite set of nonzero integers is defined similarly.

For example, -60 is a common multiple of -6 and -15, but $[-6, -15] = 30$.

There is a close relationship between the greatest common divisor and the least common multiple of two nonzero integers. Because of this, it is frequently possible to establish properties of one of the quantities if similar properties are known to hold for the other. This relationship is given in Theorem 6. Before proving it we state a needed result. The proof is left for the reader (Problem 1).

■ THEOREM 5 / If m is a common multiple of the nonzero integers a and b, then $[a, b]|m$.

■ THEOREM 6 / If a and b are nonzero integers, then

$$[a, b](a, b) = |ab|$$

PROOF: Let $d = (a, b)$ and $m = [a, b]$. The rational number $|ab|/d$ is obviously an integer. Since

$$\frac{|ab|}{d} = a \cdot \left(\pm \frac{b}{d} \right) = b \cdot \left(\pm \frac{a}{d} \right)$$

then $|ab|/d$ is a positive common multiple of a and b, and is no smaller than the least common multiple. Therefore,

$$\frac{|ab|}{d} \geq m \tag{1.3}$$

On the other hand, because $|ab|$ is a common multiple of a and b, it follows from Theorem 5 that $|ab|/m$ is a positive integer. Since m is a multiple of a, say $m = ka$, then

$$k \cdot \frac{|ab|}{m} = \frac{\pm k \cdot ab}{ka} = \pm b$$

and, therefore,

$$\frac{|ab|}{m} \Big|_b$$

In a similar way we see that $(|ab|/m)|a$. Thus, $|ab|/m$ is a positive common divisor of a and b and is no larger than the greatest common divisor, that is,

$$\frac{|ab|}{m} \leq d$$

Combining this result with inequality (1.3), we obtain

$$|ab| = md = [a, b](a, b)$$

EXERCISES

1. Calculate $[-10, -15, -20, -25]$. [*Hint:* See Problem 3.]

2. If a and b are relatively prime positive integers, prove that

$$[a, b] = ab$$

3. Does the relationship $[a_1, a_2, a_3] (a_1, a_2, a_3) = |a_1 a_2 a_3|$ hold in general?

4. Let a, b, m, and n be positive integers, $(m, n) = 1$. If $a/b = m/n$, prove that a positive integer t exists such that $a = tm$, $b = tn$.

5. Prove that the product of three consecutive integers is divisible by 6.

PROBLEMS

1. Prove Theorem 5. [*Hint:* Divide m by $[a, b]$ obtaining $m = [a, b]q + r$, $0 \leq r < [a, b]$. Show that r is a common multiple of a and b.]

2. Use Theorem 6 and Problem 2 of 1.5 to prove: If m is a positive integer, then $[ma, mb] = m[a, b]$.

3. *Prove:* $[a_1, a_2, \cdots, a_n] = [[a_1, a_2, \cdots, a_{n-1}], a_n]$.

1.7 / THE EUCLIDEAN ALGORITHM

The Greek mathematician Euclid (300 B.C.) is credited with the following method for calculating the greatest common divisor of two integers. Because of this, the method is called the *Euclidean algorithm.*

If the integers a and b are to have a greatest common divisor, one of them, say b, must be nonzero. The first step is to divide a by b, obtaining

$$a = bq + r \qquad 0 \leq r < |b|$$

If $r = 0$ we stop. If $r > 0$, we divide b by r, obtaining

$$b = rq_1 + r_1 \qquad 0 \leq r_1 < r$$

If $r_1 = 0$ we stop. Otherwise, we continue as before, obtaining

$$r = r_1 q_2 + r_2 \qquad 0 \leq r_2 < r_1$$

We now continue this process until we have a zero remainder, obtaining the chain of equations

$$a = bq + r \qquad 0 < r < |b|$$
$$b = rq_1 + r_1 \qquad 0 < r_1 < r$$
$$r = r_1 q_2 + r_2 \qquad 0 < r_2 < r_1$$

$$\cdots$$

$$r_{n-2} = r_{n-1}q_n + r_n \qquad 0 < r_n < r_{n-1}$$
$$r_{n-1} = r_n q_{n+1}$$

It is obvious that we must eventually obtain a zero remainder because the sequence $|b|, r_1, r_2, \cdots$ is a decreasing sequence of positive integers (use of the well-ordering principle) and we are assuming that r_n is the last nonzero remainder. We now apply Corollary 4.6 $n + 2$ times, obtaining

$$(a, b) = (b, r) = (r, r_1) = (r_1, r_2) = \cdots = (r_{n-1}, r_n) = (r_n, 0) = r_n$$

Thus, the greatest common divisor of a and b is equal to the last nonzero remainder obtained by the successive divisions in the Euclidean algorithm.

Example I.

(*a*) Use the Euclidean algorithm to calculate the greatest common divisor of 232 and 136.
(*b*) Calculate the least common multiple of 232 and 136.

SOLUTION: (*a*) $232 = 1 \cdot 136 + 96$

$$136 = 1 \cdot \ 96 + 40$$
$$96 = 2 \cdot \ 40 + 16$$
$$40 = 2 \cdot \ 16 + \ 8$$
$$16 = 2 \cdot \ \ 8 + \ 0$$

Therefore, $(232, 136) =$ the last nonzero remainder $= 8$.
(*b*) Using Theorem 6, we find that

$$[232, 136] = \frac{232 \cdot 136}{(232, 361)} = \frac{31{,}552}{8} = 3944$$

The basic theorem proved about the greatest common divisor is Theorem 4: *The greatest common divisor is the smallest sum of multiples.* We can use the Euclidean algorithm to write the greatest common divisor in this manner. The process is as follows: Solving the next to the last equation for r_n, we can express r_n in terms of r_{n-1} and r_{n-2}. Substituting the value of r_{n-1} from the second equation from the bottom, we can write r_n as in terms of r_{n-2} and r_{n-3}. Continuing this successive substitution we eventually write $r_n = (a, b)$ as a sum of multiples of a and b.

Example 2.

Write $(136, 232)$ as a sum of multiples of 136 and 232.

SOLUTION: From the next to the last line in the chain of equations in Example 1, we obtain
$$8 = 40 - 2 \cdot 16$$

Substituting the value of 16, we obtain
$$8 = 40 - 2(96 - 2 \cdot 40) = 5 \cdot 40 - 2 \cdot 96$$

Continuing the successive substitution,

$$8 = 5(136 - 96) - 2 \cdot 96 = 5 \cdot 136 - 7 \cdot 96$$
$$= 5 \cdot 136 - 7(232 - 136) = 12 \cdot 136 - 7 \cdot 232$$

The work involved in the Euclidean algorithm can frequently be shortened if we make one modification: *Instead of choosing the smallest nonzero remainder at each step, choose the remainder that is smallest in absolute value.* If this is done, the greatest common divisor is equal to the absolute value of the last nonzero remainder.

EXERCISES

1. Use the Euclidean algorithm to calculate (187, 221) and write it as a sum sum of multiples of 187 and 221.

2. (*a*) Use the Euclidean algorithm and Corollary 4.2 to calculate (714, 2030, 2205) and write it as a sum of multiples of 714, 2030, and 2205.
   (*b*) Calculate [714, 2030, 2205].

1.8 / THE UNIQUE FACTORIZATION THEOREM

▪ **DEFINITION** / An integer greater than 1, not divisible by any smaller positive integer except 1, is called a *prime number*. A positive integer greater than 1 which is not a prime number is called a *composite number*.

For example, the first few primes are 2, 3, 5, 7, 11, and 13.

It is obvious that if p is a prime number and a is an integer, then (a, p) is equal to 1 or p.

The theorem proved in this section is the *unique factorization theorem for integers*. This theorem is of such importance that it is frequently called *the fundamental theorem of arithmetic*.

▪ **THEOREM 7** / An integer greater than 1 is either a prime number or is a product of prime numbers. Furthermore, the factorization into primes is unique except for the order of the factors.

PROOF: We will first prove the (intuitively obvious) fact that a composite number can be factored as a product of primes.

Suppose the proposition is false. Then there is a composite number that cannot be written as a product of primes. Let n be the smallest such number.

Since n is composite we can write

$$n = ab \qquad 1 < a < n \qquad 1 < b < n$$

Because a is smaller than n then a is a prime or is a product of primes; a similar statement holds for b. But then $n = ab$ is a product of primes, which is a contradiction. Therefore, each composite number can be factored as a product of prime numbers.

We will now show that the factorization into primes is unique.

Suppose that a composite number exists for which the factorization into primes is not unique. Let

$$m = p_1 p_2 \cdots p_j = q_1 q_2 \cdots q_k$$

by the smallest such number, where $p_1, p_2, \cdots, q_{k-1}, q_k$ are prime numbers. It follows from the remark preceding the statement of the theorem that if $p_1 \neq q_i$, then $(p_1, q_i) = 1$. Thus, if $p_1 \neq q_i$ for $i = 1, 2, \cdots, k - 1$, it follows from Corollary 4.5 that $p_1 = q_k$. In other words, p_1 must be equal to one of the q's. For purposes of notation we will assumed that $p_1 = q_1$. Then

$$\frac{m}{p_1} = p_2 p_3 \cdots p_j = q_2 q_3 \cdots q_k$$

If $k > 2$, then m is not the smallest integer for which the factorization is not unique—a contradiction. If $k = 2$,

$$\frac{m}{p_1} = p_2 p_3 \cdots p_j = q_2$$

which implies that $j = 2$. Thus,

$$\frac{m}{p_1} = p_2 = q_2$$

and the factorization of m is unique, which is also a contradiction. Therefore, the factorization into primes is unique for any positive integer.

It follows from Theorem 7 that a composite integer n can be written in the form

$$n = p_1^{\alpha_1} p_2^{\alpha_2} \cdots p_k^{\alpha_k}$$

where the exponents are nonnegative integers, at least one of them is positive, and the p_i are distinct prime numbers. This factorization is frequently called the *canonical factorization* of n. In order to have a standard notation, we will also write a prime number in the above form, with the understanding that α_1 may be 1 and the other exponents may be zero.

PROBLEM

1. Let E be the set of all even positive integers. An element of E is called "E-prime" if it is not a product of two smaller positive elements of E; for example, the first five E-prime elements are 2, 6, 10, 14, and 18.

(*a*) Prove that an element of E is either E-prime or is a product of E-prime elements.

(*b*) By an example, show that the factorization into a product of E-prime elements is not unique.

1.9 / THE GREATEST INTEGER FUNCTION

In number theory we are frequently interested in the greatest integer that is not greater than a given real number α. This number is usually denoted by the symbol $[\alpha]$. For example, $[5\frac{1}{2}] = 5$, $[-7.3] = -8$, $[\pi] = 3$. The integer $[\alpha]$ is called the *integral part of* α and the difference $\alpha - [\alpha]$ is usually called the *fractional part of* α (even though it may be irrational).

The quantity $[\alpha]$ arises naturally in our study for it enables us to explicitly express the quotient and remainder after division in terms of the original integers. For example, if b is a positive integer and if

$$a = bq + r \qquad 0 \leq r < b$$

then
$$q = \left[\frac{a}{b}\right] \quad \text{and} \quad r = b \cdot \left(\frac{a}{b} - \left[\frac{a}{b}\right]\right)$$

A similar expression holds if b is negative (see Exercise 1).

Some properties of the greatest integer function are established in the next theorem. Other properties are listed in Exercises 4 and 5.

■ THEOREM 8 /

(*a*) If m is an integer, then $[m + \alpha] = m + [\alpha]$.

(*b*) $[\alpha + \beta] - 1 \leq [\alpha] + [\beta] \leq [\alpha + \beta]$.

(*c*) If m is a positive integer, then $[\alpha/m] = [[\alpha]/m]$.

PROOF OF (*b*): Write $\alpha = [\alpha] + \theta$, where $0 \leq \theta < 1$ (θ is the fractional part of α), and $\beta = [\beta] + \varphi$, $0 \leq \varphi < 1$. Substituting and using the result of (*a*), we obtain

$$[\alpha + \beta] = [[\alpha] + [\beta] + \theta + \varphi] = [\alpha] + [\beta] + [\theta + \varphi]$$

Now $0 \le \theta + \varphi < 2$, so that

$$0 \le [\theta + \varphi] \le 1$$

Thus, $$[\alpha + \beta] \ge [\alpha] + [\beta] \ge [\alpha + \beta] - 1$$

The proofs of (*a*) and (*c*) are left for the reader.

EXERCISES

1. Let *b* be a negative integer, and let

$$a = bq + r \qquad 0 \le r < |b|$$

Express *q* and *r* in terms of *a* and *b*.

2. Prove part (*a*) of Theorem 8.

3. Prove part (*c*) of Theorem 8.

4. Prove that the integer closest to the real number α is $[\alpha + \frac{1}{2}]$.

5. Let *m* be a positive integer and let α be a real number. *Prove:*

$$[\alpha] + \left[\alpha + \frac{1}{m}\right] + \left[\alpha + \frac{2}{m}\right] + \cdots + \left[\alpha + \frac{m-1}{m}\right] = [m\alpha]$$

APPENDIX / NUMBER BASES

ORIGIN OF THE HINDU-ARABIC NUMBER SYSTEM

A number of studies have been made of the number systems and the methods of counting used in various parts of the world. Basing our remarks on these studies and on the known history of the system, we can trace, with reasonable accuracy, the development of the Hindu-Arabic notation for assigning symbols to stand for the natural numbers.

Our primitive ancestor probably counted on his fingers. We conjecture that when he counted to five·fingers he said " one hand." When he reached ten fingers (or possibly ten fingers and ten toes) he said "one man." (Thus the use of the word *digit* for both a number symbol and a finger.)

When society developed to the point where more elaborate calculations were needed, one of our ancestors invented the abacus—a computing device that effectively extended the number of fingers at his disposal for counting purposes.

A possible prototype of the primitive abacus is illustrated in Figure 1.1. Recall that our primitive man did not actually need ten fingers in counting if he replaced the number "ten fingers" with its equivalent "one man." In our prototype of the abacus we have a frame of parallel wires, each strung with nine beads. To count the number "one" a bead is pushed to the top of the wire at the extreme right. Beads are pushed to the top of that wire in sequential order until all nine are up, representing the number "nine." To count the number "ten" the nine beads are pushed down and one bead is pushed up on the wire next to the one on the extreme right. To represent "one hundred" a bead is pushed up on the third wire from the right. Thus, the number "three hundred twenty-seven" is represented on the abacus in Figure 1.1.

There are many variations in the form of the abacus. Our prototype in Figure 1.1 is comparatively sophisticated because it has only nine beads on

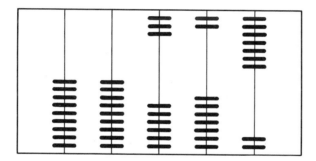

Figure 1.1 Prototype of a primitive abacus.

each wire. A more primitive model would probably have ten beads on each wire although only nine are actually needed. When the abacus was used in a society where the counting was based on "hands" rather than "men," it probably had four (or five) beads on each wire.[1]

The last stage of development is the invention of symbols to represent the numbers. It is natural to base the notation on the abacus. There are two standard ways to do this.

The first method is to assign a symbol to stand for a bead on one of the wires of the abacus, a different symbol for a bead on a different wire, and so on. To represent a number, we repeat the necessary symbols as many times as there are beads pushed up on the corresponding wires. For example, in the Roman number system the symbol XXVIII stands for 2 beads on the

---

[1]The names of the numerals in the French language seem to indicate a system based on the number twenty.

"tens" wire, 1 bead on the "fives" wire, and 3 on the "units" wire; that is, the number 28.[2]

The second method is to assign symbols to represent the number of beads pushed up on a wire and let the *position* of the symbols indicate which wires are being described. If 9 beads are on each wire, 9 symbols are needed. Using the symbols currently popular, we write the number "three hundred twenty-seven" as "327" (3 beads on the "hundreds" wire, 2 on the "tens" wire and 7 on the "units" wire).

The Babylonians and the Hindus had systems of the second type—the Babylonians' system based on the number sixty and the Hindus' system based on ten.

The second method has one defect. *How does one represent a number if one of the wires has no beads pushed up?* The great invention of the Hindus was a symbol, now written "0", to indicate this fact. In all probability the symbol was at first only a place holder, but it soon became apparent that by using this symbol calculations could be carried out as efficiently without the abacus as with it.[3]

We do not know exactly when the Hindus invented the system (probably after A.D. 600), but about A.D. 800 it was adopted in the Arab world and was gradually introduced into Europe. The major force behind its adoption was Leonardo Pisano (also called Fibonacci) of Pisa who urged its adoption in the early thirteenth century. The monks and scholars continued to use Roman numerials, but the new system was quickly adopted by the Italian merchants. Despite minor setbacks,[4] the usage spread, and by the sixteenth century the Hindu-Arabic numbers were used throughout Europe.

NUMBER BASES

We have observed that the number ten plays a special role in our number system. The obvious question follows: *Does the number ten have any special properties which make it more suitable for the special role than the other positive integers?* The answer, of course, is *no*. If our ancestors had been born with twelve fingers we would probably have a system based on the number twelve or on the number twenty-four (assuming they had twelve toes as well).

---

[2]The Roman number system is more complicated than as indicated above because the principle of subtraction is also used.

[3]We need the ten symbols "0, 1, 2, 3, 4, 5, 6, 7, 8, 9," the multiplication and addition tables (each with 100 entries), the associative, commutative, and distributive laws.

[4]For example, the use of Hindu-Arabic numbers was forbidden to the Florentine merchants in 1299.

We will now prove that any integer g greater than 1 can be used as a base for a system of enumeration similar to that of the Hindus. Obviously, the only requirements such a number must fulfill are:

(*a*) There must exist g symbols to represent the numbers, 0, 1, 2, $\cdots$, $g - 1$, and

(*b*) if m is a natural number, we must be able to write

$$m = a_t g^t + a_{t-1} g^{t-1} + \cdots + a_1 g + a_0 \quad (0 \le a_i < g)$$

For example, if g is 7 and m is 68, we can write

$$68 = 1 \cdot 7^2 + 2 \cdot 7 + 5$$

Thus, in the system based on seven (assuming the symbols 0, 1, 2, 3, 4, 5, 6 represent the integers "zero" through "six") we would write sixty-eight as 125.

In order not to confuse this number with the number one hundred twenty-five it is customary to use subscripts[5] to indicate the base; for example,

$$68_{10} = 125_7$$

Since the assignment of g symbols causes no theoretical difficulty, we must only prove that condition (*b*) always holds.

■ **THEOREM 9** / Let g be an integer greater than 1. If m is a natural number, there exist integers $a_0, a_1, \cdots, a_t, 0 \le a_i < g$, such that

$$m = a_t g^t + a_{t-1} g^{t-1} + \cdots + a_1 g + a_0$$

PROOF: We divide m by g, obtaining

$$m = q_0 g + a_0 \qquad 0 \le a_0 < g$$

Obviously, $q_0 \ge 0$. If q_0 is positive, we divide q_0 by g obtaining

$$q_0 = q_1 g + a_1 \qquad 0 \le a_1 < g$$

We now continue in this fashion until one of the quotients is equal to zero, obtaining the following chain of equations:

$$m = q_0 g + a_0 \qquad 0 \le a_0 < g \qquad q_0 > 0$$

$$q_0 = q_1 g + a_1 \qquad 0 \le a_1 < g \qquad q_1 > 0$$

---

[5]The subscripts are written in base 10.

$$q_1 = q_2 g + a_2 \qquad 0 \leq a_2 < g \qquad q_2 > 0$$

$$\cdots$$

$$q_{t-2} = q_{t-1} g + a_{t-1} \qquad 0 \leq a_{t-1} < g \qquad q_{t-1} > 0$$

$$q_{t-1} = q_t g + a_t \qquad 0 \leq a_t < g \qquad q_t = 0$$

Since q_t is the first zero quotient, then a_t, which is equal to q_{t-1}, is positive. We now substitute successively:

$$m = q_0 g + a_0$$
$$= (q_1 g + a_1)g + a_0 = q_1 g^2 + a_1 g + a_0$$
$$= (q_2 g + a_2)g^2 + a_1 g + a_0 = q_2 g^3 + a_2 g^2 + a_1 g + a_0$$
$$\cdots$$
$$= (q_{t-1} g + a_{t-1})g^{t-1} + \cdots + a_1 g + a_0$$
$$= q_{t-1} g^t + a_{t-1} g^{t-1} + \cdots + a_1 g + a_0$$
$$= a_t g^t + a_{t-1} g^{t-1} + \cdots + a_1 g + a_0$$

The proof of Theorem 9 gives us a practical method to change from base 10 to base g. Note that the "units" digit, a_0, is the remainder when m is divided by g. The next digit is the remainder when q_0, the quotient just obtained, is divided by g, and so on.

Example.

Write 2314_{10} in the base 7.

SOLUTION:

$$2314 = 330 \cdot 7 + 4 \qquad a_0 = 4$$
$$330 = 47 \cdot 7 + 1 \qquad a_1 = 1$$
$$47 = 6 \cdot 7 + 5 \qquad a_2 = 5$$
$$6 = 0 \cdot 7 + 6 \qquad a_3 = 6$$

Thus, $2314_{10} = 6514_7$.

It is customary to use the symbols 0, 1, 2, $\cdots$, 9 to represent the same numbers as in base 10 whenever this is feasible. Thus, in the above example, the seven digits are "0, 1, 2, 3, 4, 5, 6". If the base g is larger than 10, new symbols must be invented. For example, in the base 12, we need a symbol for ten and a symbol for eleven.

EXERCISES

1. Make addition and multiplication tables for the base 2. Convert 237_{10} and 194_{10} to base 2 and multiply them together. Check your answers by converting back to base 10.

2. Follow the instructions in Exercise 1 for the base 20.

[The reader will observe that in Exercise 1, the multiplication and addition tables are simple (and easily learned) although the calculations are laborious. In Exercise 2, the tables are large (and difficult to memorize), but the calculations are easy. In general, the larger the base the simpler the calculations, with the drawback that the tables are more difficult to prepare and memorize. For practical purposes, base 10 seems to be as convenient as any other.]

PROBLEMS

THE GAME OF NIM

In the ancient Chinese game of Nim, two players alternate in withdrawing stones from 3 piles that have been formed by a third person. At his turn, a player must remove at least 1 stone from one of the piles and he may remove as many as he wishes from that one pile. The person who removes the last stone from the last pile wins the game.

Analysis of the Game / After each turn write the number of stones in each pile in base 2, arranging the three numbers so that corresponding digits lie in a column. For example, if the numbers are 17, 21, and 35, we write

$$17_{10} = 0\ 1\ 0\ 0\ 0\ 1\ _2$$

$$21_{10} = 0\ 1\ 0\ 1\ 0\ 1\ _2$$

$$35_{10} = 1\ 0\ 0\ 0\ 1\ 1\ _2$$

We say that a player is in a position of Type A if, after his turn, each column contains an even number of one's. If at least one column contains an odd number of one's, we say the player is in a Type B position. Thus, the player who leaves 17, 21, 35, as above, is in a Type B position, while a player who leaves 17, 21, 4 is in a Type A position. [If we write 17, 21, and 4 in base 2, we obtain

$$17_{10} = 1\ 0\ 0\ 0\ 1\ _2$$

$$21_{10} = 1\ 0\ 1\ 0\ 1\ _2$$

$$4_{10} = 0\ 0\ 1\ 0\ 0\ _2$$

which has an even number of one's in each column.]

1. Show that if a player is in a Type A position the other player *must* go to a Type B position at his next turn. If a player is in a Type B position it is possible for the other player to go to a Type A position.

Thus, if a careful player is once able to get into a Type A position he can remain in such a position throughout the rest of the game and the other player will be forced to remain in a Type B position. Since the winning position (0, 0, 0) is of Type A, the player who stays in a Type A position is assured of winning the game.

RUSSIAN FARMER'S MULTIPLICATION

The following multiplication technique was used by the peasants during the Middle Ages in Russia and some parts of Europe.

To multiply two positive integers, successively divide one of them by 2, neglecting the remainders, and then write the quotients in a column. We successively double the other integer as many times as we halved the first, arranging the results in a similar column. Next we remove from the second column all entries for which the corresponding numbers in the first column are even. Finally, we add together the remaining numbers in the second column. The sum is seen to be the product of the two original numbers. As an example, we multiply 25 by 17:

$$
\begin{array}{cc}
25 & 17 \\
12 & \cancel{34} \\
6 & \cancel{68} \\
3 & 136 \\
1 & 272 \\
\hline
& 425 = 25 \cdot 17
\end{array}
$$

2. Prove that the method described above always works. [*Hint:* Show that the final addition is equivalent to multiplying the second number by the first when the first number is written in base 2.]

LINEAR DIOPHANTINE EQUATIONS / 2

2.1 / INTRODUCTION

Let α, β, γ be real numbers, not both α and β equal to zero. The equation $\alpha x + \beta y = \gamma$ is called a linear equation because the corresponding graph is a straight line in the XY-plane.

The problem of solving this equation becomes complicated if we wish to restrict ourselves to integral solutions. For example, the equation $x + y = 1$ obviously has an infinity of integral solutions; however, the equation $6x + 8y = 7$ has none. (If we substitute integers for x and y, the left-hand side is even and is thus not equal to 7.)

■ DEFINITION / A problem to be solved in integers is called a *diophantine problem*, after the Greek mathematician Diophantus (about A.D. 300). An equation of form $ax + by = c$ (a, b, c integers, not both a and b equal to zero) is called a *linear diophantine equation* (*in two variables*) if it is to be solved in integers.

The study of diophantine problems is one of the oldest branches of mathematics. Undoubtedly, one reason for this is the fact that man has used the positive integers much longer than the other number systems. Diophantine equations also furnish a natural vehicle for puzzles and problems of a mathematical nature.

Although Diophantus receives credit for the first systematic investigation of diophantine equations, partial results had been obtained by the Greeks of earlier times. Actually, considered by modern standards, Diophantus was not very systematic in his study. He was usually content to find only one solution of an equation, and he did not allow negative solutions.[1] He used

---

[1] Diophantus apparently had no conception of negative numbers apart from their role in subtraction.

so many special techniques that a person who had studied his solution of one problem might have no idea of how to attack a similar problem.

The Hindus, on the other hand, did make a systematic study of linear and certain nonlinear diophantine equations. Aryabhatta (born A.D. 476) completely solved the linear diophantine equation in two variables by a method called *the pulverizier*, a variation of the method we shall use to prove Theorem 1.

During the middle ages, the Arabs served as custodians of the Greek and Hindu knowledge, eventually introducing much of it into Europe. Although several Arab mathematicians considered diophantine equations during this period, they made no original contribution to the subject.

Diophantine problems, formulated as puzzles, were popular in medieval Europe. They were usually solved, of course, by trial-and-error methods. In the seventeenth century, the French mathematician Bachet (1581–1638), unaware of the work of the Hindus, also solved the linear diophantine equation in its most general form. Although this ended the mathematicians' search for solutions to particular problems of this type, the laymen continued to enjoy the linear diophantine puzzle.

Some interesting puzzles come from the medieval period. One of the oldest in our possession is the following from the tenth century. It is believed to be from a copy of a collection of puzzles prepared for Charlemagne by the monk Alcuin.

> One hundred measures of grain are distributed among 100 persons so that each man receives three measures, each woman two measures and each child half a measure. How many men, women, and children are there?

A number of problems similar to this one have been transmitted through the ages virtually intact as part of the folklore. They can frequently be recognized by one of the following two characteristics: (1) the special role of the number 100, and (2) the use of prices not compatible with those of the present time. For example, the following problem was popular with the author's high school classmates:

> Pigs cost 3 pennies each, sheep 2 pennies each, and rabbits are 5 for a penny. A man is given 100 pennies and told to buy 100 animals. How many does he buy of each kind?

In this chapter we shall prove necessary and sufficient conditions which insure that the linear diophantine equation has a solution, derive the general (parametric) form of the solution, and study the technique of solution used by Euler.

2.2 / THE DIOPHANTINE EQUATION $ax + by = c$

∎ **THEOREM 1** / The linear diophantine equation $ax + by = c$ has a solution if, and only if, the greatest common divisor of a and b divides c.

PROOF: (Part I) Let $d = (a, b)$ and suppose that $d|c$. There exists an integer k such that $c = kd$. Since d is a sum of multiples of a and b, we may write

$$am + bn = d$$

Multiplying this equation by k, we obtain

$$a(mk) + b(nk) = dk = c$$

so that $x = mk$, $y = nk$ is a solution.

(Part II) Suppose that x_0, y_0 is a solution of the equation. Then

$$ax_0 + by_0 = c.$$

Since d divides a and b, then d divides c.

Observe that the proof of Theorem 1, together with the Euclidean algorithm, provides us with a practical method to obtain one solution of the equation. We write (a, b) as a sum of multiples of a and b and then multiply by an appropriate constant.

The problem of solving a linear diophantine equation can be considered from a geometrical standpoint. A point in the XY-plane is called a *lattice point* if its coordinates are integers. Thus, solving the diophantine equation $ax + by = c$ is equivalent to finding all lattice points that lie on the straight-line graph of the equation $ax + by = c$ in the XY-plane. The slope of this line is equal to the rational number

$$-\frac{a}{b} = \frac{-a/d}{b/d}$$

where $d = (a, b)$. Therefore, if x_0, y_0 is a solution, the pair

$$x_0 + kb/d, \quad y_0 - ka/d$$

is also a solution for any integer k. Figure 2.1 pictures the situation for the diophantine equation $2x + 3y = 2$.

We will now establish that these are the only solutions.

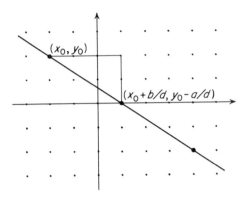

Figure 2.1 Graph of the linear diophantine equation $2x + 3y = 2$.

■ THEOREM 2 / Let $(a, b) = d$. If x_0, y_0 is a solution of the diophantine equation $ax + by = c$, the general solution of the equation is

$$x = x_0 + kb/d, \quad y = y_0 - ka/d$$

where the parameter k is an integer.

(Because d is a common divisor of a and b, the rational numbers b/d and a/d are obviously integers.)

PROOF: We established above that if k is an integer, then $x_0 + kb/d$, $y_0 - ka/d$ is also a solution (see also Exercise 5). We must now show that all solutions are of this form.

Suppose that x_1, y_1 is a solution of the diophantine equation. Then

$$ax_1 + by_1 = c = ax_0 + by_0$$

so that
$$a(x_1 - x_0) = -b(y_1 - y_0) \tag{2.1}$$

Since $(a, b) = d$, there exist relatively prime integers a' and b' such that $a = a'd$, $b = b'd$ (Corollary 4.3 of Chapter 1). If we substitute in (2.1) and cancel d, we obtain

$$a'(x_1 - x_0) = -b'(y_1 - y_0) \tag{2.2}$$

Thus, $b' | a'(x_1 - x_0)$ and $(a', b') = 1$. From Corollary 4.4 of Chapter 1, it follows that

$$b' | (x_1 - x_0)$$

that is,
$$x_1 - x_0 = kb'$$

for some integer k. If we substitute this value into (2.2) and cancel b', we obtain

$$y_1 - y_0 = -ka'$$

Thus,

$$x_1 = x_0 + kb' = x_0 + kb/d, \; y_1 = y_0 - ka' = y_0 - ka/d$$

Since x_1, y_1 was an arbitrary solution, this implies that all solutions are of the desired form.

Example I.

Solve the diophantine equation

$$738x + 621y = 45$$

SOLUTION: We use the Euclidean algorithm to calculate $(738, 621)$:

$$738 = 1 \cdot 621 + 117$$
$$621 = 5 \cdot 117 + 36$$
$$117 = 3 \cdot 36 + 9$$
$$36 = 4 \cdot 9$$

Since $(738, 621) = 9$, which divides 45, the equation has a solution. Working backwards through the above chain of equations, we write 9 as a sum of multiples of 738 and 621:

$$9 = 117 - 3 \cdot 36 = 16 \cdot 117 - 3 \cdot 621 = 16 \cdot 738 - 19 \cdot 621$$

Multiplying by 5, we obtain

$$45 = 80 \cdot 738 - 95 \cdot 621$$

so that $x_0 = 80$, $y_0 = -95$ is a solution. The general solution is

$$x = 80 + \frac{621}{9} k = 80 + 69k$$

$$y = -95 - \frac{738}{9} k = -95 - 82k$$

A few of the solutions are listed in Table 2.1.

Table 2.1

k	x	y
-2	-58	69
-1	11	-13
0	80	-95
1	149	-177

Example 2.

Obtain all positive solutions of

$$7x + 5y = 100$$

SOLUTION: The greatest common divisor of 7 and 5 is 1. By inspection we write

$$3 \cdot 7 - 4 \cdot 5 = 1$$

Thus, one solution of the original equation is

$$x_0 = 300, \ y_0 = -400$$

The general solution is

$$x = 300 + 5k$$

$$y = 400 - 7k$$

Because we wish to find the positive solutions, we solve the inequalities

$$300 + 5k > 0$$

$$-400 - 7k > 0$$

and obtain $-60 < k < -57\frac{1}{7}$. Therefore, the diophantine equation has exactly two positive solutions corresponding to the values $k = -59, k = -58$. See Table 2.2.

Table 2.2

k	x	y
−59	5	13
−58	10	6

EXERCISES

1. Solve the two diophantine problems stated in the text of Section 2.1.

2. Solve the diophantine equations
   (a) $57x - 87y = 342$;
   (b) $1411x + 1547y = 224$.

3. Obtain all positive solutions of the diophantine equations in Exercise 2.

4. Find a solution of $105x - 273y - 195z = 1365$.

5. Show by direct substitution that if x_0, y_0 is a solution of $ax + by = c$ and $d = (a, b)$, then $x_0 + kb/d$, $y_0 - ka/d$ is also a solution for any integer k.

PROBLEMS

1. Prove that if a and b are relatively prime positive integers, the diophantine equation

$$ax - by = c$$

has an infinity of positive solutions.

2. Establish necessary and sufficient conditions which insure that the linear diophantine equation

$$a_1x_1 + a_2x_2 + \cdots + a_nx_n = b$$

has a solution.

2.3* / THE METHOD OF EULER

From the theoretical standpoint, we have completely solved the problem of obtaining solutions to linear diophantine equations. We have a simple test that can be used to determine whether solutions exist. If so, we have a method to obtain one solution that can then be used to obtain all solutions.

From the practical standpoint, however, much is still to be desired. The use of the Euclidean algorithm is cumbersome, especially if the equation is in more than two variables. Furthermore, the solutions obtained are apt to be very large in comparison with some of the other solutions. An alternate method of solution that does not have these defects would be convenient.

Such a method is ascribed to the great Swiss mathematician L. Euler (1707–1783). It involves a simple process, repeated several times. The process is easy to understand, requiring little more than the division algorithm and the closure properties of the integers under addition and subtraction.[2]

Although lengthy, it is no longer than the process involving the Euclidean algorithm and is frequently much shorter (especially if the equation is in more than two variables).

Euler's method is best introduced by an example.

Example.

Solve the diophantine equation

$$738x + 621y = 45$$

---

[2]The fact that the sum and difference of two integers are also integers.

SOLUTION: Assume that x, y is a solution of the equation. The first step is to solve for the unknown that has the smallest coefficient in absolute value; in this case, y. Using the fact that $738 = 621 + 117$ and $45 = 0 \cdot 621 + 45$, we obtain

$$y = \frac{-738x + 45}{621} = -x + \frac{-117x + 45}{621}$$

If x and y are integers, then $(-117x + 45)/621$ is also an integer, which we will call t. We now rewrite the expression for t as the dipohantine equation

$$621t = -117x + 45$$

which has smaller coefficients than the original equation. We now repeat the process, solving for x, which has the smallest coefficient in absolute value:

$$x = \frac{-621t + 45}{117} = -5t + \frac{-36t + 45}{117}$$

$$= -5t + u \qquad \text{where} \qquad u = \frac{-36t + 45}{117}$$

This gives us the equation

$$36t + 117u = 45$$

Solving for t we obtain

$$t = \frac{-117u + 45}{36} = -3u + 1 + \frac{-9u + 9}{36} = -3u + 1 + v$$

where $36v = -9u + 9$ and v is an integer.

Solving for u we now obtain

$$u = -4v + 1$$

To obtain one solution, we pick a convenient value of v, say $v = 0$, and work back through the chain of equations:

$$v = 0$$

$$u = -4v + 1 = 1$$

$$t = -3u + 1 + v = -2$$

$$x = -5t + u = 11$$

$$y = -x + t = -13$$

Thus, $x = 11$, $y = -13$ is a solution.

To obtain the general solution, we let v be the parameter and substitute into the chain of equations:

$$u = -4v + 1$$

$$t = -3u + 1 + v = 13v - 2$$
$$x = -5t + u = -69v + 11$$
$$y = -x + t = 82v - 13$$

Thus, the general solution is $x = -13 + 82v$, $y = 11 - 69v$.

This solution should be compared with the solution obtained in Example 1 of Section 2.2.

EXERCISES

1. Use Euler's method to solve

$$51w + 102x + 34y + 170z = 1377$$

2. Where does Euler's method break down if we attempt to use it to solve

$$738x + 621y = 51?$$

3. An apartment building contains apartments at two rental rates: Those of Type A rent for $87 per month and those of Type B for $123 per month. When all apartments are rented the gross income is $8733 per month. How many apartments are there of each type?

4. Into the bright and refreshing outskirts of a forest, full of numerous trees with their branches bent down with the weight of flowers and fruits, trees such as jambu trees, lime trees, plantains, areca palms, jack trees, date-palms, hintala trees, palyras, punnaga trees and mango trees—the various quarters of which were filled with the many sounds of crowds of parrots and cuckoos near found springs containing lotuses with bees roaming about them—a number of weary travelers entered with joy.

There were 63 equal heaps of plantain fruits put together with 7 more of the same fruits. These were distributed equally among the 23 travelers so as to leave no remainder. Tell me now the number of fruits in each heap. (Mahaviracarya, A.D. 850.)

INTRODUCTION TO THE THEORY OF CONGRUENCES / 3

3.1 / INTRODUCTION

Many problems in number theory lead to the consideration of a set of integers in which any two elements differ by a multiple of a fixed integer. For example, the general solution of the diophantine equation $14x + 10y = 12$ is $x = -2 + 5k$, $y = 4 - 7k$. Thus, the value of x in a solution must come from the set of all integers of form $-2 + 5k$; that is, the set

$$\{\cdots, -12, -7, -2, 3, 8, 13, \cdots\}$$

and the value of y must come from the set

$$\{\cdots, -10, -3, 4, 11, 18, 25, \cdots\}$$

In the first set any two elements differ by a multiple of 5, in the second set, any two elements differ by a multiple of 7.

The study of sets of this type is facilitated by the concept of congruence, due to C. F. Gauss (1777–1855). We will develop parallels between the concepts of congruence and equality and then return to our study of these sets.

■ DEFINITION / Let a, b, and m be integers, $m > 0$. We say that *a is congruent to b, modulo m* $(a \equiv b \pmod{m})$ if m divides $a - b$.

For example, $6 \equiv 13 \pmod{7}$ and $-23 \equiv 7 \pmod{15}$. In the example preceding the definition the first set of integers contains all numbers congruent to $-2 \pmod 5$ and the second set all numbers congruent to 4 $\pmod 7$.

The similarity between the symbols for equality and congruence is not accidental. We will prove that congruence $\pmod m$ has many properties similar to those of equality. The notation is important for two basic reasons: (1) It enables us to solve certain problems involving divisibility by the use of algebraic methods; and (2) the notation suggests certain problems that probably would not have been formulated otherwise.

The first theorem states that congruence (mod m) is an equivalence relation.[1]

■ THEOREM 1 / Let m be a positive integer.

(a) If a is an integer, then $a \equiv a \pmod{m}$.

(b) If $a \equiv b \pmod{m}$, then $b \equiv a \pmod{m}$.

(c) If $a \equiv b$ and $b \equiv c \pmod{m}$, then $a \equiv c \pmod{m}$.

PROOF OF THE TRANSITIVE PROPERTY: Since $a \equiv b$ and $b \equiv c \pmod{m}$ then $a - b$ and $b - c$ are multiples of m. It follows that the sum of these numbers, $a - c$, is a multiple of m. Thus, $a \equiv c \pmod{m}$.

The proofs of the other two properties are left for the reader (Exercise 2).

EXERCISES

1. Which moduli are used to measure the following times?

   (a) The days of the week.

   (b) The hours of the day.

   (c) The minutes after the hour.

2. Prove the reflexive and symmetric properties of congruence (mod m).

3. Which of the following are equivalence relations? If a relation is not an equivalence relation, which properties does it lack?

   (a) The relation "less-than-or-equals" for integers.

   (b) The relation "is a descendant of" for persons.

   (c) The relation "is congruent to" for triangles.

   (d) The relation "is complementary to" for angles.

   (e) The relation "$a|b$" for integers.

---

[1] A *relation* on a set S is a collection R of ordered pairs of elements of S. If the ordered pair (a, b) is in the relation R, it is customary to write aRb rather than $(a, b) \in R$.

An *equivalence relation* on S is a relation R, having the properties:

Reflexive Property: aRa for each a in S;

Symmetric Property: If aRb, then bRa;

Transitive Property: If aRb and bRc, then aRc.

Examples of equivalence relations are: (1) equality of numbers; (2) similarity of triangles; (3) concentricity of circles.

PROBLEMS

1. Discuss the concept of congruence, modulo zero.

2. Let m be a positive integer. Suppose that

$$a_1 = mq_1 + r_1 \qquad 0 \le r_1 < m$$

and
$$a_2 = mq_2 + r_2 \qquad 0 \le r_2 < m$$

Prove that $a_1 \equiv a_2 \pmod{m}$ if, and only if, $r_1 = r_2$.

3.2 / ARITHMETIC PROPERTIES OF CONGRUENCE

We have shown that congruence (mod m) has properties similar to equality. We will now prove that we can add and multiply congruences in a manner similar to that in which we operate using equality.

■ THEOREM 2 / If $a \equiv a' \pmod{m}$ and $b \equiv b' \pmod{m}$, then $a + b \equiv a' + b' \pmod{m}$ and $ab \equiv a'b' \pmod{m}$.

PROOF OF THE MULTIPLICATION PROPERTY: Because $a \equiv a'$ and $b \equiv b'$ (mod m), there exist integers k and n such that

$$a - a' = km \qquad b - b' = nm$$

Multiplying, we obtain

$$ab = (a' + km)(b' + nm) = a'b' + m(a'n + b'k + knm)$$

Thus, $m|(ab - a'b')$ and so

$$ab \equiv a'b' \pmod{m}$$

The proof of the addition property is left for the reader.

One of the important properties of the integers is the cancellation law for multiplication: *If $ab = ac$ and $a \ne 0$, then $b = c$.* A natural conjection would be that a corresponding cancellation law holds for the integers under congruence; that is, *If $ab \equiv ac \pmod{m}$ and $a \not\equiv 0 \pmod{m}$, then $b \equiv c \pmod{m}$.* It is easy, however, to construct an example to show that this cannot be correct. For example, $8 \cdot 3 \equiv 8 \cdot 5 \pmod{16}$ but $3 \not\equiv 5 \pmod{16}$. We see then that a cancellation law for multiplication must be more complicated when we are concerned with congruence rather than with equality. The correct form of the cancellation law is given in the following theorem.

■ THEOREM 3 / (The Cancellation Law) If $ab \equiv ac$ (mod m), then $b \equiv c$ (mod m/d), where $d = (a, m)$.

PROOF: We divide a and m by d writing

$$a = a'd, \ m = m'd \quad \text{where } (a', m') = 1 \quad \text{(see Corollary 4.3 of Chapter 1)}$$

Because $ab \equiv ac$ (mod m), we can write

$$ab - ac = km$$

Substituting from above and cancelling d, we obtain

$$a'd(b - c) = km'd$$
$$a'(b - c) = km'$$

Thus, $m' | a'(b - c)$ and $(m', a') = 1$. From Corollary 4.4 of Chapter 1, it follows that m', equal to m/d, divides $b - c$. Thus,

$$b \equiv c \ (\text{mod } m/d)$$

In one important special case we obtain a cancellation law similar to the one under equality.

■ COROLLARY 3.1 / If $(a, m) = 1$ and $ab \equiv ac$ (mod m), then $b \equiv c$ (mod m).

EXERCISES

1. *Prove:* If $a \equiv b$ (mod m) and n is a positive integer, then $a^n \equiv b^n$ (mod m). Show by an example that the converse is not necessarily true.

2. *Prove:* If $f(x)$ is a polynomial with integral coefficients, and if $a \equiv b$ (mod m), then $f(a) \equiv f(b)$ (mod m).

3. Let p be a prime number. *Prove:* If $ab \equiv ac$ (mod p) and $a \not\equiv 0$ (mod p), then $b \equiv c$ (mod p).

4. Let p be a prime number. *Prove:* If $a^2 \equiv 1$ (mod p) then $a \equiv \pm 1$ (mod p).

PROBLEMS

" CASTING OUT NINES "

1. If n is a positive integer, prove that n is congruent to the sum of its digits (written in base 10), modulo 9; that is, if

$$n = a_k 10^k + a_{k-1} 10^{k-1} + \cdots + a_1 10 + a_0$$

then
$$n \equiv a_k + a_{k-1} + \cdots + a_1 + a_0 \pmod{9}$$

[This fact was used extensively for checking numerical calculations before the invention of the desk calculator. For example, in order to check the computation when multiplying 8207 by 1530, we proceed as follows:

$$8207 \equiv 8 + 2 + 7 \equiv 8 \pmod{9}$$

$$1530 \equiv 1 + 5 + 3 \equiv 0 \pmod{9}$$

$$12{,}556{,}710 \equiv 1 + 2 + 5 + 5 + 6 + 7 + 1 \equiv 0 \pmod{9}.$$

Since $8 \cdot 0 \equiv 0 \pmod{9}$ the answer checks. Note that this does *not* tell us that the answer is correct. It only tells us that if we have a mistake the error is a multiple of 9. In other words, we can expect the method to detect errors $\frac{8}{9}$ of the time.]

2. Obtain a rule similar to "casting out nines" for the modulus 11.

3. Generalize the results of Problems 1 and 2 for an arbitrary base g.

3.3 / THE LINEAR CONGRUENCE $ax \equiv b \pmod{m}$

Consider the linear congruence $ax \equiv b \pmod{m}$. By a *solution* of this congruence we mean an integer x_0 such that $ax_0 \equiv b \pmod{m}$. The central problems of this section will be to decide when the above congruence has a solution, and to determine all solutions.

Suppose x_0 is a solution of the above congruence. Then there exists an integer y_0 such that

$$ax_0 - b = y_0 m$$

Thus, $ax_0 - my_0 = b$, so that x_0, y_0 is a solution of the linear diophantine equation

$$ax - my = b$$

On the other hand, if the linear diophantine equation $ax - my = b$ has a solution x_0, y_0, then

$$ax_0 - my_0 = b$$

and so
$$ax_0 \equiv b \pmod{m}$$

Thus, we have proved the following important fact: *The linear congruence $ax \equiv b \pmod{m}$ has x_0 as a solution if, and only if, there is a integer y_0 such that x_0, y_0 is a solution of the linear diophantine equation $ax - my = b$.*

We are now in a position to state the basic theorem on linear congruences by paraphrasing Theorems 1 and 2 of Chapter 2.

■ **THEOREM 4** / The linear congruence $ax \equiv b \pmod{m}$ has a solution if, and only if, the greatest common divisor of a and m divides b. If this is the case, and if x_0 is a solution of the congruence, then the general solution is

$$x \equiv x_0\left(\bmod \frac{m}{d}\right)$$

where
$$d = (a, m)$$

The details of the proof are left for the reader.

Example 1.

Because $(42, 91) = 7$, the linear congruence

$$42x \equiv 50 \pmod{91}$$

does not have a solution.

Example 2.

Solve $42x \equiv 50 \pmod{76}$.

SOLUTION: Because $(42, 76)$ divides 50, the congruence has a solution. From the cancellation law we obtain

$$21x \equiv 25 \pmod{38}$$

Thus,

$$21x \equiv 25 \equiv 25 + 38 \equiv 63 \pmod{38}$$

Dividing by 21 (the g. c. d. of 21 and 38 is 1) we obtain

$$x \equiv 3 \pmod{38}$$

which is the general solution. If we wish to write the solution in terms of the original modulus, we have

$$x \equiv 3 \quad \text{or} \quad x \equiv 41 \pmod{76}$$

In some cases we wish to write the general solution of the congruence $ax \equiv b \pmod{m}$ in terms of the modulus m. From Theorem 4, we see that the general solution is $x \equiv x_0 \pmod{m/d}$; thus, x is a solution if and only if

x is in the set

$$\left\{ \cdots, x_0 - 2\frac{m}{d}, x_0 - \frac{m}{d}, x_0, x_0 + \frac{m}{d}, x_0 + 2\frac{m}{d}, \cdots \right\}$$

It is easy to see that every number in this set is congruent to one of the numbers

$$x_0, x_0 + \frac{m}{d}, \cdots, x_0 + (d-1)\frac{m}{d}$$

modulo m, and that these numbers are incongruent to each other. Thus, we obtain the following corollary.

■ **COROLLARY 4.1** / If x_0 is a solution of $ax \equiv b \pmod{m}$ and if $d = (a, m)$, the numbers

$$x_0, x_0 + \frac{m}{d}, \cdots, x_0 + (d-1)\frac{m}{d}$$

form a complete set of incongruent solutions, modulo m; that is, the numbers are incongruent $\pmod{m}$, they are all solutions, and any solution is congruent to one of the numbers in the set $\pmod{m}$.

■ **COROLLARY 4.2** / Let $d = (a, m)$. If $d|b$, the linear congruence $ax \equiv b$ $\pmod{m}$ has exactly d incongruent solutions, modulo m.

EXERCISES

1. Solve each of the following linear congruences. If a solution exists write the general solution in terms of the original modulus.

(a) $23x \equiv 41 \pmod{52}$

(b) $68x \equiv 100 \pmod{120}$

(c) $42x \equiv 37 \pmod{63}$

(d) $70x \equiv 50 \pmod{90}$

2. Construct a formal proof of Theorem 4.

3. Let x_0 be a solution of $ax \equiv b \pmod{m}$ and let $d = (a, m)$. Prove that the numbers

$$x_0, x_0 + \frac{m}{d}, \cdots, x_0 + (d-1)\frac{m}{d}$$

are solutions of the congruence, that they are incongruent, modulo m, and that any solution of the congruence is congruent to one of these numbers, modulo m.

PROBLEM

1. Discuss the linear congruence $ax + by \equiv c$ (mod m). Generalize the result to the congruence $a_1 x_1 + a_2 x_2 + \cdots + a_n x_n \equiv c$ (mod m). (For a related problem, see Problem 2 of Section 2.2.)

3.4 / RESIDUE CLASSES

■ DEFINITION / A set of integers containing exactly those integers which are congruent, modulo m, to a fixed integer is called a *residue class, modulo m*.

Example.

There are seven residue classes, modulo 7, namely the sets:

$$\{\cdots, -14, -7, 0, \ 7, 14, 21, \cdots\}$$
$$\{\cdots, -13, -6, 1, \ 8, 15, 22, \cdots\}$$
$$\{\cdots, -12, -5, 2, \ 9, 16, 23, \cdots\}$$
$$\{\cdots, -11, -4, 3, 10, 17, 24, \cdots\}$$
$$\{\cdots, -10, -3, 4, 11, 18, 25, \cdots\}$$
$$\{\cdots, \ -9, -2, 5, 12, 19, 26, \cdots\}$$
$$\{\cdots, \ -8, -1, 6, 13, 20, 27, \cdots\}$$

The first set contains all those integers congruent to 0 (mod 7), the second set, those congruent to 1, $\cdots$, the seventh set those congruent to 6 (mod 7).

We will use the symbol $\mathscr{R}_a$ (mod m) to represent the residue class, modulo m, that contains the integers congruent to a, modulo m. Thus, each residue class can be denoted by an infinity of symbols. For example, the first residue class above can be represented by any of the following symbols: $\cdots$, $\mathscr{R}_{-14}$, $\mathscr{R}_{-7}$, $\mathscr{R}_0$, $\mathscr{R}_7$, $\mathscr{R}_{14}$, $\cdots$.

Several of the elementary properties of residue classes follow from Theorem 1. They are given in the following theorem.

■ THEOREM 5 / Let m be a positive integer.

(*a*) $\mathscr{R}_a = \mathscr{R}_b$, if and only if $a \equiv b$ (mod m).

(*b*) Two residue classes (mod m) are either disjoint or equal.

(*c*) There are exactly m distinct residue classes (mod m) and they contain all of the integers.

PROOF: (*a*) If $a \equiv b \pmod{m}$, it follows from the transitive property of congruence that an integer is congruent to $a \pmod{m}$ if, and only if, it is congruent to $b \pmod{m}$. Thus, $\mathcal{R}_a = \mathcal{R}_b$.

Suppose $\mathcal{R}_a = \mathcal{R}_b$. Because a is in $\mathcal{R}_a$, a is in $\mathcal{R}_b$. Thus, $a \equiv b \pmod{m}$.

(*b*) Suppose $\mathcal{R}_a$ and $\mathcal{R}_b$ have an element c in common. Then $c \equiv a \pmod{m}$ and $c \equiv b \pmod{m}$. From the symmetric and transitive properties of congruence, it follows that $a \equiv b \pmod{m}$. From (*a*) it now follows that $\mathcal{R}_a = \mathcal{R}_b$. Thus, either $\mathcal{R}_a$ and $\mathcal{R}_b$ are disjoint or they are equal.

(*c*) If a is an integer, we can divide a by m writing

$$a = mq + r \qquad 0 \leq r < m$$

Thus, $a \equiv r \pmod{m}$ and so $\mathcal{R}_a = \mathcal{R}_r$. This implies that a is in one of the residue classes $\mathcal{R}_0, \mathcal{R}_1, \cdots, \mathcal{R}_{m-1}$. Because the integers $0, 1, 2, \cdots, m - 1$ are incongruent $\pmod{m}$, it follows that there are exactly m residue classes $\pmod{m}$.

Using the residue class concept we can reformulate our results on the linear congruence $ax \equiv b \pmod{m}$. Because the general solution of the congruence is

$$x \equiv x_0 \left(\bmod \frac{m}{d} \right)$$

we see that x is a solution if, and only if, x is in $\mathcal{R}_{x_0} \pmod{m/d}$. Using Corollary 4.1, we find that x is a solution if, and only if, x is in one of the residue classes

$$\mathcal{R}_{x_0}, \mathcal{R}_{x_0 + m/d}, \cdots, \mathcal{R}_{x_0 + (d-1)m/d} \pmod{m}$$

Example.

In Example 2 of Section 3.3 we found the general solution of $42x \equiv 50 \pmod{76}$ to be

$$x \equiv 3 \pmod{38}$$

Thus, x is a solution of the congruence if and only if x is in $\mathcal{R}_3 \pmod{38}$.

EXERCISES

1. (*a*) List six elements from each of the following residue classes modulo 17:

$$\mathcal{R}_7, \mathcal{R}_{29}, \mathcal{R}_{72}, \mathcal{R}_5, \mathcal{R}_{-47}, \mathcal{R}_{-80}.$$

(*b*) Which of the above residue classes are equal?

2. Write the solutions of the linear congruences in Exercise 1 of Section 3.3 using residue classes.

PROBLEMS

(Knowledge of elementary modern algebra is required.)

THE RING OF RESIDUE CLASSES (mod *m*)

We define the operations " $\oplus$ " and " $\circ$ " on the residue classes, modulo m, as follows:

$$\mathscr{R}_a \oplus \mathscr{R}_b = \mathscr{R}_{a+b}$$

$$\mathscr{R}_a \circ \mathscr{R}_b = \mathscr{R}_{ab}$$

For example, modulo 7,

$$\mathscr{R}_1 \oplus \mathscr{R}_{17} = \{\cdots, -6, 1, 8, 15, \cdots\} \oplus \{\cdots, -4, 3, 10, 17, \cdots\}$$
$$= R_{18} = \{\cdots, -3, 4, 11, 18, \cdots\}$$

1. Show that the two operations are "well defined," that is, the operations depend only on the residue classes involved and not on the particular subscripts used to represent the residue classes.

2. Show that the residue classes (mod m) form a commutative ring with identity under the operations " $\oplus$ " and " $\circ$ ".

3. Show that the ring of residue classes (mod m) is a field if, and only if, m is a prime number.

3.5 / SYSTEMS OF LINEAR CONGRUENCES

Consider the system of linear congruences

$$\begin{cases} a_1 x \equiv b_1 \ (\text{mod } m_1) \\ a_2 x \equiv b_2 \ (\text{mod } m_2) \\ \quad \cdots \\ a_n x \equiv b_n \ (\text{mod } m_n) \end{cases}$$

By a *solution* of this system we mean an integer x_0 which is a solution of each congruence in the system.

Because each congruence in the above system determines a residue class, the solutions of the system are the numbers in the intersection of these classes. Thus, we may replace any one of the above congruences by a different congruence that defines the same residue class.

In Part II of the solution of the following example, we demonstrate an efficient method for solving a system of linear congruences.

Example 1.

Solve the system $\begin{cases} 5x \equiv 7 \ (\text{mod } 12) \\ 4x \equiv 12 \ (\text{mod } 14) \end{cases}$.

PART I: By the methods of Section 3.3, we see that x_0 is a solution of $5x \equiv 7$ (mod 12) if and only if x_0 is in $\mathcal{R}_{11}$ (mod 12), and x_0 is a solution of $4x \equiv 12$ (mod 14) if and only if x_0 is in $\mathcal{R}_3$ (mod 7). Thus, x_0 is a solution of the system of congruences if, and only if, x_0 is in the intersection of the two residue classes $\mathcal{R}_{11}$ (mod 12) and $\mathcal{R}_3$ (mod 7). Therefore, the system $\begin{cases} x \equiv 11 \ (\text{mod } 12) \\ x \equiv 3 \ \ (\text{mod } 7) \end{cases}$ has the same solutions as the original system.

PART II: Suppose x_0 is a solution of the system. Then $x_0 \equiv 11$ (mod 12), and so we can write

$$x_0 = 11 + 12s$$

Substituting this into the second congruence, we obtain

$$x_0 \equiv 11 + 12s \equiv 3 \ (\text{mod } 7)$$

Thus,

$$12s \equiv -8 \ (\text{mod } 7)$$

$$-2s \equiv -8 \ (\text{mod } 7)$$

$$s \equiv \ \ 4 \ (\text{mod } 7)$$

If we now write $s = 4 + 7t$ and substitute into the expression for x_0, we obtain

$$x_0 = 11 + 12s = 59 + 84t$$

Thus, $$x_0 \equiv 59 \ (\text{mod } 84)$$

We have shown that if a solution x_0 exists, it must be congruent to 59, modulo 84. If we now substitute back in the original system, we see that any number congruent to 59, modulo 84, is indeed a solution. Thus, the general solution is

$$x \equiv 59 \ (\text{mod } 84)$$

We now prove the fundamental theorem for systems of linear congruences. This theorem and its corollary give necessary and sufficient conditions which insure that a system has a solution and determine the form of the general solution.

■ THEOREM 6 / The system of congruences $\begin{cases} x \equiv a \ (\text{mod } m) \\ x \equiv b \ (\text{mod } n) \end{cases}$ has a solution if, and only if, $(m, n)|(a - b)$. If this is the case and if x_0 is a solution, the general solution is

$$x \equiv x_0 \ (\text{mod } [m, n])$$

PROOF: (Part I) The integer x_0 is a solution of the system of congruences if, and only if, there exists an integer k such that

$$x_0 = a + km$$

and

$$a + km \equiv b \ (\text{mod } n)$$

By Theorem 4 such a number k will exist if, and only if,

$$(m, n)|(a - b)$$

(Part II) Suppose that $(m, n)|(a - b)$ and that x_0 is a solution of the system of congruences. If x_1 is also a solution, then

$$x_1 \equiv a \equiv x_0 \ (\text{mod } m)$$

and

$$x_1 \equiv b \equiv x_0 \ (\text{mod } n)$$

Thus, $x_1 - x_0$ is a common multiple of m and n and, by Theorem 5 of Chapter 1, $[m, n]|(x_1 - x_0)$. In terms of congruences,

$$x_1 \equiv x_0 \ (\text{mod } [m, n])$$

Conversely, if $x_1 \equiv x_0 \ (\text{mod } [m, n])$, then obviously

$$x_1 \equiv x_0 \equiv a \ (\text{mod } m)$$

and

$$x_1 \equiv x_0 \equiv b \ (\text{mod } n)$$

and so x_1 is also a solution of the system. Thus, the general solution is

$$x \equiv x_0 \ (\text{mod } [m, n])$$

Several results can be proved for systems of more than two congruences. Two corollaries will be stated, the proofs will be left for the reader.

■ COROLLARY 6.1 / The system of linear congruences

$$\begin{cases} x \equiv a_1 \ (\text{mod } m_1) \\ x \equiv a_2 \ (\text{mod } m_2) \\ \qquad \cdots \\ x \equiv a_n \ (\text{mod } m_n) \end{cases}$$

has a solution if, and only if, $(m_j, m_k)|(a_j - a_k)$, for each pair of subscripts j, k. If this is the case and if x_0 is a solution, the general solution is

$$x \equiv x_0 \pmod{[m_1, m_2, \cdots, m_n]}$$

For the special case in which the moduli $m_1, m_2, \cdots, m_n$ are relatively prime in pairs, it is obvious that the system in Corollary 6.1 will have a solution. In this case we can write the solution of the system in closed form. This fact was known to the Chinese mathematician Sun-tse (first century A.D.) and the corresponding theorem is known as the Chinese Remainder Theorem.

■ COROLLARY 6.2 / (The Chinese Remainder Theorem.) Suppose $m_1, m_2, \cdots, m_n$ are pairwise relatively prime, that is, $(m_i, m_j) = 1$ if $i \neq j$. Let $M = m_1 m_2 \cdots m_n$. We define numbers $b_1, b_2, \cdots, b_n$ by choosing $y = b_j$ as a solution of

$$y \frac{M}{m_j} \equiv 1 \pmod{m_j} \qquad (j = 1, 2, \cdots, n)$$

The general solution of the system

$$\begin{cases} x \equiv a_1 \pmod{m_1} \\ x \equiv a_2 \pmod{m_2} \\ \cdots \\ x \equiv a_n \pmod{m_n} \end{cases}$$

is

$$x \equiv a_1 b_1 \frac{M}{m_1} + a_2 b_2 \frac{M}{m_2} + \cdots + a_n b_n \frac{M}{m_n} \pmod{M}$$

Corollary 6.2 furnishes the most efficient method for solving several systems of congruences when the same sets of moduli appear in each system.

Example 2.

Solve the systems of congruences

$$\begin{cases} x \equiv 5 \pmod 7 \\ x \equiv 8 \pmod{19} \end{cases}, \quad \begin{cases} x \equiv 4 \pmod 7 \\ x \equiv 16 \pmod{19} \end{cases}, \quad \begin{cases} x \equiv 1 \pmod 7 \\ x \equiv -8 \pmod{19} \end{cases}$$

and

$$\begin{cases} x \equiv 2 \pmod 7 \\ x \equiv 5 \pmod{19} \end{cases}$$

Because $y = b_1$ is a solution of $19y \equiv 1 \pmod 7$, we may choose $b_1 = 3$. Similarly, we choose $b_2 = -8$. Then

$$b_1 \frac{M}{m_1} = 3 \cdot 19 = 57$$

and
$$b_2 \frac{M}{m_2} = -8 \cdot 7 = -56$$

We now find the solutions of the systems by substituting into the congruence in Corollary 6.2:

System   I: $x \equiv 5 \cdot 57 + 8(-56) \equiv 103 \pmod{133}$.

System II: $x \equiv 4 \cdot 57 + 16(-56) \equiv 130 \pmod{133}$.

System III: $x \equiv 1 \cdot 57 - 8(-56) \equiv 106 \pmod{133}$.

System IV: $x \equiv 2 \cdot 57 + 5(-56) \equiv 100 \pmod{133}$.

EXERCISES

1. Calculate the intersection of the residue classes:
   (a) $\mathcal{R}_7 \pmod{15} \cap \mathcal{R}_4 \pmod{21} \cap \mathcal{R}_{15} \pmod{37}$,
   (b) $\mathcal{R}_{12} \pmod{26} \cap \mathcal{R}_{18} \pmod{21} \cap \mathcal{R}_7 \pmod{36}$.

2. Solve: (a) $\begin{cases} x \equiv 2 \pmod 5 \\ x \equiv 3 \pmod 7 \end{cases}$ (b) $\begin{cases} x \equiv 1 \pmod 5 \\ x \equiv 4 \pmod 7 \end{cases}$ (c) $\begin{cases} x \equiv 4 \pmod 5 \\ x \equiv 1 \pmod 7 \end{cases}$.

3. (Ancient Hindu Problem) If eggs are taken from a basket two, three, four, five, and six at a time there are left over, respectively, one, two, three, four, and five eggs. If they are taken out seven at a time, there are no eggs left over. How many eggs are in the basket?

4. (Ancient Chinese Problem) A number of units of work are to be performed by workmen. If sets of 2, 3, 6, and 12 men work for certain numbers of whole days there remain, respectively, 1, 2, 5, and 5 units of work not completed. How many units are there?

PROBLEMS

1. Prove Corollary 6.1.

2. Prove Corollary 6.2.

3.6 / INTRODUCTION TO HIGHER ORDER CONGRUENCES

The fundamental problem in the theory of equations is that of finding all solutions of $f(x) = 0$, where $f(x)$ is a polynomial. A related number theory problem is that of finding all solutions of

$$f(x) \equiv 0 \pmod{m}$$

where $f(x)$ is an *integral polynomial*, that is, a polynomial with integral coefficients.

If a is a solution of $f(x) = 0 \pmod{m}$, then any integer congruent to a, modulo m, is also a solution. Therefore, our problem is to find all incongruent solutions of $f(x) \equiv 0 \pmod{m}$. In general, this problem is very difficult and many of the techniques of solution depend partially on trial-and-error methods. In this section we will prove some general theorems concerning these solutions.

Our first result is a theorem which shows us that if m is not a power of a prime, the problem of solving $f(x) \equiv 0 \pmod{m}$ can be reduced to that of solving a system of congruences in which the moduli are smaller than m.

■ THEOREM 7 / Let $M = m_1 \cdot m_2 \cdots m_n$, where the integers $m_1, m_2, \cdots, m_n$ are relatively prime in pairs. The integer a is a solution of

$$f(x) \equiv 0 \pmod{M}$$

if, and only if, a is a solution of the system

$$\begin{cases} f(x) \equiv 0 \pmod{m_1} \\ f(x) \equiv 0 \pmod{m_2} \\ \quad \cdots \\ f(x) \equiv 0 \pmod{m_n} \end{cases}$$

PROOF: If $f(a) \equiv 0 \pmod{M}$, then obviously $f(a) \equiv 0 \pmod{m_i}$ $(i = 1, 2, \cdots, n)$. Conversely, suppose a is a solution of the system

$$f(x) \equiv 0 \pmod{m_i} \qquad (i = 1, 2, \cdots, n)$$

Then $f(a)$ is a solution of the system

$$\begin{cases} y \equiv 0 \pmod{m_1} \\ y \equiv 0 \pmod{m_2} \\ \quad \cdots \\ y \equiv 0 \pmod{m_n} \end{cases}$$

and it follows from Corollary 6.2 that $f(a) \equiv 0 \pmod{m_1 \cdot m_2 \cdots m_n}$. Thus, a is a solution of $f(x) \equiv 0 \pmod{M}$.

Example I.

Let $f(x) = x^5 - 3x^4 + 7x^3 - 2x^2 - 9x + 6$. Solve $f(x) \equiv 0 \pmod{165}$.

SOLUTION: Since $165 = 11 \cdot 5 \cdot 3$, we first find all solutions of $f(x) \equiv 0 \pmod{11}$, $f(x) \equiv 0 \pmod{5}$, and $f(x) \equiv 0 \pmod{3}$.

By substituting the values $x = 0, 1, 2, \cdots, 10$, we find the solutions of $f(x) \equiv 0$ (mod 11) to be

$$x \equiv 1 \qquad x \equiv 6 \qquad \text{and} \qquad x \equiv 8 \text{ (mod 11)}$$

Similarly, the solutions of $f(x) \equiv 0$ (mod 5) are

$$x \equiv 1 \qquad x \equiv 2 \qquad \text{and} \qquad x \equiv 3 \text{ (mod 5)}$$

and the solutions of $f(x) \equiv 0$ (mod 3) are

$$x \equiv 0 \qquad \text{and} \qquad x \equiv 1 \text{ (mod 3)}$$

Consequently, there are 18 solutions, corresponding to the 18 systems of linear congruence that we can write with one member from each of the above three sets of "partial solutions."

For example, from the systems

$$\begin{cases} x \equiv 1 \text{ (mod 11)} \\ x \equiv 1 \text{ (mod } 5) \\ x \equiv 0 \text{ (mod } 3) \end{cases} \quad \text{and} \quad \begin{cases} x \equiv 6 \text{ (mod 11)} \\ x \equiv 3 \text{ (mod } 5) \\ x \equiv 1 \text{ (mod } 3) \end{cases}$$

we obtain, respectively, the solutions $x \equiv 111$ (mod 165) and $x \equiv 28$ (mod 165).

One of the basic theorems in the theory of equations is the factor theorem. We will prove a corresponding theorem for congruences and use it to determine the maximum number of incongruent solutions of a polynomial congruence with a prime modulus.

■ **THEOREM 8** / (The Factor Theorem.) Let $f(x)$ be an integral polynomial of degree $n > 0$. The integer a is a solution of

$$f(x) \equiv 0 \text{ (mod } m)$$

if, and only if, there exists an integral polynomial $g(x)$ of degree $n - 1$ such that

$$f(x) \equiv (x - a) \cdot g(x) \text{ (mod } m)$$

PROOF: If $f(x) \equiv (x - a) \cdot g(x)$ (mod m)

then $\qquad f(a) \equiv (a - a) \cdot g(a) \equiv 0 \text{ (mod } m)$

To prove the converse, we divide $f(x)$ by $x - a$, obtaining a quotient polynomial $g(x)$ and a constant remainder r. Obviously, $g(x)$ has integral coefficients and is of degree $n - 1$, while r is an integer. Thus,

$$f(x) = (x - a) \cdot g(x) + r$$

If we substitute $x = a$, we obtain

$$f(a) = (a - a) g(a) + r \equiv r \ (\text{mod } m)$$

Because a is a solution of $f(x) \equiv 0 \ (\text{mod } m)$, we also know that $f(a) \equiv 0$ $(\text{mod } m)$. Thus, $r \equiv 0 \ (\text{mod } m)$, implying that

$$f(x) \equiv (x - a) g(x) \ (\text{mod } m)$$

The next two theorems are only valid if the modulus is a prime. (Example 1 furnishes a counterexample for the two propositions if we allow the modulus to be composite.)

■ THEOREM 9 / Let p be a prime number and $f(x)$ an integral polynomial of degree n. If $a_1, a_2, \cdots, a_t$ are incongruent solutions of $f(x) \equiv 0 \ (\text{mod } p)$, there exists an integral polynomial $g_t(x)$ of degree $n - t$ such that

$$f(x) \equiv (x - a_1)(x - a_2) \cdots (x - a_t) g_t(x) \ (\text{mod } p)$$

PROOF: By Theorem 8 there is an integral polynomial $g_1(x)$ of degree $n - 1$ such that

$$f(x) \equiv (x - a_1) \cdot g_1(x) \ (\text{mod } p)$$

Since a_2 is a solution of $f(x) \equiv 0 \ (\text{mod } p)$, then

$$f(a_2) \equiv (a_2 - a_1) \cdot g_1(a_2) \equiv 0 \ (\text{mod } p)$$

Since $a_2 - a_1 \not\equiv 0 \ (\text{mod } p)$, then

$$g_1(a_2) \equiv 0 \ (\text{mod } p)$$

We now apply Theorem 8 again and write

$$g_1(x) \equiv (x - a_2) \cdot g_2(x) \ (\text{mod } p)$$

and substitute, obtaining

$$f(x) \equiv (x - a_1) \cdot (x - a_2) \cdot g_2(x) \ (\text{mod } p)$$

where the degree of $g_2(x)$ is $n - 2$.

If we repeat this argument using successively $a_3, a_4, \cdots, a_t$, we eventually obtain

$$f(x) \equiv (x - a_1) \cdot (x - a_2) \cdots (x - a_t) \cdot g_t(x) \ (\text{mod } p)$$

where $g_t(x)$ is an integral polynomial of degree $n - t$.

■ THEOREM 10 / (The Theorem of Lagrange.) Let p be a prime number, and let $f(x)$ be an integral polynomial of degree n. The congruence $f(x) \equiv 0$

(mod p) has at most n incongruent solutions, modulo p, unless each co-efficient of $f(x)$ is congruent to zero, modulo p.

The proof, which follows immediately from Theorem 9, is left for the reader.

EXERCISES

1. Find all 18 solutions of the congruence in Example 1. (As mentioned earlier, the most efficient way to work problems of this type is by using Corollary 6.2.)

2. Solve the following congruences:
  (a) $x^3 - 2x^2 - 5x + 10 \equiv 0$ (mod 17)
  (b) $x^2 - 11 \equiv 0$ (mod 23)
  (c) $x^2 + 11 \equiv 0$ (mod 23)

3. Solve: $2x^3 - 25x^2 + 9x + 1 \equiv 0$ (mod 715).

PROBLEMS

1. Where does the proof break down if we try to prove Theorem 9 for a composite modulus, using the same argument as for a prime modulus?

2. Prove Theorem 10.

3. Let $f(x)$ be an integral polynomial. For each positive integer k, let $\alpha(k)$ denote the number of incongruent solutions of

$$f(x) \equiv 0 \text{ (mod } k)$$

Prove: If $m_1, m_2, \cdots, m_n$ are pairwise relatively prime integers, then

$$\alpha(m_1 m_2 \cdots m_n) = \alpha(m_1)\, \alpha(m_2) \cdots \alpha(m_n)$$

4. Let $f(x)$ be an integral polynomial of positive degree. Prove that

$$f(1), f(2), \cdots, f(n), \cdots$$

are not all prime numbers.

APPENDIX / A CALENDAR PROBLEM

In this section we will derive a formula in which the day of the week is expressed as a function of the calendar date.

In the Gregorian calendar a normal year consists of 52 weeks and one day, while in a leap year an extra day is added at the end of February. Recall that a noncentury year is a leap year if it has a number divisible by 4, but a century year is a leap year only when it has a number divisible by 400. Thus, 1600 was a leap year, but 1700, 1800, and 1900 were not.

We will make two restrictions in order to simplify our formula. (1) Because a century leap year occurred 18 years after the calendar reform in 1582 we will find it convenient to develop a formula only for the years subsequent to 1600. (2) In order not to add the extra day during the course of the leap year, we will start the new year on March 1. Thus, for purposes of our computation, February 29, 1872 is considered to be the last day of the twelfth month of 1871.

To reduce the problem to one involving numbers, we assign the numbers 1, 2, $\cdots$, 12 to the months March, April $\cdots$, February, and the numbers 0, 1, $\cdots$, 6 to the days Sunday, Monday, $\cdots$, Saturday, respectively.

Let us suppose that March 1, 1600 fell on day of the week number a. Then

$$\text{March 1, 1601 fell on day } a + 1 \pmod 7$$
$$\text{March 1, 1602 fell on day } a + 2 \pmod 7$$
$$\text{March 1, 1603 fell on day } a + 3 \pmod 7$$
$$\text{March 1, 1604 fell on day } a + 4 + 1 \pmod 7$$

In general, March 1 of the year $1600 + t$ falls on day number d, where

$$d \equiv a + t + \text{(the number of elapsed leap years) (mod 7)}$$

It is not difficult to compute the number of elapsed leap years. If $t < 100$, this number is simply $[t/4]$. If $t \geq 100$, it is the number $[t/4]$, *minus* the number of elapsed century years, $[t/100]$, *plus* the number of elapsed century leap years, $[t/400]$. (These numbers would be much more difficult to calculate if we did not start with a century leap year.)

Therefore, March 1 of the year $1600 + t$ will occur on the day of the week that is congruent, modulo 7, to

$$a + t + \left[\frac{t}{4}\right] - \left[\frac{t}{100}\right] + \left[\frac{t}{400}\right]$$

If the reader substitutes the value of t obtained from the current year and sets this congruent to the day on which March 1 falls (found by checking a current calendar) he will find that $a \equiv 3 \pmod 7$. Therefore, March 1, 1600 fell on a Wednesday.

Our formula to determine d, the day on which March 1 falls in the year $1600 + t$ is thus

$$d \equiv 3 + t + \left[\frac{t}{4}\right] - \left[\frac{t}{100}\right] + \left[\frac{t}{400}\right] \pmod 7$$

We will now rewrite this formula so that we can substitute the year number directly. We write the year number N in the form

$$N = 100\,C + D \qquad 0 \le D < 100$$

For the year N we obviously have

$$t = N - 1600 = 100\,C + D - 1600$$

If we now substitute this value of t into the above formula we obtain

$$d \equiv 3 + (100\,C + D - 1600) + \left[\frac{100\,C + D - 1600}{4}\right]$$

$$- \left[\frac{100\,C + D - 1600}{100}\right] + \left[\frac{100\,C + D - 1600}{400}\right] \pmod 7$$

Using Theorem 8(a) of Chapter 1, we can rewrite this as

$$d \equiv 3 + 100\,C + D - 1600 + 25\,C + \left[\frac{D}{4}\right] - 400$$

$$- C - \left[\frac{D}{100}\right] + 16 + \left[\frac{100\,C + D}{400}\right] - 4 \pmod 7$$

Because $0 \le D < 100$, then $[D/100] = 0$. It is easy to show that

$$\left[\frac{100\,C + D}{400}\right] = \left[\frac{C}{4}\right]$$

Substituting these values into the above expression and simplifying, we obtain

$$d \equiv 3 - 2C + D + \left[\frac{C}{4}\right] + \left[\frac{D}{4}\right] \pmod 7$$

We now have a formula to compute the day of the week on which March 1 falls in a given year. In order to extend this formula to cover other dates, we consider the following information:

The number of April 1 is 3 units greater than that of March 1.
The number of May 1 is 2 units greater than that of April 1.
The number of June 1 is 3 units greater than that of May 1.
The number of July 1 is 2 units greater than that of June 1.
The number of August 1 is 3 units greater than that of July 1.
The number of September 1 is 3 units greater than that of August 1.
The number of October 1 is 2 units greater than that of September 1.
The number of November 1 is 3 units greater than that of October 1.
The number of December 1 is 2 units greater than that of November 1.

The number of January 1 is 3 units greater than that of December 1.
The number of February 1 is 3 units greater than that of January 1.

It was observed by Rev. Zeller that the function $f(m) = [2.6m - 0.2]$ takes on the same increments as the above table when m varies from 1 to 12. When $m = 1$, we obtain $f(m) = [2.6 - 0.2] = 2$. Thus, the formula for March 1 becomes

$$d \equiv 1 + [2.6 - 0.2] - 2C + D + \left[\frac{C}{4}\right] + \left[\frac{D}{4}\right] \pmod{7}$$

and the first day of the mth month falls on day

$$d' \equiv 1 + [2.6m - 0.2] - 2C + D + \left[\frac{C}{4}\right] + \left[\frac{D}{4}\right] \pmod{7}$$

From this it is obvious that the rth day of the mth month of year $100C + D$ falls on day number

$$d \equiv r + [2.6m - 0.2] - 2C + D + \left[\frac{C}{4}\right] + \left[\frac{D}{4}\right] \pmod{7}$$

Example.

Determine the day of the week on which January 17, 1932 fell.

SOLUTION: For the purposes of our computation, January 1932 is considered to be the eleventh month of 1931. Thus,

$$r = 17 \qquad m = 11 \qquad C = 19 \qquad D = 31$$

From the formula we obtain

$$d \equiv 17 + [(2.6)(11) - 0.2] - 2 \cdot 19 + 31 + \left[\frac{19}{4}\right] + \left[\frac{31}{4}\right]$$

$$\equiv 17 + 28 - 38 + 31 + 4 + 7 \equiv 0 \pmod{7}$$

Thus, January 17, 1932 was a Sunday.

EXERCISES

1. Determine the day of the week on which you were born.

2. Show that

$$\left[\frac{100C + D}{400}\right] = \left[\frac{C}{4}\right] \text{ if } 0 \le D < 100$$

THE EULER–FERMAT THEOREM / 4

4.1 / COMPLETE SYSTEMS OF RESIDUES

The most important function considered in elementary number theory is Euler's totient function φ.[1] In this chapter we will develop certain properties of this function, using the concepts of complete and reduced systems of residues.

■ DEFINITION / Let m be a positive integer. A set of integers is called a *complete system of residues, modulo m*, if the set contains exactly one element from each residue class, modulo m.

Example.

Let $m = 7$. Because 1 is in $\mathscr{R}_1$, 16 is in $\mathscr{R}_2$, -11 is in $\mathscr{R}_3$, 53 is in $\mathscr{R}_4$, -44 is in $\mathscr{R}_5$, 69 is in $\mathscr{R}_6$, and -77 is in $\mathscr{R}_7$, then

$$\{1, 16, -11, 53, -44, 69, -77\}$$

is a complete system of residues (mod 7).

Because there are exactly m distinct residue classes (mod m), namely $\mathscr{R}_0$, $\mathscr{R}_1$, $\mathscr{R}_2$, $\cdots$, $\mathscr{R}_{m-1}$, then a complete system of residues must contain exactly m elements. The simplest complete system of residues is, obviously, $0, 1, \cdots, m - 1$.

The first theorem states a different set of conditions under which a set is known to be a complete system of residues. This is important, because the conditions in the theorem are usually easier to check than are the conditions in the definition.

---

[1] Euler's function will be defined in Section 4.2.

■ THEOREM 1 / Let m be a positive integer and let S be a nonvoid set of integers. S is a complete system of residues (mod m) if, and only if,

(1) S contains m elements, and

(2) no two elements of S are congruent, modulo m.

PROOF: Obviously, if S is a complete system of residues, the two conditions are satisfied.

To prove the converse, we note that if no two elements of S are congruent, the elements of S are in different residue classes (mod m). Since S has m elements, all the residue classes must be represented among the elements of S. Thus, S is a complete system of residues (mod m).

PROBLEMS

1. Let m be a positive integer and let r be relatively prime to m. Show that the finite arithmetic progression

$$\{a, a + r, a + 2r, \cdots, a + (m - 1) \cdot r\}$$

is a complete system of residues (mod m).

2. Suppose $(m, n) = 1$. Let $\{a_1, a_2, \cdots, a_m\}$ be a complete system of residues (mod m), and let $\{b_1, b_2, \cdots, b_n\}$ be a complete system of residues (mod n). Let S be the set of all integers of form

$$a_i n + b_j m \qquad (i = 1, 2, \cdots, m; j = 1, 2, \cdots, n)$$

Show that S is a complete system of residues (mod mn).

4.2 / REDUCED SYSTEMS OF RESIDUES

Corollary 4.6 of Chapter 1 can be restated using the congruence notation as follows: *If*

$$a \equiv b \pmod{m}$$

then

$$(a, m) = (b, m)$$

In other words, if a and b are in the same residue class (mod m) then $(a, m) = (b, m)$. This leads us naturally to the following definition:

■ DEFINITION / Let $\mathcal{R}_a$ be a residue class (mod m). We say that $\mathcal{R}_a$ is *relatively prime to* m provided each element of $\mathcal{R}_a$ is relatively prime to m.

This is equivalent to saying that $\mathcal{R}_a$ is relatively prime to m if, and only if, $(a, m) = 1$.

Example I.

$\mathcal{R}_1$, $\mathcal{R}_3$, $\mathcal{R}_7$, and $\mathcal{R}_9$ (mod 10) are the residue classes that are relatively prime to 10.

Euler's totient function φ is defined as follows:

■ DEFINITION / Let m be a positive integer. $\varphi(m)$ is the number of residue classes (mod m) that are relatively prime to m.

From the above example, we see that $\varphi(10) = 4$. Similarly, since $\mathcal{R}_1$, $\mathcal{R}_3$, $\mathcal{R}_{19}$, $\mathcal{R}_{-5}$, $\mathcal{R}_{11}$, and $\mathcal{R}_{13}$ (mod 14) are the residue classes relatively prime to 14, we see that $\varphi(14) = 6$. Obviously, $\varphi(1) = 1$ since 1 is relatively prime to the single residue class (mod 1).

■ DEFINITION / A nonvoid set of integers is called a *reduced system of residues, modulo m*, if the set contains exactly one element from each residue class (mod m) that is relatively prime to m.

Example 2.

Since 1 is in $\mathcal{R}_1$, -17 is in $\mathcal{R}_3$, 87 is in $\mathcal{R}_7$, and 19 is in $\mathcal{R}_9$ (mod 10), then

$$\{1, -17, 87, 19\}$$

is a reduced system of residues (mod 10). Similarly,

$$\{1, 3, 19, -5, 11, 23\}$$

is a reduced system of residues (mod 14).

One method to obtain a reduced system of residues is to start with a complete system of residues and delete those elements that are not relatively prime to the modulus. Thus, the simplest reduced system of residues, modulo m ($m > 1$), is just the collection of all integers in the set $\{1, \cdots, m-1\}$ that are relatively prime to m.

We will now prove a theorem similar to Theorem 1 that gives us an alternate set of conditions under which a set of integers is known to be a reduced system of residues (mod m). In actual practice the conditions in the theorem are usually easier to check than are the conditions in the definition.

■ THEOREM 2 / Let m be a positive integer. A set of integers S is a reduced system of residues (mod m) if, and only if,
   (1) S contains exactly $\varphi(m)$ elements,
   (2) no two elements of S are congruent (mod m),
and (3) each element of S is relatively prime to m.

PROOF: It is obvious from the definition that a reduced system of residues must satisfy all three conditions.

To prove the converse we suppose that S is a set of integers having the three properties. Because no two elements of S are congruent, the elements are in different residue classes (mod m). Since the elements of S are relatively prime to m, they are in residue classes that are relatively prime to m. Thus, the $\varphi(m)$ elements of S are distributed among the $\varphi(m)$ residue classes that are relatively prime to m, one in each residue class. Therefore, S is a reduced system of residues, modulo m.

The conditions established in Theorem 2 are frequently easy to check when considering particular examples. As a simple application we state the following corollary (the proof is left for the reader):

■ COROLLARY 2.1 / If $\{r_1, r_2, \cdots, r_{\varphi(m)}\}$ is a reduced system of residues (mod m), and if $(a, m) = 1$, then $\{ar_1, ar_2, \cdots, ar_{\varphi(m)}\}$ is also a reduced system of residues (mod m).

EXERCISE

1. Prove Corollary 2.1.

PROBLEM

1. Let m and n be relatively prime. Let $\{a_1, a_2, \cdots, a_{\varphi(m)}\}$ and $\{b_1, b_2, \cdots, b_{\varphi(n)}\}$ be reduced systems of residues, modulo m and n, respectively. Let S be the set of all integers of form

$$a_i n + b_j m \ (i = 1, 2, \cdots, \varphi(m); j = 1, 2, \cdots, \varphi(n))$$

Prove that S is a reduced system of residues (mod mn). (This result is needed for Problem 1 of Section 4.3.)

4.3 / EVALUATION OF EULER'S TOTIENT FUNCTION

■ DEFINITION / A function α defined on the positive integers is said to be *multiplicative* if $\alpha(m\,n) = \alpha(m) \cdot \alpha(n)$ whenever m and n are relatively prime.

For example, the function α, defined in Problem 3 of Section 3.6 is a multiplicative function. The function that is identically zero is trivially a multiplicative function. The function β, defined by $\beta(n) = n^2$, is a multiplicative function.

As a first step in obtaining a formula for $\varphi(n)$, we shall prove that φ is a multiplicative function. Because it is easy to establish that $\varphi(4) = 2$ and $\varphi(5) = 4$, we can then calculate that $\varphi(20) = \varphi(4) \cdot \varphi(5) = 8$, so that a reduced system of residues (mod 20) contains eight elements. Note that the fact that φ is multiplicative does not imply that $\varphi(20) = \varphi(2) \cdot \varphi(10)$. (Why not?)

■ THEOREM 3 / The function φ is multiplicative.

PROOF: Let m and n be relatively prime positive integers and let $\{a_1, a_2, \cdots, a_{\varphi(m)}\}$ and $\{b_1, b_2, \cdots, b_{\varphi(n)}\}$ be reduced systems of residues, modulo m and n, respectively. We will calculate a set of numbers $\{c_{ij}\}$ as follows: For each pair i and j where $1 \leq i \leq \varphi(m)$, $1 \leq j \leq \varphi(n)$, we let c_{ij} be the unique solution of the system of congruences

$$\begin{cases} x \equiv a_i \ (\text{mod } m) \\ x \equiv b_j \ (\text{mod } n) \end{cases}$$

which is in the range $1 \leq x \leq mn$ (see Theorem 6 of Chapter 3). Thus, we obtain the set of $\varphi(m) \cdot \varphi(n)$ numbers listed in Table 4.1.

Table 4.1

	b_1	b_2	$\cdots$	b_j	$\cdots$	$b_{\varphi(n)}$
a_1	c_{11}	c_{12}	$\cdots$	c_{1j}	$\cdots$	$c_{1\varphi(n)}$
a_2	c_{21}	c_{22}	$\cdots$	c_{2j}	$\cdots$	$c_{2,\varphi(n)}$
$\cdots$	$\cdots$	$\cdots$	$\cdots$	$\cdots$	$\cdots$	$\cdots$
a_i	c_{i1}	c_{i2}	$\cdots$	c_{ij}	$\cdots$	$c_{i,\varphi(n)}$
$\cdots$	$\cdots$	$\cdots$	$\cdots$	$\cdots$	$\cdots$	$\cdots$
$a_{\varphi(m)}$	$c_{\varphi(m),1}$	$c_{\varphi(m),2}$	$\cdots$	$c_{\varphi(m),j}$	$\cdots$	$c_{\varphi(m),\varphi(n)}$

If we can show that this set is a reduced system of residues, modulo mn, we will know that $\varphi(mn) = \varphi(m) \cdot \varphi(n)$. The proof of this fact will be in three parts.

I. We will show that the c's are incongruent (mod mn). Suppose $c_{ij} \equiv c_{st}$ (mod mn). Then

$$a_i \equiv c_{ij} \equiv c_{st} \equiv a_s \ (\text{mod } m)$$

which, because the a's came from a reduced system of residues (mod m), implies that $i = s$. In a similar way we see that $b_j \equiv b_t$ (mod n) and, therefore,

$j = t$. Thus, if $i \neq s$ or $j \neq t$, then $c_{ij} \not\equiv c_{st} \pmod{mn}$. In other words, we have $\varphi(m) \cdot \varphi(n)$ incongruent numbers in the set $\{c_{ij}\}$.

II. Next we will show that each c_{it} is relatively prime to mn. Since $a_i \equiv c_{ij} \pmod{m}$, then

$$(c_{ij}, m) = (a_i, m) = 1$$

and, similarly

$$(c_{ij}, n) = (b_j, n) = 1$$

Since c_{ij} is relatively prime to both m and n, then c_{ij} is relatively prime to m.

III. Let $\mathcal{R}_k$ be a residue class $\pmod{mn}$, that is relatively prime to mn. We will show that one of the c's is in $\mathcal{R}_k$. Since $\mathcal{R}_k$ is relatively prime to mn, the integer k is relatively prime to mn, and thus also to m and n. Since $\{a_1, \cdots, a_{\varphi(m)}\}$ is a reduced system of residues, modulo m, there is an element in this set, say a_i, that is congruent to $k \pmod{m}$. Similarly, there is an element b_j that is congruent to $k \pmod{n}$. Thus, k is a solution of

$$\begin{cases} x \equiv a_i \pmod{m} \\ x \equiv b_j \pmod{m} \end{cases}$$

and so, by Theorem 6 of Chapter 3, $k \equiv c_{ij} \pmod{mn}$. Thus, c_{ij} is in the residue class $\mathcal{R}_k \pmod{mn}$.

Hence, the numbers in the constructed set are all in different residue classes, and a residue class is represented in the set if, and only if, it is relatively prime to mn. Therefore, the set is a reduced system of residues, modulo mn; and $\varphi(m) \cdot \varphi(n)$, the number of elements in the constructed set, is equal to $\varphi(mn)$.

Because φ is multiplicative, we will be able to evaluate the function if we can evaluate it for powers of each prime p.

■ **THEOREM 4** / If p is a prime number and α is a positive integer, $\varphi(p^\alpha) = p^\alpha \cdot (1 - 1/p) = p^{\alpha - 1} \cdot (p - 1)$.

PROOF: Because the set of integers

$$\{1, 2, \cdots, p, p + 1, \cdots, 2p, \cdots, 3p, \cdots, p^{\alpha - 1}p\}$$

is a complete system of residues, modulo p^α, we can obtain a reduced system by deleting from this set all elements that are not relatively prime to p^α. Since p is a prime, the only numbers not relatively prime to p^α are the multiples of p. Thus, we must delete the $p^{\alpha - 1}$ numbers

$$\{p, 2p, 3p, \cdots, p^{\alpha - 1}p\}$$

Therefore,

$$\varphi(p^\alpha) = p^\alpha - p^{\alpha - 1} = p^{\alpha - 1}(p - 1) = p^\alpha\left(1 - \frac{1}{p}\right)$$

∎ **COROLLARY 4.1** / If $n = p_1^{\alpha_1} p_2^{\alpha_2} \cdots p_k^{\alpha_k}$, where the p's are distinct prime numbers, then

$$\varphi(n) = n\left(1 - \frac{1}{p_1}\right)\left(1 - \frac{1}{p_2}\right) \cdots \left(1 - \frac{1}{p_k}\right)$$

The proof, which follows directly from Theorem 4 and the multiplicative property of φ, is left for the reader.

Example.

Calculate $\varphi(7^2 \cdot 13^4 \cdot 19)$.

SOLUTION: $\varphi(7^2 \cdot 13^4 \cdot 19) = \varphi(7^2) \cdot \varphi(13^4) \cdot \varphi(19)$ (by Theorem 3)

$$= 7(7-1) \cdot 13^3 (13-1) \cdot (19-1)$$

$$= 1,680,932$$

EXERCISES

1. Calculate $\varphi(9702)$ and $\varphi(873)$.

2. Prove that $\varphi(n)$ is even if $n > 2$.

3. Prove Corollary 4.1.

4. Find all solutions of $\varphi(n) = 14$.

5. If α is a multiplicative function, not identically zero, prove that $\alpha(1) = 1$.

PROBLEM

1. Use Problem 1 of Section 4.2 to devise a new proof that φ is multiplicative.

4.4 / THE EULER–FERMAT THEOREM

The significance of Euler's totient function in elementary number theory rests primarily on certain of its properties that are superficially unrelated to the definition of the function. Two of these properties will be established in Theorem 5 and Theorem 7.

A special case of Theorem 5 was proved by Fermat and the general theorem was later proved by Euler. We will reverse the historical order and prove the generalization first. (Also see Problem 3.)

■ **THEOREM** 5 / (Euler–Fermat) If m is a positive integer and $(a, m) = 1$, then

$$a^{\varphi(m)} \equiv 1 \pmod{m}$$

PROOF: Let $\{r_1, r_2, \cdots, r_{\varphi(m)}\}$ be a reduced system of residues (mod m). It follows from Corollary 2.1 that $\{ar_1, ar_2, \cdots, ar_{\varphi(m)}\}$ is also a reduced system of residues (mod m). Thus, each ar_i is congruent to one, and only one, of the elements in the original set. Therefore, the products of the elements in the sets are congruent; that is,

$$(ar_1) \cdot (ar_2) \cdots (ar_{\varphi(m)}) \equiv r_1 r_2 \cdots r_{\varphi(m)} \pmod{m}$$

Because each r_i is relatively prime to m, we apply the cancellation law for congruences to obtain $a^{\varphi(m)} \equiv 1 \pmod{m}$.

■ **COROLLARY** 5.1 / (Fermat's Theorem) If p is a prime number and a is an integer, then

$$a^p \equiv a \pmod{p}$$

PROOF: If $(a, p) = 1$, then $\varphi(p) = p - 1$. By Theorem 5,

$$a^{p-1} \equiv 1 \pmod{p}$$

and so $\qquad\qquad a^p \equiv a \pmod{p}$

If $(a, p) \neq 1$, then $a \equiv 0 \pmod{p}$. Thus,

$$a^p \equiv 0 \equiv a \pmod{p}$$

Example.

Calculate $7^{1015} \pmod{31}$.
Because $\varphi(31) = 30$ and $(7, 31) = 1$,

$$7^{30} \equiv 1 \pmod{31}$$

Since $1015 = 30 \cdot 33 + 25$,

$$7^{1015} \equiv 7^{30 \cdot 33 + 25} \equiv 1^{33} \cdot 7^{25} \equiv 7^{25} \pmod{31}$$

To calculate $7^{25} \pmod{31}$ we first calculate $7^n \pmod{31}$ where $n = 2, 4, 8, 16$, obtaining

$$7^2 \equiv 49 \equiv -13 \pmod{31}$$
$$7^4 \equiv 169 \equiv 14 \pmod{31}$$
$$7^8 \equiv 196 \equiv 10 \pmod{31}$$
$$7^{16} \equiv 100 \equiv 7 \pmod{31}$$

Thus, $7^{25} \equiv 7 \cdot 7^8 \cdot 7^{16} \equiv 7 \cdot 10 \cdot 7 \equiv 490 \equiv 25 \equiv -6 \pmod{31}$.

EXERCISES

1. Calculate 3^{1000} (mod 7).

2. Calculate 7^{1000} (mod 54).

3. Use Fermat's theorem to prove: If p is a prime, then $(a \pm b)^p \equiv a^p \pm b^p$ (mod p).

PROBLEMS

1. If p is a prime and $1 \le k \le p - 1$, show that the binomial coefficient $\binom{p}{k}$ is divisible by p.

2. Prove Fermat's theorem by induction on a. [*Hint:* Expand $a^p \equiv [(a - 1) + 1]^p$ (mod p) by the binomial theorem (Problem 3 of Section 1.2) and use Problem 1.]

3. (*Knowledge of elementary modern algebra is required.*) Prove that the Euler-Fermat theorem follows from the fact that the order of an element of a finite group divides the order of the group.

4.5* / APPLICATION TO HIGHER ORDER CONGRUENCES

Fermat's theorem can frequently be used to obtain information about the solutions of the congruence

$$f(x) \equiv 0 \ (\text{mod } p)$$

where $f(x)$ is an integral polynomial.

The most obvious use of the theorem is in reducing the congruence to one of lower degree, if $f(x)$ has degree greater than or equal to p.

Example I.

Let $f(x) = 3x^{10} - 7x^9 + 4x^8 - 3x^7 + 2x^6 - x^5 + x^3 - 4x^2 - x + 3$.

Show that the congruence $f(x) \equiv 0$ (mod 5) has the same solutions as

$$3x^3 + x^2 + x + 2 \equiv 0 \ (\text{mod } 5)$$

SOLUTION: If x is any integer, from Fermat's theorem we obtain

$$x^5 \equiv x, \ x^6 \equiv x^2, \ x^7 \equiv x^3, \ x^8 \equiv x^4, \ x^9 \equiv x, \text{ and } x^{10} \equiv x^2 \ (\text{mod } 5)$$

Substituting these values into the congruence $f(x) \equiv 0$ (mod 5) and reducing the coefficients (mod 5), we see that x is a solution of the above congruence if and only if x is a solution of

$$(1) \quad 4x^4 + 3x^3 + x^2 + x + 3 \equiv 0 \text{ (mod 5)}$$

In this particular congruence, $x \equiv 0$ (mod 5) is obviously not a solution, so that any solution must be relatively prime to 5. Thus, we can apply the Euler–Fermat theorem, obtaining $x^4 \equiv 1$ (mod 5) for each solution x. If we substitute this into the congruence (1), we see that any solution of $f(x) \equiv 0$ (mod 5) must also be a solution of

$$(2) \quad 3x^3 + x^2 + x + 2 \equiv 0 \text{ (mod 5)}$$

Because $x \equiv 0$ (mod 5) is not a solution of this last congruence, any solution of (2) must also be a solution of (1). Thus, $f(x) \equiv 0$ (mod 5) and $x^3 + x^2 + x + 2 \equiv 0$ (mod 5) have the same solutions.

For the rest of this section we will assume that the degree of the polynomial congruence $f(x) \equiv 0$ (mod p) is n, where $0 < n < p$.

A problem of interest is that of determining when the integral polynomial $f(x)$ is congruent (mod p) to a product of distinct linear terms. This is equivalent (see Theorem 9 of Chapter 3) to determining when $f(x) \equiv 0$ (mod p) has n incongruent solutions (mod p). Before devising a test for this property, we make one further observation: If

$$f(x) = a_n x^n + a_{n-1} x^{n-1} + \cdots + a_1 x + a_0, \quad a_n \not\equiv 0 \text{ (mod } p)$$

there is a polynomial

$$g(x) = x^n + b_{n-1} x^{n-1} + \cdots + b_1 x + b_0$$

such that $f(x) \equiv 0$ (mod p) and $g(x) \equiv 0$ (mod p) have the same solutions. We obtain $g(x)$ by multiplying $f(x)$ by a solution of

$$a_n y \equiv 1 \text{ (mod } p)$$

and reducing the coefficients (mod p).

■ **THEOREM 6** / Let p be a prime number and let $f(x)$ be an integral polynomial of degree n, $0 < n < p$, which has a leading coefficient of 1. Divide $x^p - x$ by $f(x)$ obtaining a quotient $q(x)$ and a remainder $r(x)$, where the degree of $r(x)$ is less than n. The congruence $f(x) \equiv 0$ (mod p) has n incongruent solutions (mod p) if, and only if, each coefficient of $r(x)$ is divisible by p.

PROOF: We write $x^p - x = f(x) \cdot q(x) + r(x)$. Since the leading coefficient of $f(x)$ is 1, then $q(x)$ and $r(x)$ have integral coefficients.

Part I. Suppose $f(x) \equiv 0$ (mod p) has n incongruent solutions. Because $r(x)$ is congruent (mod p) to

$$x^p - x - f(x) \cdot q(x)$$

and (by Fermat's theorem) any solution of $f(x) \equiv 0$ (mod p) is also a solution of $x^p - x \equiv 0$ (mod p), then $r(x) \equiv 0$ (mod p) has at least n incongruent solutions. From the Theorem of Lagrange (Theorem 10 of Chapter 3), it follows that each coefficient of $r(x)$ is divisible by p.

Part II. Suppose each coefficient of $r(x)$ is divisible by p. Then $r(x) \equiv 0$ (mod p) and $x^p - x \equiv 0$ (mod p) have p incongruent solutions. Thus,

$$f(x) \cdot q(x) \equiv x^p - x - r(x) \equiv 0 \text{ (mod } p)$$

also has p incongruent solutions. Since $f(x) \cdot q(x)$ has degree p and since any solution of $f(x)q(x) \equiv 0$ (mod p) must be a solution of $f(x) \equiv 0$ or $g(x) \equiv 0$ (mod p), it follows that $f(x) \equiv 0$ (mod p) has n incongruent solutions and $q(x) \equiv 0$ (mod p) has $p - n$ incongruent solutions (mod p).

Example 2.

Determine whether the congruences

$$(a) \quad x^4 + 2x^3 + 2x^2 + x + 2 \equiv 0 \text{ (mod 5)}$$

and $\qquad\qquad (b) \quad 2x^4 + 3x^3 - 3x^2 + 8x \equiv 0 \text{ (mod 5)}$

have four incongruent solutions.

SOLUTION: (*a*) Dividing $x^5 - x$ by $x^4 + 2x^3 + 2x^2 + x + 2$ we obtain

$$x^5 - x = (x^4 + 2x^3 + 2x^2 + x + 2) \cdot (x - 2) + (2x^3 + 3x^2 - x + 4)$$

Since the coefficients of the remainder are not divisible by 5, the congruence does not have four incongruent solutions.

(*b*) Multiplying $2x^4 + 3x^3 - 3x^2 + 8x$ by 3, we see that

$$x^4 + 4x^3 + x^2 + 4x \equiv 0 \text{ (mod 5)}$$

has the same solutions as (*b*). Since

$$x^5 - x = (x^4 + 4x^3 + x^2 + 4x)(x - 4) + (15x^3 + 15x)$$

congruence (*b*) has four incongruent solutions.

■ COROLLARY 6.1 / Let p be a prime number and let n be a positive divisor of $p - 1$. The congruence

$$x^n - 1 \equiv 0 \text{ (mod } p)$$

has exactly n incongruent solutions.

PROOF: It follows from the algebraic identity

$$x^p - x = (x^{p-1} - 1)x = (x^n - 1)(x^{p-1-n} + x^{p-1-2n} + \cdots + x^n + 1)x$$

that the remainder is zero when $x^p - x$ is divided by $x^n - 1$.

EXERCISES

1. Use the Euler–Fermat theorem to reduce $f(x) \equiv 0 \pmod{p}$ to give $g(x) \equiv 0 \pmod{p}$ where $g(x)$ has degree less than $p - 1$. Shown that $g(x) \equiv 0 \pmod{p}$ does not have the same solution sets as $f(x) \equiv 0 \pmod{p}$.
   (a) $f(x) = x^5 + 2x^4 + 3x^3 - 2x^2 - x$, $p = 5$;
   (b) $f(x) = 3x^6 - x^5 + 3x^4 + x^3 + x^2 - x + 2$, $p = 5$.

2. Use Theorem 6 to determine if the following polynomial congruences have n incongruent solutions.
   (a) $x^4 - 2x^3 + x^2 - 3x + 1 \equiv 0 \pmod{7}$, $n = 4$.
   (b) $5x^4 - x^3 + 4x^2 + 4x + 3 \equiv 0 \pmod{11}$, $n = 4$.

3. Show that the congruence $x^p + a \equiv 0 \pmod{p}$ has only the solution $x \equiv -a \pmod{p}$.

4. Suppose $f(x) = a_p x^p + a_{p-1} x^{p-1} + \cdots + a_1 x + a_0$ where $a_0 \not\equiv 0 \pmod{p}$ and $a_{p-1} + a_0 \equiv 0 \pmod{p}$. Prove that $f(x) \equiv 0 \pmod{p}$ has at most $p - 3$ incongruent solutions.

4.6 / AN IMPORTANT THEOREM

A second important property of Euler's totient function will be established in Theorem 7. Before proving this theorem we introduce a new symbol.

■ NOTATION / If n is a positive integer and α is a function defined on the positive integers, the symbol "$\sum_{d|n} \alpha(d)$" means the sum of all of the numbers $\alpha(d)$ as d ranges over the positive divisors of n.

For example, if $\alpha = \varphi$ and $n = 10$, then

$$\sum_{d|10} \varphi(d) = \varphi(1) + \varphi(2) + \varphi(5) + \varphi(10) = 1 + 1 + 4 + 4 = 10$$

If α is defined by $\alpha(m) = m$ and $n = 15$, then

$$\sum_{d|15} \alpha(d) = \sum_{d|15} d = 1 + 3 + 5 + 15 = 24$$

One observation will be made at this time:

$$\sum_{d|n} \alpha(d) = \sum_{d|n} \alpha\left(\frac{n}{d}\right)$$

This is obvious if we notice that as *d* ranges over all divisors of *n*, so does *n/d*.

■ THEOREM 7 / If *n* is a positive integer, then $\sum_{d|n} \varphi(d) = n$.

We will prove the theorem by partitioning the set $\{1, 2, \cdots, n\}$ into non-overlapping subsets, each of which contains $\varphi(d)$ elements, where *d* is one of the divisors of *n*. The reader will probably have a better understanding of the proof if he verifies it for a particular example (see Exercise 1).

PROOF: Let $d_1, d_2, \cdots, d_t$ be the positive divisors of *n*. If *k* is a positive integer, then the greatest common divisor of *k* and *n* is one of the d_j. For fixed d_j we will determine how many integers *k* from the set $\{1, 2, \cdots, n\}$ have d_j as greatest common divisor with *n*.

Suppose $(k, n) = d_j$. We can write $k = k'd_j$, $n = n'd_j$, where $(k', n') = 1$. Since $1 \le k \le n$, then $1 \le k' \le n'$. Thus, k' is a number in the set $\{1, 2, \cdots, n'\}$ which is relatively prime to n'. Since there are $\varphi(n') = \varphi(n/d_j)$ such numbers, then there are $\varphi(n/d_j)$ values of *k* (since $k = k' \cdot d_j$) in the set $\{1, 2, \cdots, n\}$ which have d_j as the greatest common divisor with *n*.

Since each of the *n* elements in the original set is in one of these subsets, then

$$n = \varphi\left(\frac{n}{d_1}\right) + \varphi\left(\frac{n}{d_2}\right) + \cdots + \varphi\left(\frac{n}{d_t}\right) = \sum_{d|n} \varphi\left(\frac{n}{d}\right)$$

Using the remark preceding the statement of the theorem, we obtain

$$\sum_{d|n} \varphi(d) = \sum_{d|n} \varphi\left(\frac{n}{d}\right) = n$$

EXERCISE

1. Verify the proof of Theorem 7 for the case $n = 65$.

4.7 / THE EXPONENT TO WHICH a BELONGS (mod m)

Let *m* be a positive integer and let *a* be relatively prime to *m*. We know that $\varphi(m)$ is a solution of the congruence $a^x \equiv 1$ (mod *m*). In certain problems it is necessary to know the smallest positive solution of this congruence. For example, this number plays a fundamental role in the theory of decimal expansions of rational numbers.

■ DEFINITION / We say that *a belongs to the exponent k (mod m)* if k is the smallest positive integer x such that $a^x \equiv 1 \pmod{m}$.

Example I.

If we consider the powers of 5 (mod 7), we obtain

$$5^1 \equiv 5 \pmod{7}$$

$$5^2 \equiv 4 \pmod{7}$$

$$5^3 \equiv 6 \pmod{7}$$

$$5^4 \equiv 2 \pmod{7}$$

$$5^5 \equiv 3 \pmod{7}$$

$$5^6 \equiv 1 \pmod{7}$$

Thus, 5 belongs to the exponent 6 (mod 7).

The reader should observe that the powers of 5 form a reduced system of residues (mod 7).

Instead of considering all of the powers of the integer a, it is convenient to restrict the exponents that need to be considered by using the following theorem and its corollary.

■ THEOREM 8 / If $a^t \equiv 1 \pmod{m}$ and a belongs to the exponent k (mod m), then $k|t$.

PROOF: We divide t by k, obtaining

$$t = kq + r \qquad 0 \le r < k$$

Then

$$1 \equiv a^t \equiv a^{kq + r} \equiv (a^k)^q a^r \equiv 1^q \cdot a^r \equiv a^r \pmod{m}$$

Since r is less than k, the *smallest positive* solution of $a^x \equiv 1 \pmod{m}$, then r must be zero. Thus, $t = k \cdot q$, and so $k|t$.

■ COROLLARY 8.1 / If a belongs to the exponent k (mod m), then $k|\varphi(m)$.

Example 2.

Find the exponent k to which 19 belongs (mod 47).

SOLUTION: Since $\varphi(47) = 46$, k must be one of the numbers 1, 2, 23, 46. Computing the powers of 19, we find

$$19^2 \equiv \ 361 \equiv 32 \ (\text{mod } 47)$$

$$19^4 \equiv 1024 \equiv 37 \ (\text{mod } 47)$$

$$19^8 \equiv 1369 \equiv \ 6 \ (\text{mod } 47)$$

$$19^{16} \equiv \ 36 \ \ \ \ \ \ (\text{mod } 47)$$

Thus, $19^{23} \equiv 19^{16} \cdot 19^4 \cdot 19^2 \cdot 19 \equiv 36 \cdot 37 \cdot 32 \cdot 19 \equiv -1 \ (\text{mod } 47)$, and $19^{46} \equiv (-1)^2 \equiv 1 \ (\text{mod } 47)$, so that 19 belongs to the exponent 46 (mod 47).

When finding the exponent to which a belongs for a composite modulus it is usually easiest to use the following theorem. The proof is left for the reader (Exercises 1 and 2).

∎ THEOREM 9 / If a belongs to the exponent s (mod m) and to the exponent t (mod n), then a belongs to the exponent $[s, t]$ (mod $[m, n]$).

Example 3.

Find the exponent to which 19 belongs (mod $7 \cdot 47$).

SOLUTION: Since $19 \equiv 5$ (mod 7) then from Example 1 it follows that 19 belongs to the exponent 6 (mod 7). We found in Example 2 that 19 belongs to the exponent 46 (mod 47). From Theorem 9 it follows that 19 belongs to the exponent $[6, 46] = 138$ (mod $7 \cdot 47$).

EXERCISES

1. Prove Theorem 9.

2. Extend the result of Theorem 9 by induction; that is, *prove:* if a belongs to the exponents $k_1, k_2, \cdots, k_n$ modulo $m_1, m_2, \cdots, m_n$, respectively, then a belongs to the exponent $[k_1, k_2, \cdots, k_n]$ (mod $[m_1, m_2, \cdots, m_n]$).

3. Find the exponent to which 10 belongs (mod $3^2 \cdot 7 \cdot 11 \cdot 13$).

PROBLEMS

1. Let p be a prime number. If a belongs to the exponent k (mod p), prove that a belongs to either the exponent k or the exponent kp (mod p^2).

2. Let p be a prime number. If a belongs to the exponent k (mod p^n), where $n > 1$, and a does not belong to the exponent k (mod p^{n+1}), then a belongs to the exponent kp (mod p^{n+1}), to the exponent kp^2 (mod p^{n+2}), $\cdots$, to the exponent kp^j (mod p^{n+j}), $\cdots$. The restriction $n > 1$ is only needed when $p = 2$.

4.8 / PRIMITIVE ROOTS

■ DEFINITION / The integer a is called a *primitive root* (*mod m*) if a belongs to the exponent $\varphi(m)$ (mod m).

For example, in Section 4.7, we established that 19 is a primitive root (mod 7) and (mod 47).

Primitive roots play a key role in many theoretical investigations. For example, we will use the fact several times in Chapter 9 that primitive roots exist if m is a prime. In the appendix to this chapter we will use primitive roots to define functions similar to the logarithm function which can be used to reduce certain nonlinear congruences to equivalent linear congruences.

In this section we will prove that primitive roots exist if the modulus m is a prime. Our method will be to determine the number of primitive roots for this case.

■ LEMMA / Let p be a prime number and let d be a divisor of $p - 1$. The number of incongruent numbers belonging to the exponent d (mod p) is either zero or $\varphi(d)$.

PROOF: Let a belong to the exponent d (mod p). The numbers $a, a^2, \cdots, a^d$ are incongruent (mod p) and each is a solution of

$$x^d - 1 \equiv 0 \text{ (mod } p) \tag{4.1}$$

It follows from Lagrange's theorem (Theorem 10 of Chapter 3) that these are the only solutions of (4.1). Thus, any number belonging to the exponent d (mod p) must be congruent (mod p) to one of these numbers. Obviously, the number a^k belongs to the exponent d if, and only if, k is relatively prime to d. Thus, there are exactly $\varphi(d)$ numbers in the above set belonging to the exponent d (mod p).

■ THEOREM 10 / If p is a prime number and d is a positive divisor of $p - 1$, there are exactly $\varphi(d)$ incongruent numbers belonging to the exponent d (mod p).

PROOF: For each integer d, $1 \leq d \leq p - 1$, let $\alpha(d)$ be the number of integers k, $1 \leq k \leq p - 1$, which belong to the exponent d (mod p). From Theorem 8 we obtain the fact that

$$\alpha(d) = 0 \qquad \text{if } d \nmid (p - 1)$$

from the lemma, that

$$0 \leq \alpha(d) \leq \varphi(d) \qquad \text{if } d | (p - 1)$$

and from Theorem 7 that

$$\sum_{d | (p - 1)} \varphi(d) = p - 1$$

Because each of the $p - 1$ integers in the range $1 \leq k \leq p - 1$ belongs to some exponent (mod p), then

$$p - 1 = \alpha(1) + \alpha(2) + \cdots + \alpha(p - 1) = \sum_{d | (p - 1)} \alpha(d) \leq \sum_{d | (p - 1)} \varphi(d) = p - 1$$

Thus, $\alpha(d) = \varphi(d)$; the number of integers belonging to d (mod p) is equal to $\varphi(d)$, if $d | (p - 1)$.

■ COROLLARY 10.1 / If p is a prime number, there are exactly $\varphi(p - 1)$ incongruent primitive roots (mod p).

Theorem 10 is surprising to many students. A natural conjecture is that $\alpha(d)$ is a function of both d and p. However, Theorem 10 informs us that the value of $\alpha(d)$ depends only on d (providing d divides $p - 1$). For example, since 7 divides $p - 1$ when $p = 29$, 43, 71, 113, and 127, then for each of these primes there are exactly six incongruent numbers belonging to the exponent 7.

Primitive roots are important in number theory primarily because of the following theorem. The proof is left for the reader.

■ THEOREM 11 / Let g be a primitive root (mod p). The numbers $g, g^2, \cdots, g^{p-1}$ form a reduced system of residues (mod p).

EXERCISES

1. Find all primitive roots (mod m) for $m = 7$ and $m = 14$.

2. How many primitive roots exist (mod 28)?

3. Prove Theorem 11.

4.9* / EXISTENCE OF PRIMITIVE ROOTS (mod *m*)

In this section we will prove that certain moduli have primitive roots and all others do not. The results are summarized in Corollary 13.1.

■ DEFINITION / The positive integer *t* is said to be a *universal exponent for the modulus m* if

$$a^t \equiv 1 \;(\text{mod } m)$$

for all *a* relatively prime to *m*.

For example, the Euler–Fermat theorem states that $\varphi(m)$ is a universal exponent for *m*.

■ DEFINITION / The function λ is defined as follows:

(1) $\lambda(m) = \varphi(m)$ if $m = 2$, $m = 4$, $m = p^\alpha$, or $m = 2 \cdot p^\alpha$, where *p* is an odd prime,

(2) $\lambda(2^\alpha) = \frac{1}{2}\varphi(2^\alpha)$ if $\alpha \geq 3$,

and (3) $\lambda(2^\alpha p_1^{\alpha_1} \cdots p_k^{\alpha_k}) = [\lambda(2^\alpha), \lambda(p_1^{\alpha_1}), \cdots, \lambda(p_k^{\alpha_k})]$ if $\alpha \geq 2$ or $k \geq 2$ and the p_i are distinct odd primes.

Example.

Since $4400 = 2^4 \cdot 5^2 \cdot 11$, then

$$\lambda(4400) = [\lambda(2^4), \lambda(5^2), \lambda(11)] = [\tfrac{1}{2}\varphi(2^4), \varphi(5^2), \varphi(11)]$$

$$= [4, 20, 10] = 20$$

■ THEOREM 12 / $\lambda(m)$ is a universal exponent for *m*.

PROOF: (Part I) If $m = 2$, $m = 4$, $m = p^\alpha$, or $m = 2p^\alpha$, the proposition to be proved is identical to the Euler–Fermat theorem.

(Part II) Suppose $m = 2^\alpha$ ($\alpha \geq 3$). Let *a* be relatively prime to 2^α. Then *a* is odd and so we can write

$$a = 4n \pm 1$$

The proposition will be proved by induction on α.
If $\alpha = 3$, we obtain

$$a^{\lambda(8)} = a^2 = 16n^2 \pm 8n + 1 \equiv 1 \;(\text{mod } 8)$$

Assume that $\qquad a^{\lambda(2^k)} \equiv 1 \;(\text{mod } 2^k) \qquad$ for $k \geq 3$

We rewrite this congruence as the equation

$$a^{\lambda(2^k)} = 1 + b \cdot 2^k$$

and square, obtaining

$$a^{2 \cdot \lambda(2^k)} = 1 + 2b \cdot 2^k + b^2 \cdot 2^{2k} \equiv 1 \ (\text{mod } 2^{k+1})$$

Since $\qquad \lambda(2^{k+1}) = \frac{1}{2} \varphi(2^{k+1}) = \frac{1}{2} \cdot 2\varphi(2^k) = 2 \cdot \lambda(2^k)$

then $\qquad\qquad a^{\lambda(2^{k+1})} \equiv 1 \ (\text{mod } 2^{k+1})$

From the principle of mathematical induction, it follows that

$$a^{\lambda(2^\alpha)} \equiv 1 \ (\text{mod } 2^\alpha), \qquad \alpha = 3, 4, \cdots$$

(Part III) Suppose $m = 2^\alpha p_1^{\alpha_1} \cdots p_k^{\alpha_k}$ where either $\alpha \geq 2$ or $k \geq 2$. If a is relatively prime to m, a is relatively prime to each of the moduli $2^\alpha, p_1^{\alpha_1}, \cdots, p_k^{\alpha_k}$. From the previous parts of the proof, it follows that

$$a^{\lambda(2^\alpha)} \equiv 1 \ (\text{mod } 2^\alpha)$$

$$a^{\lambda(p_1^{\alpha_1})} \equiv 1 \ (\text{mod } p_1^{\alpha_1})$$

$$\cdots$$

$$a^{\lambda(p_k^{\alpha_k})} \equiv 1 \ (\text{mod } p_k^{\alpha_k})$$

Since $\lambda(m) = [\lambda(2^\alpha), \lambda(p_1^{\alpha_1}), \cdots, \lambda(p_k^{\alpha_k})]$, then

$$a^{\lambda(m)} \equiv 1 \ (\text{mod } 2^\alpha)$$

$$a^{\lambda(m)} \equiv 1 \ (\text{mod } p_1^{\alpha_1})$$

$$\cdots$$

$$a^{\lambda(m)} \equiv 1 \ (\text{mod } p_k^{\alpha_k})$$

Since $a^{\lambda(m)} - 1$ is a common multiple of the moduli $2^\alpha, p_1^{\alpha_1}, \cdots, p_k^{\alpha_k}$, it follows that the least common multiple of these numbers divides $a^{\lambda(m)} - 1$. Therefore,

$$a^{\lambda(m)} \equiv 1 \ (\text{mod } 2^\alpha p_1^{\alpha_1} \cdots p_k^{\alpha_k})$$

Theorem 12 is frequently useful when computing the exponent to which a belongs (mod m). For example, since $\lambda(4400) = 20$, 3 must belong to one of the exponents 1, 2, 4, 5, 10, 20 (mod 4400).

■ **COROLLARY 12.1** / If $m = 2^\alpha$ ($\alpha \geq 3$) or $m = 2^\alpha p_1^{\alpha_1} \cdots p_k^{\alpha_k}$, where $\alpha \geq 2$ or $k \geq 2$, there are no primitive roots (mod m).

SKETCH OF THE PROOF: We must show that in these cases $\lambda(m) < \varphi(m)$. The details are left for the reader (Problem 1).

Thus, we can have primitive roots (mod m) only in the following cases: $m = 2$, $m = 4$, $m = p^\alpha$, or $m = 2p^\alpha$, where p is an odd prime. In Theorem 13 we will prove that primitive roots exist for all of these cases. In order to simplify the proof we prove two lemmas.

■ **LEMMA 1** / Let p be an odd prime and let k be a positive integer. If g is a primitive root (mod p^k), then g belongs to the exponent $\varphi(p^k)$ or to the exponent $\varphi(p^{k+1})$ (mod p^{k+1}).

PROOF: Suppose g belongs to the exponent n (mod p^{k+1}). By Theorem 8 we know that $n | \varphi(p^{k+1})$. Since g belongs to the exponent $\varphi(p^k)$ (mod p^k) and $g^n \equiv 1$ (mod p^k), it follows that $\varphi(p^k) | n$. Since $\varphi(p^{k+1}) = p\varphi(p^k)$, n must be either $\varphi(p^k)$ or $\varphi(p^{k+1})$.

■ **LEMMA 2** / Let p be an odd prime. There exists an odd integer that is a primitive root (mod p) and (mod p^2).

PROOF: Let g be a primitive root (mod p). We may assume that g is odd; otherwise, $g + p$ is an odd primitive root and we may use it instead of g. If $g^{\varphi(p)} \not\equiv 1$ (mod p^2), then by Lemma 1, g is a primitive root (mod p^2).

If $g^{\varphi(p)} \equiv 1$ (mod p^2) we will consider the integer $g + 2p$, which is also an odd primitive root (mod p). Using the binomial theorem, we obtain

$$(g + 2p)^{\varphi(p)} = g^{\varphi(p)} + \binom{\varphi(p)}{1} g^{\varphi(p)-1} 2p$$

$$+ \binom{\varphi(p)}{2} g^{\varphi(p)-2}(2p)^2 + \cdots + (2p)^{\varphi(p)}$$

$$\equiv g^{\varphi(p)} + \binom{\varphi(p)}{1} g^{\varphi(p)-1} 2p \pmod{p^2}$$

$$\equiv 1 + (p-1)g^{\varphi(p)-1} 2p \pmod{p^2}$$

$$\equiv 1 - 2pg^{\varphi(p)-1} \pmod{p^2}$$

Since $2g^{\varphi(p)-1}$ is relatively prime to p, then

$$(g + 2p)^{\varphi(p)} \not\equiv 1 \pmod{p^2}$$

From Lemma 1 it follows that $g + 2p$ is a primitive root (mod p) and (mod p^2).

■ **THEOREM 13** / Let p be an odd prime number. If $m = 2$, $m = 4$, $m = p^\alpha$, or $m = 2p^\alpha$, then primitive roots exist, modulo m.

PROOF: (Part I) If $m = 2$ or $m = 4$, we can verify from the definition that 3 is a primitive root (mod m).

(Part II) Suppose $m = p^\alpha$ where p is an odd prime. By Lemma 2 there exists an odd integer g that is a primitive root (mod p) and (mod p^2). We make the inductive assumption that g is a primitive root (mod p^α) for $\alpha = 1, 2, \cdots, k$ ($k \geq 2$). We will now prove that g is a primitive root (mod p^{k+1}).

Suppose g is not a primitive root (mod p^{k+1}). From Lemma 1 it follows that

$$g^{\varphi(p^k)} \equiv 1 \ (\text{mod } p^{k+1}) \tag{4.2}$$

Because g is a primitive root (mod p^{k-1}) and (mod p^k), it follows from Lemma 1 that we can write

$$g^{\varphi(p^{k-1})} = 1 + mp^{k-1} \qquad m \not\equiv 0 \ (\text{mod } p) \tag{4.3}$$

If we raise both sides of this equation to the power p, we obtain

$$g^{p \cdot \varphi(p^{k-1})} = (1 + mp^{k-1})^p \equiv 1 + mp^k \qquad (\text{mod } p^{k+1})$$

Since $p\varphi(p^{k-1}) = \varphi(p^k)$, then from (4.2),

$$g^{\varphi(p^k)} \equiv 1 \equiv g^{p\varphi(p^{k-1})} \equiv 1 + mp^k \qquad (\text{mod } p^{k+1})$$

Thus, $m \equiv 0 \ (\text{mod } p)$, contradicting Equation (4.3). Because our initial assumption was false, then $g^{\varphi(p_k)} \not\equiv 1 \ (\text{mod } p^{k+1})$, which, by Lemma 1, implies that g is a primitive root (mod p^{k+1}).

By the principle of mathematical induction, it follows that the odd integer g is a primitive root (mod p^α) ($\alpha = 1, 2, \cdots$).

(Part III) Suppose $m = p^\alpha$. Let g be an odd primitive root (mod p^α). Then g is also a primitive root (mod 2). By Theorem 9, g belongs to the exponent $[1, \varphi(p^\alpha)]$ (mod $[2, p^\alpha]$). Since $\varphi(2p^\alpha) = \varphi(p^\alpha)$, then g belongs to the exponent $\varphi(2p^\alpha)$ (mod $2p^\alpha$).

The results of Corollary 12.1 and Theorem 13 are summarized in the following corollary:

∎ COROLLARY 13.1 / Let m be an integer greater than 1. Primitive roots exist (mod m) if, and only if,

$$m = 2 \qquad m = 4 \qquad m = p^\alpha \qquad \text{or} \qquad m = 2p^\alpha$$

where p is an odd prime number.

PROBLEM

1. Prove Corollary 12.1.

APPENDIX / THE THEORY OF INDICES

In Theorem 11 we established that if p is a prime number and g is a primitive root (mod p), the numbers

$$g, g^2, \cdots, g^{p-1}$$

constitute a reduced system of residues (mod p). Thus, if a is relatively prime to p, there is a unique integer k, $1 \le k \le p - 1$, such that $g^k \equiv a$ (mod p).

■ DEFINITION / Let g be a primitive root, modulo the prime p, and let a be relatively prime to p. The smallest positive integer k, such that $g^k \equiv a$ (mod p), is called the *index of a* (*with respect to the primitive root g for the prime p*), and is denoted by the symbols

$$k = \text{ind}_g a = \text{ind } a$$

Example I.

Construct a table of indices for the prime 13.

SOLUTION: We base our table on the primitive root 2. The powers of 2 (mod 13) are

$$2^1 \equiv 2 \qquad 2^5 \equiv 6 \qquad 2^9 \equiv 5$$
$$2^2 \equiv 4 \qquad 2^6 \equiv 12 \qquad 2^{10} \equiv 10$$
$$2^3 \equiv 8 \qquad 2^7 \equiv 11 \qquad 2^{11} \equiv 7$$
$$2^4 \equiv 3 \qquad 2^8 \equiv 9 \qquad 2^{12} \equiv 1$$

Thus, our table is

n	1	2	3	4	5	6	7	8	9	10	11	12
ind n	12	1	4	2	9	5	11	3	8	10	7	6

The next theorem shows that indices have properties similar to those of logarithms. We will first prove a useful lemma that establishes a correspondence between numbers (mod p) and indices (mod $p - 1$).

■ LEMMA / Let g be a primitive root, modulo the prime p, and let a be relatively prime to p. Then $g^t \equiv a$ (mod p) if, and only if, $t \equiv \text{ind}_g a$ (mod $p - 1$).

PROOF: If $t \equiv \text{ind}_g\, a \pmod{p - 1}$, we can write

$$t = \text{ind } a + m \cdot (p - 1)$$

Thus,

$$g^t \equiv g^{\text{ind } a + m(p - 1)} \equiv g^{\text{ind } a}(g^{p - 1})^m \equiv g^{\text{ind } a} \equiv a \pmod{p}$$

On the other hand, if $g^t \equiv a \equiv g^{\text{ind } a} \pmod{p}$, then

$$g^{|t - \text{ind } a|} \equiv 1 \pmod{p}$$

Since g belongs to the exponent $p - 1 \pmod{p}$, it follows from Theorem 8 that

$$t \equiv \text{ind } a \pmod{p - 1}$$

■ THEOREM 14 / If n is a positive integer and a and b are not divisible by the prime number p, then

(a) $\text{ind } ab \equiv \text{ind } a + \text{ind } b \pmod{p - 1}$

and (b) $\text{ind } a^n \equiv n \text{ ind } a \pmod{p - 1}$.

The proofs are similar to the corresponding proofs for logarithms and are left for the reader (Exercises 2 and 3).

Example 2.

Solve $5x^{10} \equiv 7 \pmod{13}$.

SOLUTION: Using Theorem 14 and our table of indices for the prime 13, we obtain

$$5x^{10} \equiv 7 \pmod{13}$$

$$\text{ind } (5x^{10}) = \text{ind } 7$$

$$\text{ind } 5 + 10 \text{ ind } x \equiv \text{ind } 7 \pmod{12}$$

$$10 \text{ ind } x \equiv \text{ind } 7 - \text{ind } 5$$

$$\equiv 11 - 9 \equiv 2 \pmod{12}$$

$$5 \text{ ind } x \equiv \quad 1 \pmod{6} \text{ (cancellation law)}$$

$$\text{ind } x \equiv \quad 5 \pmod{6}$$

Thus, $\text{ind } x = 5$ or $\text{ind } x = 11$. Using our table again we find the solutions of the original congruence are

$$x \equiv 6 \pmod{13}$$

or

$$x \equiv 7 \pmod{13}$$

Compared to logarithms, indices have two defects: (1) Tables must be constructed for each prime modulus [and there are $\varphi(p - 1)$ possible tables for each prime p]; (2) the entries in the tables are not in ascending order as is the case with logarithms. Thus, it is convenient to have two sets of tables, one to convert indices to numbers and one to convert numbers to indices. Such tables of indices for the primes less than 100 are found at the end of the book.

Example 3.

Prove that the congruence $23\ x^5 \equiv 17 \pmod{71}$ has no solution.

SOLUTION: ind $(23\ x^5) = $ ind 17

$$5 \text{ ind } x \equiv \text{ ind } 17 - \text{ ind } 23 \equiv 49 - 15 \equiv 34 \pmod{70}$$

Because the greatest common divisor of 5 and 70 does not divide 34, this congruence has no solution.

Example 4.

Solve $23 \cdot 5^x \equiv 33 \pmod{71}$.

SOLUTION: The above congruence is equivalent to

$$x \text{ ind } 5 \equiv \text{ ind } 33 - \text{ ind } 23 \pmod{70}$$
$$28\ x \equiv 57 - 15 \equiv 42 \quad \pmod{70}$$
$$2x \equiv 3 \quad\quad\quad\quad\ \pmod{5}$$
$$x \equiv 4 \quad\quad\quad\quad\ \pmod{5}$$

Tables of indices can be used to determine the exponent to which an integer belongs (mod p) and thus can be used to find all primitive roots (mod p). The method is given in the statement of the following theorem. The proof of the theorem is left for the reader (Problem 1).

■ THEOREM 15 / If a is not divisible by the prime p, then a belongs to the exponent

$$\frac{\varphi(p)}{(\varphi(p),\ \text{ind } a)}$$

(mod p).

■ COROLLARY 15.1 / The integer a is a primitive root (mod p) if, and only if,

$$(\varphi(p),\ \text{ind } a) = 1$$

Example 5.

Calculate the exponent to which 10 belongs (mod 89).

SOLUTION. From the tables we find that ind $10 = 86$. Thus, $(\varphi(89), \text{ind } 10) = (88, 86) = 2$ so that 10 belongs to the exponent

$$44 = \frac{\varphi(89)}{(\varphi(89), \text{ind } 10)} \quad (\text{mod } 89)$$

EXERCISES

1. Find all solutions of the following congruences:
   (a) $14x^{72} \equiv 81 \pmod{97}$.
   (b) $14x^{72} \equiv 83 \pmod{97}$.
   (c) $8 \cdot 50^x \equiv 41 \pmod{59}$.

2. Prove Part (a) of Theorem 14.

3. Prove Part (b) of Theorem 14.

4. Prove that $\text{ind}_g\, g = 1$ and $\text{ind}_g\, 1 = p - 1$.

PROBLEMS

1. Prove Theorem 15.

2. State necessary and sufficient conditions (in terms of indices) which insure that the congruence

$$ax^b \equiv c \pmod{p}$$

has a solution. Determine the number of incongruent solutions. Prove your result.

DECIMAL EXPANSION OF RATIONAL NUMBERS / 5

5.1 / INTRODUCTION

One of the most surprising facts about the history of mathematics is the slowness with which important concepts were developed. The ancient societies experimented with number systems for centuries before the Hindus invented the positional notation. To us, having great hindsight, the next logical step is the use of the positional notation in writing fractions.

Although the Hindu notation was introduced in Europe in the early thirteenth century, it was not until the end of the sixteenth century that decimal fractions began to be adopted and not until the beginning of the eighteenth century that the usage was universal in Europe.

Actually, the decimal notation had been anticipated over the centuries. The ancient Babylonions had a positional notation based on the number 60 which they could use to represent fractions.[1] In the fourteenth century, Oresme, Bishop of Normandy, invented a decimal fraction system which was never adopted, and in the middle of the fifteenth century Regiomontanus (Christian name: John Müller) of Germany used a decimal-like notation in trigonometry. In 1530 Christoff Rudolff of Vienna, in a book of calculating examples, used a decimal notation similar to the one now used.

Simon Stevin, a Belgian of many scientific interests, was the major force behind the adoption of decimal fractions. In *La Disme*, published in 1585, he introduced a cumbersome decimal notation and systematically developed the properties of decimal fractions. The book included an essay in which Stevin strongly urged the adoption of the decimal system, pointing out the advantages for bookkeeping, monetary units, and systems of weights and measures.

The present simplified decimal notation was first used in 1617 by the Scottish mathematician Napier, the inventor of logarithms.

---

[1] The sexagesimal system was used in Europe until the Middle Ages for the extraction of roots.

Let us review the basic principles of decimal notation. When we write

$$\alpha = n . a_1 a_2 a_3 \cdots$$

where n is a nonnegative integer and a_1, a_2, $\cdots$ are integers in the range $0 \le a_j < 10$, we mean that the series

$$n + \frac{a_1}{10} + \frac{a_2}{10^2} + \frac{a_3}{10^3} + \cdots$$

converges to the real number α. The proof that any nonnegative real number α can be represented in this manner is sketched in the problem section.

We could, of course, use a base other than 10 for our number system. A practical method of converting from base 10 to a different base is illustrated by the following example.

Example.

Convert 0.4_{10} to base 3 notation

SOLUTION: We write (using base 10 notation)

$$0.4 = \frac{a_1}{3} + \frac{a_2}{3^2} + \frac{a_3}{3^3} + \cdots \qquad 0 \le a_t < 3$$

Thus,
$$3(0.4) = 1.2 = a_1 + \frac{a_2}{3} + \frac{a_3}{3^2} + \cdots$$

implying that

$$a_1 = 1 \quad \text{and} \quad 0.2 = \frac{a_2}{3} + \frac{a_3}{3^2} + \cdots$$

Multiplying the latter expression by 3, we obtain

$$3(0.2) = 0.6 = a_2 + \frac{a_3}{3} + \frac{a_4}{3^2} + \cdots$$

so that

$$a_2 = 0 \quad \text{and} \quad 0.6 = \frac{a_3}{3} + \frac{a_4}{3^2} + \cdots$$

Continuing in this manner, we obtain

$$3(0.6) = 1.8 = a_3 + \frac{a_4}{3} + \frac{a_5}{3^2} + \cdots$$

$$a_3 = 1 \quad \text{and} \quad 0.8 = \frac{a_4}{3} + \frac{a_5}{3^2} + \cdots$$

and
$$3(0.8) = 2.4 = a_4 + \frac{a_5}{3} + \frac{a_6}{3^2} + \cdots$$

so that
$$a_4 = 2 \quad \text{and} \quad 0.4 = \frac{a_5}{3} + \frac{a_6}{3^2} + \cdots$$

Comparing the form of the two series for 0.4, we see that if we continue, we will obtain

$$a_1 = a_5 = a_9 = a_{13} = \cdots = 1$$

$$a_2 = a_6 = a_{10} = a_{14} = \cdots = 0$$

$$a_3 = a_7 = a_{11} = a_{15} = \cdots = 1$$

$$a_4 = a_8 = a_{12} = a_{16} = \cdots = 2$$

Thus,
$$0.4_{10} = (0.101210121012 \cdots)_3$$

In actual practice, rather than writing out each of the above steps we use the following scheme:

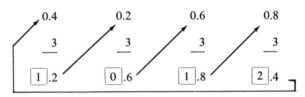

In the remainder of this chapter we will study the decimal expansions of rational numbers. We will show that the expansions are periodic, establish necessary and sufficient conditions which insure the expansion to be finite, and, finally, determine the period and the position in which the repeating block begins.

It is obvious that if k, m, n, and t are positive integers, then

$$\frac{m}{n} \qquad k + \frac{m}{n} \qquad \text{and} \qquad \frac{tm}{tn}$$

all have the same decimal part in their expansions. Thus, we may restrict ourselves to studying the expansions of proper fractions that are reduced to lowest terms; that is, we will consider the expansion of m/n, where $1 \le m < n$ and $(m, n) = 1$.

EXERCISE

1. Convert the following fractions to base g notation:
   (a) $(\frac{1}{3})_{10}$, $g = 12$.
   (b) 0.132_{10}, $g = 7$.
   (c) 41.132_{10}, $g = 7$.

PROBLEMS

1. Let n be a nonnegative integer and a_1, a_2, a_3, $\cdots$ be integers in the range $0 \le a_j < 10$. Prove that the series

$$n + \frac{a_1}{10} + \frac{a_2}{10^2} + \frac{a_3}{10^3} + \cdots$$

converges to a real number α.

2. Let α be a positive real number. Prove that there is a series

$$n + \frac{a_1}{10} + \frac{a_2}{10^2} + \frac{a_3}{10^3} + \cdots \qquad 0 \le a_i < 10$$

that converges to α. [*Hint*: Let $n = [\alpha]$. Define the sequences $\{\alpha_i\}_{i=1}^{\infty}$ and $\{a_i\}_{i=1}^{\infty}$ inductively as follows:

$$\alpha_1 = \alpha - n, \qquad a_1 = [10\alpha_1]$$
$$\alpha_2 = 10\alpha_1 - a_1, \qquad a_2 = [10\alpha_2]$$
$$\cdots$$
$$\alpha_k = 10\alpha_{k-1} - a_{k-1}, \qquad a_k = [10\alpha_k]$$
$$\cdots$$

3. Devise a rigorous proof that the method illustrated in the Example can always be used to convert fractions from base 10 to base g notation.

5.2 / FINITE DECIMAL EXPANSIONS

In this section we will establish necessary and sufficient conditions which insure that the decimal expansion of m/n is finite.

■ THEOREM 1 / Let m and n be relatively prime, $1 \le m < n$. The decimal expansion of m/n is finite if, and only if, n is of form $2^\alpha 5^\beta$ (where α and β are nonnegative integers). If this is the case, the length of the expansion is equal to the larger of the numbers α and β.

PROOF: (Part I) If m/n has a finite decimal expansion, we can write

$$\frac{m}{n} = \frac{a_1}{10} + \frac{a_2}{10^2} + \cdots + \frac{a_k}{10^k} = \frac{10^{k-1}a_1 + 10^{k-2}a_2 + \cdots + a_k}{10^k}$$

so that

$$10^k m = n(10^{k-1} a_1 + 10^{k-2} + \cdots + a_k)$$

Thus,

$$n | 10^k m \qquad \text{and} \qquad (m, n) = 1$$

implying that $n | 10^k$. It follows from the unique factorization theorem that $n = 2^\alpha 5^\beta$, where α and β are nonnegative integers, not both zero, and each less than or equal to k.

(Part II) Suppose $n = 2^\alpha 5^\beta$. For sake of argument, we will assume that $\beta \geq \alpha$. Since $n > 1$, then $\beta > 0$. Thus,

$$\frac{m}{n} = \frac{2^{\beta - \alpha} m}{10^\beta}$$

We now write the integer $2^{\beta - \alpha} m$ in the Hindu-Arabic notation

$$2^{\beta - \alpha} m = c_t 10^t + c_{t-1} 10^{t-1} + \cdots + c_1 10 + c_0$$

where each c_j is one of the ten digits. Since $5 \nmid 2^{\beta - \alpha} m$, then $5 \nmid c_0$, and so $c_0 \neq 0$. Furthermore, since $1 \leq m < n$, it follows that $\beta > t$. Thus,

$$\frac{m}{n} = \frac{2^{\beta - \alpha} m}{10^\beta} = \frac{c_t}{10^{\beta - t}} + \frac{c_{t-1}}{10^{\beta - t + 1}} + \cdots + \frac{c_1}{10^{\beta - 1}} + \frac{c_0}{10^\beta}$$

Since $c_0 \neq 0$, the βth position in the decimal expansion is the last nonzero position. Thus, the expansion is finite, of length β.

If we had assumed $\alpha \geq \beta$, we would have established in a similar way that the expansion is of length α.

5.3 / INFINITE DECIMAL EXPANSIONS

In this section we begin our investigation of infinite decimal expansions.

■ DEFINITION / The decimal expansion $a_1/10 + a_2/10^2 + a_3/10^3 + \cdots$ is said to be *periodic* if there exist positive integers k and t such that

$$a_k = a_{k+t} \qquad = a_{k+2t} \qquad = \cdots$$

$$a_{k+1} = a_{k+t+1} \qquad = a_{k+2t+1} \qquad = \cdots$$

$$\cdots$$

$$a_{k+t-1} = a_{k+2t-1} = a_{k+3t-1} = \cdots$$

The smallest such t is called the *period* of the expansion. If $k = 1$, the expansion is said to be *purely periodic*.

Example.

The expansion of $\frac{1}{3} = 0.33333 \cdots$ is purely periodic with period 1. The expansion of $13/70 = 0.1857142857142 \cdots$ is periodic with period 6, but is not purely periodic.

In order to simplify the notation, it is customary to write the repeating block of a periodic expansion with a bar over it rather than repeating it several times. Thus, we would write

$$\frac{1}{3} = 0.\overline{3}$$

$$\frac{13}{70} = 0.1\overline{857142}$$

and

$$\frac{47}{176} = 0.267\overline{045}$$

If the expansion of m/n is to be infinite, then n is not of form $2^\alpha 5^\beta$. For purposes of our notation, we let $m_1 = m$.

Thus, we can write

$$\frac{m}{n} = \frac{m_1}{n} = \frac{a_1}{10} + \frac{a_2}{10^2} + \frac{a_3}{10^3} + \cdots$$

so that

$$10m_1 = a_1 n + \left(\frac{a_2}{10} + \frac{a_3}{10^2} + \cdots\right) n$$

Since $10m_1$ and $a_1 n$ are integers, then $(a_2/10 + a_3/10^2 + \cdots)n$ is also an integer. Call it m_2. Because the expansion is not finite, then

$$0 < \frac{a_2}{10} + \frac{a_3}{10^2} + \cdots < 1$$

and so

$$0 < m_2 = \left(\frac{a_2}{10} + \frac{a_3}{10^2} + \cdots\right) n < n$$

Thus, we have

$$10m_1 = a_1 n + m_2 \qquad 0 < m_2 < n$$

That is, a_1 is the quotient when $10m_1$ is divided by n, and m_2 is the remainder.

We now repeat the process, obtaining

$$10m_2 = a_2 n + m_3 \qquad 0 < m_3 < n$$

where
$$m_3 = \left(\frac{a_3}{10} + \frac{a_4}{10^2} + \cdots \right) n$$

Eventually we obtain the chain of equations

$$10m_1 = a_1 n + m_2 \qquad 0 < m_2 < n$$
$$10m_2 = a_2 n + m_3 \qquad 0 < m_3 < n$$
$$10m_3 = a_3 n + m_4 \qquad 0 < m_4 < n \qquad\qquad (5.1)$$
$$\cdots$$
$$10m_k = a_k n + m_{k+1} \qquad 0 < m_{k+1} < n$$
$$\cdots$$

where
$$m_{k+1} = \left(\frac{a_{k+1}}{10} + \frac{a_{k+2}}{10^2} + \cdots \right) n$$

The reader should note that the above equations represent the steps in the familiar process of long division. For example, if $m = 4$ and $n = 37$, then in the long division process we obtain

```
         0.1081 ···
   37 | 4.0000 ···
        37
        ──
        30
         0
        ──
        300
        296
        ───
         40
         37
         ──
          3.
           .
            .
```

Thus, in the chain of equations we have

$$10m_1 = 40 = 1 \cdot 37 + 3$$
$$10m_2 = 30 = 0 \cdot 37 + 30$$
$$10m_3 = 300 = 8 \cdot 37 + 4$$
$$10m_4 = 40 = 1 \cdot 37 + 3$$
$$\cdots$$

■ **THEOREM** 2 / Let $(m, n) = 1$, $1 \leq m < n$, and let t be a positive integer. If, in the chain of equations, $m_k = m_{k+t}$ for some positive integer k, then the decimal expansion of m/n is periodic and there is a repeating block of length t, beginning with a_k.

PROOF: Because $m_k = m_{k+t}$,

$$10m_k = a_k n + m_{k+1}$$

$$= 10m_{k+t} = a_{k+t} n + m_{k+t+1}$$

where $0 < m_{k+1} < n$ and $0 < m_{k+t+1} < n$. From the uniqueness of division, it follows that

$$a_k = a_{k+t} \quad \text{and} \quad m_{k+1} = m_{k+t+1}$$

Thus,
$$10m_{k+1} = a_{k+1} n + m_{k+2}$$

$$= 10m_{k+t+1} = a_{k+t+1} n + m_{k+t+2}$$

which implies that

$$a_{k+1} = a_{k+t+1} \quad \text{and} \quad m_{k+2} = m_{k+t+2}$$

Continuing in this fashion (this statement disguises a proof by mathematical induction), we see that if j is a nonnegative integer, then

$$m_{k+j} = m_{k+t+j}$$

and
$$a_{k+j} = a_{k+t+j}$$

Applying this result for the nonnegative integers, $j, j + t, j + 2t, \cdots$, we obtain

$$a_{k+j} = a_{k+t+j} = a_{k+2t+j} = a_{k+3t+j} = \cdots$$

By letting j take on the values $0, 1, 2, \cdots, t - 1$, we find that

$$a_k = a_{k+t} \quad = a_{k+2t} \quad = a_{k+3t} \quad = \cdots$$

$$a_{k+1} = a_{k+t+1} \quad = a_{k+2t+1} = a_{k+3t+1} = \cdots$$

$$\cdots$$

$$a_{k+t-1} = a_{k+2t-1} = a_{k+3t-1} = a_{k+4t-1} = \cdots$$

Thus,

$$\frac{m}{n} = 0 . a_1 a_2 \cdots a_{k-1} \overline{a_k a_{k+1} \cdots a_{k+t-1}}$$

EXERCISE

1. Write out the chain of equations (5.1) for $m = 5, n = 28$.

5.4 / PERIODICITY OF THE EXPANSION OF m/n: SPECIAL CASE

In this section we consider the expansion of m/n where $1 \leq m < n$ and n is relatively prime to $10m$. We will show that the expansion is purely periodic in this case and will determine the period.

■ **THEOREM 3** / If $1 \leq m < n$ and n is relatively prime to $10m$, the decimal expansion of m/n is purely periodic. If $10^k \equiv 1 \pmod{n}$, there is a repeating block of length k that begins with the first position of the expansion.

PROOF: Since $(10m, n) = 1$ then $(10, n) = 1$. Thus, there is an integer k such that $10^k \equiv 1 \pmod{n}$. If we replace each of the equations in the chain (5.1) by a congruence (mod n), we obtain

$$10m_1 \equiv m_2 \pmod{n}$$

$$10m_2 \equiv m_3 \pmod{n}$$

$$10m_3 \equiv m_4 \pmod{n} \qquad (5.2)$$

$$\ldots$$

$$10m_k \equiv m_{k+1} \pmod{n}$$

$$\ldots$$

By substituting successively in the chain of congruences, we have

$$10m_1 \equiv m_2 \pmod{n}$$

$$10^2 m_1 \equiv m_3 \pmod{n}$$

$$10^3 m_1 \equiv m_4 \pmod{n}$$

$$\ldots$$

$$10^k m_1 \equiv m_{k+1} \pmod{n}$$

Thus, since $10^k \equiv 1 \pmod{n}$,

$$m_1 \equiv 10^k m_1 \equiv m_{k+1} \pmod{n}$$

and, since $0 < m_1 < n, 0 < m_{k+1} < n$, this implies that

$$m_1 = m_{k+1}$$

From Theorem 2 it follows that the expansion is purely periodic and a repeating block of length k exists that begins in the first position.

We will now prove a converse to part of Theorem 3.

■ THEOREM 4 / Suppose that $1 \le m < n$, and $10m$ is relatively prime to n. If there is a repeating block of length k in the expansion of m/n, then $10^k \equiv 1$ (mod n).

PROOF: Suppose the repeating block begins in the tth position. Then

$$m_t = \left(\frac{a_t}{10} + \frac{a_{t+1}}{10^2} + \cdots + \frac{a_{t+k-1}}{10^{t+k}} + \frac{a_t}{10^{t+k+1}} + \cdots \right) n$$

$$= \left(\frac{a_{t+k}}{10} + \frac{a_{t+k+1}}{10^2} + \cdots + \frac{a_{t+2k-1}}{10^{t+k}} + \frac{a_{t+k}}{10^{t+k+1}} + \cdots \right) n$$

$$= m_{t+k}$$

From the chain of congruences (5.2), we obtain

$$10m_t \equiv m_{t+1} \pmod{n}$$

$$10^2 m_t \equiv m_{t+2} \pmod{n}$$

$$\cdots$$

$$10^k m_t \equiv m_{t+k} \equiv m_t \pmod{n}$$

From the cancellation law for congruences it now follows that

$$10^k \equiv 1 \pmod{n}$$

Thus, we have proved that if $1 \le m < n$ and $(10m, n) = 1$, the decimal expansion of m/n is purely periodic and k is the length of a repeating block in the expansion if, and only if, $10^k \equiv 1$ (mod n). Since the smallest such integer k is the exponent to which 10 belongs (mod n), then this number is the period of the expansion. We summarize these results in Theorem 5.

■ THEOREM 5 / Suppose $1 \le m < n$ and that $(10m, n) = 1$. The decimal expansion of m/n is purely periodic and the period of the expansion is equal to the exponent to which 10 belongs (mod n).

Example.

Calculate the period of the decimal expansion of $\dfrac{4}{7 \cdot 89}$

SOLUTION: In Example 5 of the appendix to Chapter 4, we found that 10 belongs to the exponent 44 (mod 89). Using tables of indices (or direct computation) we find that 10 belongs to the exponent 6 (mod 7). From Theorem 9 of Chapter 4 it follows that 10 belongs to the exponent $[6, 44] = 132$ (mod $7 \cdot 89$). Thus, the period of the expansion of $\dfrac{4}{7 \cdot 89}$ is 132.

EXERCISE

1. Calculate the periods of the decimal expansions of:

(a) $\dfrac{7}{13 \cdot 17 \cdot 89}$;

(b) $\dfrac{5}{9 \cdot 11 \cdot 59 \cdot 97}$.

5.5 / PERIODICITY OF THE EXPANSION OF m/n: GENERAL CASE

We have considered two special cases of the decimal expansion of m/n. In Section 5.2 we considered the case where n is of form $2^\alpha 5^\beta$, and in Section 5.4 the case where n is relatively prime to 10. Before considering the general case we prove a lemma.

■ **LEMMA** / Let m, n_1, n_2 be integers, n_1 and n_2 both greater than 1. Suppose that $1 \le m < n_1 n_2$, that $(m, n_1 n_2) = 1$, and that $(n_1, n_2) = 1$. There exist integers m_1, m_2, and q,

$$1 \le m_i < n_i \qquad \text{and} \qquad (m_i, n_i) = 1 \qquad (i = 1, 2)$$

such that

$$\frac{m}{n_1 n_2} = \frac{m_1}{n_1} + \frac{m_2}{n_2} + q$$

PROOF: Since n_1 and n_2 are relatively prime, there exist integers x and y such that

$$m = x n_2 + y n_1 \tag{5.3}$$

We now divide x by n_1, obtaining

$$x = n_1 q_1 + m_1 \qquad 0 \le m_1 < n_1 \tag{5.4}$$

Similarly, we write

$$y = n_2 q_2 + m_2, \qquad 0 \le m_2 < n_2$$

On substituting in (5.3), dividing by $n_1 n_2$, and simplifying , we obtain

$$\frac{m}{n_1 n_2} = \frac{m_1}{n_1} + \frac{m_2}{n_2} + q \qquad \text{where} \qquad q = q_1 + q_2$$

It follows from (5.4) and (5.3) that

$$(m_1, n_1) | m$$

Thus, $(m_1, n_1) | (m, n_1)$, which implies that m_1 and n_1 are relatively prime. Since $n_1 \ge 2$, this means that

$$1 \le m_1 < n_1 \qquad \text{and} \qquad (m_1, n_1) = 1$$

A similar proof shows that

$$1 \le m_2 < n_2 \qquad \text{and} \qquad (m_2, n_2) = 1$$

■ THEOREM 6 / Suppose $(m, n) = 1$ and $1 \le m < n$. Write $n = 2^\alpha 5^\beta n'$ where $(n', 10) = 1$. The decimal expansion of m/n is periodic with period equal to the exponent to which 10 belongs (mod n'). The repeating block begins in position $t + 1$, where $t = \max \{\alpha, \beta\}$.

PROOF: If $\alpha = \beta = 0$ or if $n' = 1$, the hypothesis reduces to that of Theorem 1 or Theorem 5 (special cases of this theorem).

Assume that not both α and β are zero and that $n' > 1$. By the Lemma there exist integers m' and m'' such that

$$\frac{m}{2^\alpha 5^\beta n'} = \frac{m'}{n'} + \frac{m''}{2^\alpha 5^\beta} + q$$

where q is an integer, $1 \le m' < n'$, $1 \le m'' < 2^\alpha 5^\beta$, $(m', n') = 1$, and $(m'', 2^\alpha 5^\beta) = 1$. Since q is an integer, the decimal expansion of $m/2^\alpha 5^\beta n'$ is determined by the expansion of

$$\frac{m'}{n'} + \frac{m''}{2^\alpha 5^\beta}$$

From Theorem 5 we know that the expansion of m'/n' is purely periodic with period equal to the exponent to which 10 belongs (mod n'). Although we usually consider the repeating block to start in the first position, we may start it in any position; in particular, the $(t + 1)$st position. From Theorem 1, the expansion of $m''/2^\alpha 5^\beta$ is finite of length t. If we now add the two fractions we see that the tth term of the expansion of m'/n' is changed (and possibly other terms as well), although no term after the tth term is changed. Thus, the expansion of $m/2^\alpha 5^\beta n'$ is periodic, with the period equal to the exponent to which 10 belongs (mod n'), and the repeating block begins in the $(t + 1)$st position, where $t = \max \{\alpha, \beta\}$.

EXERCISES

1. Find the periods and the positions in which the repeating blocks begin for the decimal expansions of:

(a) $\dfrac{3}{2 \cdot 5^2 \cdot 7^2 \cdot 11 \cdot 13}$;

(b) $\dfrac{23}{100 \cdot 99 \cdot 59 \cdot 97}$.

2. Show that the integer q is necessary in the statement of the Lemma by considering the lemma for $m = 1$, $n_1 = 5$, $n_2 = 7$. In general, what values may q assume?

PERFECT NUMBERS / 6

6.1 / INTRODUCTION

From ancient times magic properties have been associated with certain numbers. Some of the more favored numbers were 7 and 40 (as evidenced from their use in the Bible), 6 (the number of days necessary for the creation of the world), and 28 (the length of the lunar cycle).

The ancient Greeks made extensive classifications of numbers according to their magic properties. One such classification depended on the sums of the proper divisors of the numbers (the so-called *aliquot parts*). A number is *perfect* if it is equal to the sum of its proper divisors (such as 6, 28, and 496), *deficient* if the sum is less than the number, and *abundant* if the sum is greater than the number. Two numbers are *amicable* if the proper divisors of each sums to the other (such as 220 and 284).

Perfect numbers, being between abundancy and deficiency, signified perfection and were greatly desired. Amicable numbers played an important role in astrological calculations involving love potions, talismans, and so on, especially among the Arabs of a later millennium.

In Europe, numerology was taken quite seriously until modern times. For example, Alcuin (eighth century) noted that because the second origin of mankind was associated with the deficient number 8 (the number of souls on Noah's Ark), while the first origin was associated with the perfect number 6, the second creation was inferior to the first. As late as the sixteenth century the mathematician Peter Bungus worked with great industry to assign the number 666 (the symbol of the Antichrist in Revelation XIII, 18) to Martin Luther.[1] This attack on Luther was, to some extent, provoked, since Luther's friend Stifel had previously assigned the same number to Pope Leo X.

---

[1] Bungus assigned numbers to the letters of the alphabet as follows: $a = 1$, $b = 2, \cdots, k = 10, l = 20, \cdots$. After misspelling Luther's name he found that $M_{30}, A_1 R_{80} T_{100} I_9 N_{40} L_{20} V_{200} T_{100} E_5 R_{80} A_1$ sums to 666.

It will be proved in this chapter that an even number is perfect if, and only if, it is of a certain form. A few results concerning odd perfect numbers will be mentioned.

6.2 / THE SIGMA AND TAU FUNCTIONS

To facilitate our study of perfect numbers we introduce two functions defined on the positive integers. In number theory it is customary to call these functions *arithmetic functions* or *number-theoretic functions* rather than sequences.

■ DEFINITION / If n is a positive integer, we let $\tau(n)$ denote the number of positive divisors of n, and $\sigma(n)$ the sum of the positive divisors.

Example.

Since 10 has the positive divisors 1, 2, 5, and 10, then $\tau(10) = 4$ and $\sigma(10) = 1 + 2 + 5 + 10 = 18$.

Using the notation of Section 4.6, we could have defined these functions by

$$\tau(n) = \sum_{d \mid n} 1, \qquad \sigma(n) = \sum_{d \mid n} d$$

In this section we will obtain formulas to express $\tau(n)$ and $\sigma(n)$ in terms of the prime divisor of n.

■ THEOREM 1 / The functions σ and τ are multiplicative.

PROOF: We must show that if m and n are relatively prime, then $\sigma(mn) = \sigma(m)\sigma(n)$ and $\tau(mn) = \tau(m)\tau(n)$.

Let $m_1, m_2, \cdots, m_{\tau(m)}$ be the positive divisors of m, and $n_1, n_2, \cdots, n_{\tau(n)}$ the positive divisors of n. Consider the set of products

$$\{m_1 n_1, m_2 n_1, m_3 n_1, \cdots, m_{\tau(m)} n_1$$
$$m_1 n_2, m_2 n_2, m_3 n_2, \cdots, m_{\tau(m)} n_2 \qquad (6.1)$$
$$\cdots$$
$$m_1 n_{\tau(n)}, m_2 n_{\tau(n)}, m_3 n_{\tau(n)}, \cdots, m_{\tau(m)} n_{\tau(n)}\}$$

Each number in this set is obviously a positive divisor of mn. On the other hand, if d is a positive divisor of mn, then (d, m) is one of the divisors of m, say m_i, and (d, n) is one of the divisors of n, say n_j. Since $d \mid mn$ and $(m, n) = 1$, it follows from the unique factorization theorem that $d = m_i n_j$. Thus, each positive divisor of *mn* is in this set. Since we will count the elements of (6.1) we must be sure that no number is duplicated in the set. Suppose

$$m_h n_i = m_j n_k$$

Because *m* and *n* are relatively prime, then m_j and n_i are also relatively prime. Therefore, since $m_j | m_h n_i$, it follows that $m_j | m_h$. In a similar way, we see that $m_h | m_j$. Thus, $m_h = m_j$, so that $h = j$. Similarly, we see that $i = k$. Thus, the numbers in (6.1) are all different.

Because the numbers in the set (6.1) are the positive divisors of *mn*, then $\tau(mn)$ is equal to the number of elements in the set and $\sigma(mn)$ is the sum of the elements. Therefore,

$$\tau(mn) = \tau(m)\tau(n)$$

and

$$\sigma(mn) = m_1 n_1 + m_2 n_1 + m_3 n_1 + \cdots + m_{\tau(m)} n_1 +$$
$$+ m_1 n_2 + m_2 n_2 + m_3 n_2 + \cdots + m_{\tau(m)} n_2 +$$
$$\cdots$$
$$+ m_1 n_{\tau(m)} + m_2 n_{\tau(n)} + m_3 n_{\tau(n)} + \cdots + m_{\tau(m)} n_{\tau(n)}$$
$$= (m_1 + m_2 + \cdots + m_{\tau(m)})(n_1 + n_2 + \cdots + n_{\tau(n)})$$
$$= \sigma(m)\sigma(n)$$

Thus, σ and τ are multiplicative functions.

We will now be able to evaluate the σ and τ functions if we know the values of $\sigma(p^\alpha)$ and $\tau(p^\alpha)$ for each prime *p*.

■ THEOREM 2 / If *p* is a prime number, then

$$\sigma(p^\alpha) = \frac{p^{\alpha+1} - 1}{p - 1}$$

and

$$\tau(p^\alpha) = \alpha + 1$$

SKETCH OF THE PROOF: The proof follows trivially from the fact that the positive divisors of p^α are

$$1, p, p^2, \cdots, p^\alpha$$

We can combine the results of Theorem 1 and Theorem 2 as follows:

■ COROLLARY 2.1 / If $p_1, p_2, \cdots, p_k$ are distinct prime numbers, then

$$\sigma(p_1^{\alpha_1} p_2^{\alpha_2} \cdots p_k^{\alpha_k}) = \frac{p_1^{\alpha_1+1} - 1}{p_1 - 1} \cdot \frac{p_2^{\alpha_2+1} - 1}{p_2 - 1} \cdots \frac{p_k^{\alpha_k+1} - 1}{p_k - 1}$$

and

$$\tau(p_1^{\alpha_1} p_2^{\alpha_2} \cdots p_k^{\alpha_k}) = (\alpha_1 + 1)(\alpha_2 + 1) \cdots (\alpha_k + 1)$$

Example.

Calculate $\sigma(n)$ and $\tau(n)$ if $n = 1{,}274{,}000$.

SOLUTION: Since $1{,}274{,}000 = 2^4 \cdot 7^2 \cdot 5^3 \cdot 13$, then

$$\sigma(n) = \sigma(2^4)\sigma(7^2)\sigma(5^3)\sigma(13)$$

$$= \frac{2^5 - 1}{1} \cdot \frac{7^3 - 1}{6} \cdot \frac{5^4 - 1}{4} \cdot \frac{13^2 - 1}{12}$$

$$= 31 \cdot 57 \cdot 156 \cdot 14 = 3{,}859{,}128$$

and

$$\tau(n) = \tau(2^4)\tau(7^2)\tau(5^3)\tau(13)$$

$$= 5 \cdot 3 \cdot 4 \cdot 2 = 120$$

EXERCISES

1. Calculate $\sigma(n)$ and $\tau(n)$:
   (a) $n = 76$;
   (b) $n = 1460$.

2. *Prove*: If m and n are relatively prime positive integers and d is a positive divisor of mn, then

$$d = (m, d) \cdot (n, d)$$

3. *Prove*: $\tau(n)$ is odd if, and only if, n is a square.

6.3 / EVEN PERFECT NUMBERS

We can reformulate the definition of a perfect number as follows:

■ DEFINITION / A positive integer n is called a *perfect* number if $\sigma(n) = 2n$.

Let us examine the form of the three perfect numbers mentioned in Section 6.1:

$$6 = 2 \cdot 3 \quad = \quad 2(2^2 - 1)$$
$$28 = 4 \cdot 7 \quad = \quad 2^2(2^3 - 1)$$
$$496 = 16 \cdot 31 \quad = \quad 2^4(2^5 - 1)$$

We see that each of these numbers is of form

$$2^{k-1}(2^k - 1)$$

where $2^k - 1$ is a prime. The following theorem, due to Euclid, shows that any number of this form is perfect.

■ THEOREM 3 / If $2^k - 1$ is a prime number, then

$$2^{k-1}(2^k - 1)$$

is a perfect number.

SKETCH OF THE PROOF: Use Corollary 2.1 to show that

$$\sigma(2^{k-1}(2^k - 1)) = 2^k(2^k - 1)$$

The details are left for the reader.

Two thousand years after Euclid, Euler was able to prove that all even perfect numbers are of the type found by Euclid. Euler proved the following theorem:

■ THEOREM 4 / If n is an even perfect number, there exists a prime number $(2^k - 1)$ such that

$$n = 2^{k-1}(2^k - 1)$$

PROOF: Since n is even we can write $n = 2^t m$, where m is an odd integer. Since n is perfect, then

$$\sigma(n) = \sigma(2^t)\sigma(m) = (2^{t+1} - 1)\sigma(m)$$

$$= 2n \qquad\qquad (6.2)$$

$$= 2^{t+1}m$$

Thus, $(2^{t+1} - 1)\,|\,2^{t+1}m$, implying, since $2^{t+1} - 1$ is odd, that $(2^{t+1} - 1)\,|\,m$. Therefore,

$$m = (2^{t+1} - 1)u$$

where u is an integer. Suppose u is greater than 1. Then 1, u, and $(2^{t+1} - 1) \cdot u$ are distinct divisors of m, so that

$$\sigma(m) \geq 1 + u + (2^{t+1} - 1)u > 2^{t+1}u$$

Therefore,

$$\sigma(n) = (2^{t+1} - 1)\sigma(m) > (2^{t+1} - 1)2^{t+1}u = 2^{t+1}m = 2n$$

which contradicts (6.2). Thus, $u = 1$ and

$$m = 2^{t+1} - 1$$

If we assume that m is not a prime, we get a contradiction similar to the one above. Thus,

$$m = 2^{t+1} - 1 \text{ is a prime}$$

and

$$n = 2^t (2^{t+1} - 1)$$

If we let $k = t + 1$, we have the desired result.

As we have seen, our search for even perfect numbers has been reduced to a search for prime numbers of form $2^k - 1$. Such primes are called *Mersenne primes* after Martin Mersenne (1588–1648). We will prove one rather trivial result about Mersenne primes.

■ THEOREM 5 / If $2^k - 1$ is a prime number, then k is also a prime.

PROOF: If k is not a prime, we can write $k = ab$, where a and b are both greater than 1. Thus,

$$2^k - 1 = 2^{ab} - 1 = (2^a - 1)(2^{a(b-1)} + 2^{a(b-2)} + \cdots + 2^a + 1)$$

so that $2^k - 1$ is not a prime.

At the present time twenty Mersenne primes are known and there are, of course, twenty corresponding perfect numbers. The known Mersenne primes are

$$M_2 = 2^2 - 1 = 3 \qquad M_{13} = 8,191$$
$$M_3 = 2^3 - 1 = 7 \qquad M_{17} = 131,071$$
$$M_5 = 31 \qquad\qquad M_{19} = 524,287$$
$$M_7 = 127 \qquad\qquad M_{31} = 2,147,483,647$$
$$M_{61}, M_{89}, M_{107}, M_{127}, M_{521}, M_{607}, M_{1279}$$
$$M_{2203}, M_{2281}, M_{3217}, M_{4253}, M_{4423}$$

Very little is known about Mersenne primes. We do not know if their number is finite or infinite. If it is finite, we have no bounds for the largest such number and, consequently, we do not know if the above list is exhaustive.

EXERCISES

1. *Prove*: If n is a perfect number, then $\sum_{d|n} \dfrac{1}{d} = 2$.

2. Show that the definition of *amicable numbers* can be reformulated as:

m and n are amicable if and only if

$$\sigma(m) = \sigma(n) = m + n$$

3. Define the sequences P_n and Q_n by

$$P_n = 3 \cdot 2^n - 1, \; Q_n = 9 \cdot 2^{2n-1} - 1 \qquad (n = 1, 2, \cdots)$$

Show that if P_{n-1}, P_n, and Q_n are prime numbers, then

$$a = 2^n P_{n-1} P_n \qquad \text{and} \qquad b = 2^n Q_n$$

are amicable.

4. Use Exercise 3 to find two sets of amicable numbers.

PROBLEM

1. Show that if a and b are even integers such that

$$\sigma(a) = 2b \qquad \text{and} \qquad \sigma(b) = 2a$$

then there exist Mersenne primes $2^p - 1$ and $2^q - 1$ such that

$$a = 2^{q-1}(2^p - 1) \qquad \text{and} \qquad b = 2^{p-1}(2^q - 1)$$

6.4* / REMARKS ON ODD PERFECT NUMBERS

The theory of odd perfect numbers is not as well developed as that of even perfect numbers. To this date no odd perfect number has been discovered and many mathematicians believe that such numbers do not exist. Unfortunately, no one has been able to prove this conjecture.

Most of the theorems proved about odd perfect numbers state conditions that such numbers must satisfy, many of them concerning the prime factors. Using these conditions it is sometimes possible to establish other results, such as bounds on the number of distinct prime factors, or bounds on the size of the numbers themselves. A few of the many established facts are summarized below. For a more detailed listing and for references to the following results the reader is referred to the survey paper by McCarthy in the list of special references.

Euler obtained the first significant result on odd perfect numbers: If n is an odd perfect number, the n is of form

$$n = p^{\alpha} q_1^{2\beta_1} q_2^{2\beta_2} \cdots q_t^{2\beta_t}$$

where $p, q_1, q_2, \cdots, q_t$ are distinct odd primes and

$$p \equiv \alpha \equiv 1 \pmod 4$$

It has since been proved that it is impossible to have all of the β's equal to 1, and Brauer and Kanold have proved that it is impossible to have one of the β's equal to 2 and the others equal to 1. Kanold proved that if $\beta_2 = \beta_3 = \cdots = \beta_t = 1$, then $t \geq 9$ and $n > 10^{36}$. If, in addition, $\alpha = 1$, then $q_1 = 3, 2\beta_1 \geq 12$, and $t \geq 13$.

It was established in the last century by Sylvester that n must have at least 4 distinct prime factors and if $n \not\equiv 0 \pmod 3$, at least 7 distinct prime factors. This bound has since been improved. We now know that $t \geq 5$ if $3 \mid n$ and $t \geq 8$ if $3 \nmid n$. Kanold has proved, in addition, that n must have at least one prime factor greater than or equal to 61.

An odd perfect number must be fairly large. Near the turn of the century it was established that if n is an odd perfect number then $n > 2 \cdot 10^6$. This was improved to $(1.4) \cdot 10^{14}$ by Kanold. In the 1956 Supplement to his book *Number Theory and Its History*, Ore announced that one of his students, J. B. Muskat, had raised this bound to 10^{18}.

PROBLEMS

1. Let p be a prime. Prove that if $n = p^\alpha$, then n is not an odd perfect number.

2. Let p and q be distinct odd primes. Prove that $p^\alpha q^\beta$ is not a perfect number. (Thus, an odd perfect number must have at least 3 distinct prime factors.)

3. Prove Euler's result: If n is an odd perfect number, then

$$n = p^\alpha q_1^{2\beta_1} q_2^{2\beta_2} \cdots q_t^{2\beta_t}$$

where $p, q_1, q_2, \cdots, q_t$ are distinct odd primes and $p \equiv \alpha \equiv 1 \pmod 4$.

ARITHMETIC FUNCTIONS / 7

7.1 / INTRODUCTION

In the preceding chapters we have studied three arithmetic functions, σ, τ, and φ, and have observed that they are associated with sums of form $\sum_{d|n} \alpha(d)$; that is,

$$\sum_{d|n} \varphi(d) = n \qquad \text{(Theorem 7 of Chapter 4)}$$

$$\sum_{d|n} 1 = \tau(n) \qquad \text{(Definition)}$$

and
$$\sum_{d|n} d = \sigma(n) \qquad \text{(Definition)}$$

In this chapter we will study arithmetic functions with particular emphasis on sums of the above type. A new notation will be introduced in order to facilitate our work.

7.2 / THE CALCULUS OF ARITHMETIC FUNCTIONS

We now define a "binary operation"[1] on the collection of arithmetic functions that will produce a third function from any two given functions. We will use a product notation to indicate this operation.

---

[1] A function from the set of all ordered pairs of elements of a set S to S is called a *binary operation on* S. If " $\bigcirc$ " denotes the binary operation, it is customary to write " $a \bigcirc b = c$ " rather than " $\bigcirc(a, b) = c$."

The binary operation " $\bigcirc$ " is said to be *associative* if $a \bigcirc (b \bigcirc c) = (a \bigcirc b) \bigcirc c$ for all a, b, c in S. It is said to be *commutative* if $a \bigcirc b = b \bigcirc a$ for all a, b in S.

Examples of binary operations are:
(1) addition and multiplication of numbers (commutative and associative);
(2) subtraction of numbers (neither commutative nor associative);
(3) multiplication of nth order matrices (associative, but not commutative).

■ DEFINITION / Let α and β be arithmetic functions. The function $\alpha \circ \beta$ called the *convolution product of* α *and* β, is defined by

$$(\alpha \circ \beta)(n) = \sum_{d|n} \alpha(d)\beta\left(\frac{n}{d}\right)$$

Example.

Calculate $(\varphi \circ \tau)$ (n) $(n = 1, 2, 3, 4)$.

SOLUTION: $(\varphi \circ \tau)(1) = \sum_{d|1} \varphi(d)\tau\left(\frac{1}{d}\right) = \varphi(1)\tau(1) = 1$

$(\varphi \circ \tau)(2) = \sum_{d|2} \varphi(d)\tau\left(\frac{2}{d}\right) = \varphi(1)\tau(2) + \varphi(2)\tau(1)$

$\qquad = 1 \cdot 2 + 1 \cdot 1 = 3$

$(\varphi \circ \tau)(3) = \varphi(1)\tau(3) + \varphi(3)\tau(1)$

$\qquad = 1 \cdot 2 + 2 \cdot 1 = 4$

$(\varphi \circ \tau)(4) = \varphi(1)\tau(4) + \varphi(2)\tau(2) + \varphi(4)\tau(1)$

$\qquad = 1 \cdot 3 + 1 \cdot 2 + 2 \cdot 1 = 7$

The function $\varphi \circ \tau$ will be considered again in Problem 1 and in Exercise 1.

The use of this notation leads to a convenient calculus of arithmetic functions. We will establish several useful properties of convolution multiplication that will enable us to manipulate these functions with comparative ease.

■ THEOREM 1 / Convolution multiplication is commutative; that is,

$$\alpha \circ \beta = \beta \circ \alpha$$

PROOF: Let n be a positive integer. As d ranges over the divisors of n, so does n/d. Let $d' = n/d$. Then

$$(\alpha \circ \beta)(n) = \sum_{d|n} \alpha(d)\beta\left(\frac{n}{d}\right) = \sum_{d'|n\alpha} \left(\frac{n}{d'}\right)\beta(d')$$

$$= \sum_{d'|n} \beta(d')\alpha\left(\frac{n}{d'}\right) = (\beta \circ \alpha)(n)$$

Since $(\alpha \circ \beta)(n) = (\beta \circ \alpha)(n)$ for each positive integer n, the functions $\alpha \circ \beta$ and $\beta \circ \alpha$ are equal.

In the next theorem we will establish one of the most important properties of convolution multiplication: the associative property. Many of the other properties (such as the Möbius inversion formula of Section 7.4) are consequences of this property.

Before proving Theorem 2 we make an observation that will be used in several of the proofs that follow: *Many sums can be rewritten as double sums.* For example,

Let α and β be arithmetic functions and let m and n be positive integers. Then

$$\sum_{\substack{d|m \\ D|n}} \alpha(d)\beta(D) = \sum_{d|m} \alpha(d) \sum_{D|n} \beta(D)$$

PROOF: Let $d_1, d_2, \cdots, d_s$ and $D_1, D_2, \cdots, D_t$ be the positive divisors of m and n, respectively. Then

$$\sum_{\substack{d|m \\ D|n}} \alpha(d)\beta(D) = \sum_{\substack{j = 1,2,\cdots,s \\ k = 1,2,\cdots,t}} \alpha(d_j)\beta(D_k)$$

$$= \alpha(d_1)\beta(D_1) + \alpha(d_2)\beta(D_1) + \cdots + \alpha(d_s)\beta(D_1)$$

$$+ \alpha(d_1)\beta(D_2) + \alpha(d_2)\beta(D_2) + \cdots + \alpha(d_s)\beta(D_2)$$

$$\cdots$$

$$+ \alpha(d_1)\beta(D_t) + (\alpha d_2)\beta(D_t) + \cdots + \alpha(d_s)\beta(D_t)$$

$$= \{\alpha(d_1) + \cdots + \alpha(d_s)\} \cdot \{\beta(D_1) + \cdots + \beta(D_t)\}$$

$$= \sum_{d|m} \alpha(d) \sum_{D|n} \beta(D)$$

■ **THEOREM 2 /** Convolution multiplication is associative; that is, if α, β, and γ are arithmetic functions, then

$$(\alpha \circ \beta) \circ \gamma = \alpha \circ (\beta \circ \gamma)$$

PROOF: We must show that if n is a positive integer, then $((\alpha \circ \beta) \circ \gamma)(n) = (\alpha \circ (\beta \circ \gamma))(n)$. If we consider the first of these expressions, we see that

$$((\alpha \circ \beta) \circ \gamma)(n) = \sum_{d|n}(\alpha \circ \beta)(d)\,\gamma\left(\frac{n}{d}\right)$$

$$= \sum_{d|n}\left(\sum_{s|d}\alpha(s)\beta\left(\frac{d}{s}\right)\right)\gamma\left(\frac{n}{d}\right)$$

$$= \sum_{d|n}\sum_{s|d}\alpha(s)\beta\left(\frac{d}{s}\right)\gamma\left(\frac{n}{d}\right)$$

Since $s|d$, we let $d = st$. Thus, the above sum is equal to the single sum

$$\sum_{st|n}\alpha(s)\beta(t)\gamma\left(\frac{n}{st}\right) \tag{7.1}$$

We will now consider the expression $(\alpha \circ (\beta \circ \gamma))(n)$. We write

$$(\alpha \circ (\beta \circ \gamma))(n) = \sum_{d|n} \alpha(d)(\beta \circ \gamma)\left(\frac{n}{d}\right) = \sum_{d|n} \alpha(d)\left(\sum_{m|n/d} \beta(m)\gamma\left(\frac{n}{md}\right)\right)$$

$$= \sum_{d|n} \sum_{m|n/d} \alpha(d)\beta(m)\gamma\left(\frac{n}{md}\right)$$

This double sum indicates that we consider all positive integers m and d such that $m|(n/d)$; that is, such that $md|n$. Thus, we can replace the double sum by a single sum and obtain

$$(\alpha \circ (\beta \circ \gamma))(n) = \sum_{md|n} \alpha(d)\beta(m)\gamma\left(\frac{n}{md}\right)$$

which is identical to expression (7.1) for $((\alpha \circ \beta) \circ \gamma)(n)$ except for the labeling of the divisors of n. Thus,

$$((\alpha \circ \beta) \circ \gamma)(n) = \sum_{st|n} \alpha(s)\beta(t)\gamma\left(\frac{n}{st}\right) = \sum_{md|n} \alpha(d)\beta(m)\gamma\left(\frac{n}{md}\right) = (\alpha \circ (\beta \circ \gamma))(n)$$

Since $\alpha \circ (\beta \circ \gamma)$ and $(\alpha \circ \beta) \circ \gamma$ have the same value for each positive integer n, the two functions are equal.

Rather than write $\alpha \circ (\beta \circ \gamma)$ or $(\alpha \circ \beta) \circ \gamma$ we will write $\alpha \circ \beta \circ \gamma$.

We will next prove that the multiplicative functions form a special subset of the arithmetic functions.

■ **THEOREM 3** / If α and β are multiplicative arithmetic functions, so is $\alpha \circ \beta$.

PROOF: Let m and n be relatively prime positive integers. If d is a divisor of mn, d can be written as $d = st$ where $s|m$ and $t|n$. Obviously,

$$(s, t) = \left(\frac{m}{s}, \frac{n}{t}\right) = 1$$

Thus,

$$(\alpha \circ \beta)(mn) = \sum_{d|mn} \alpha(d)\beta\left(\frac{mn}{d}\right) = \sum_{\substack{s|m \\ t|n}} \alpha(st)\beta\left(\frac{m}{s} \cdot \frac{n}{t}\right)$$

Because α and β are multiplicative, $\alpha(st) = \alpha(s)\alpha(t)$,

$$\beta\left(\frac{m}{s} \cdot \frac{n}{t}\right) = \beta\left(\frac{m}{s}\right)\beta\left(\frac{n}{t}\right)$$

and the above sum is equal to

$$\sum_{\substack{s|m \\ t|n}} \alpha(s)\beta\left(\frac{m}{s}\right)\alpha(t)\beta\left(\frac{n}{t}\right)$$

which, in turn, is equal to the product of the sums

$$\sum_{s|m}\alpha(s)\beta\left(\frac{m}{s}\right) \quad \text{and} \quad \sum_{t|n}\alpha(t)\beta\left(\frac{n}{t}\right)$$

Therefore,

$$(\alpha \circ \beta)(mn) = \sum_{\substack{s|m \\ t|n}}\alpha(s)\beta\left(\frac{m}{s}\right)\alpha(t)\beta\left(\frac{n}{t}\right) = \left(\sum_{s|m}\alpha(s)\beta\left(\frac{m}{s}\right)\right)\left(\sum_{t|n}\alpha(t)\beta\left(\frac{n}{t}\right)\right)$$

$$= (\alpha \circ \beta)(m) \cdot (\alpha \circ \beta)(n)$$

and $\alpha \circ \beta$ is multiplicative.

One additional definition will be made in this section.

▪ **DEFINITION** / We say that the arithmetic function α is *totally multiplicative* if

$$\alpha(mn) = \alpha(m)\alpha(n)$$

for each pair of positive integers m and n.

Example.

The function defined by $\alpha(n) = n^2$ is totally multiplicative. The function σ is multiplicative, but is not totally multiplicative.

EXERCISES

1. Let p be a prime number. Show that

$$(\varphi \circ \tau)(p) = p + 1$$

and
$$(\varphi \circ \tau)(p^2) = p^2 + p + 1$$

2. Let $\beta = \tau \circ \tau \circ \tau$.
   (a) Is β multiplicative?
   (b) Calculate $\beta(n)$ for $n = 1, 2, \cdots, 10$.

3. Let p be a prime and let β be the function of Exercise 2. Calculate $\beta(p)$ and $\beta(p^2)$.

4. Let α and β be totally multiplicative functions. Does $\alpha \circ \beta$ have to be multiplicative? Totally multiplicative?

PROBLEM

1. Prove: $\varphi \circ \tau = \sigma$. [*Hint*: See Exercise 1.]

7.3 / INVERSE FUNCTIONS UNDER CONVOLUTION MULTIPLICATION

■ DEFINITION / The function ϵ is defined as follows:

$$\epsilon(1) = 1$$
$$\epsilon(n) = 0 \qquad \text{if } n > 1$$

The function ϵ is called the *identity* for convolution multiplication since

$$\epsilon \circ \alpha = \alpha \circ \epsilon = \alpha \qquad (7.2)$$

if α is an arithmetic function (see Exercise 2).

We see from (7.2) that the function ϵ plays a role in convolution multiplication that is similar to the role played by the number 1 in ordinary multiplication. We are thus led to the following definition:

■ DEFINITION / Let α and β be arithmetic functions. β is called *the inverse of* α (*under convolution multiplication*) if

$$\alpha \circ \beta = \epsilon$$

This fact is indicated by writing $\beta = \alpha^{-1}$.

Thus, α^{-1} is a function having the property $\alpha^{-1} \circ \alpha = \alpha \circ \alpha^{-1} = \epsilon$. It is easy to show (Problem 1) that if α has an inverse, it is unique. Consequently, we may speak of *the* inverse of α. In Theorem 4, we establish necessary and sufficient conditions which insure that an inverse will exist.

■ THEOREM 4 / The arithmetic function α has an inverse if, and only if, $\alpha(1) \neq 0$.

PROOF: Suppose $\alpha(1) \neq 0$. Define the function β inductively by

$$\beta(1) = \frac{1}{\alpha(1)}$$

$$\beta(n) = -\frac{1}{\alpha(1)} \cdot \sum_{\substack{d \mid n \\ d < n}} \beta(d)\alpha\left(\frac{n}{d}\right) \qquad \text{if } n > 1 \qquad (7.3)$$

We will prove that $\beta = \alpha^{-1}$. If $n = 1$, then

$$(\beta \circ \alpha)(1) = \beta(1)\alpha(1) = 1 = \epsilon(1)$$

If $n > 1$, then

$$(\beta \circ \alpha)(n) = \sum_{d|n} \beta(d)\alpha\left(\frac{n}{d}\right) = \sum_{\substack{d|n \\ d<n}} \beta(d)\alpha\left(\frac{n}{d}\right) + \beta(n)\alpha(1)$$

$$= \sum_{\substack{d|n \\ d<n}} \beta(d)\alpha\left(\frac{n}{d}\right) + \left\{\frac{-1}{\alpha(1)} \sum_{\substack{d|n \\ d<n}} \beta(d)\alpha\left(\frac{n}{d}\right)\right\}\alpha(1)$$

$$= 0 = \epsilon(n)$$

Since $(\beta \circ \alpha)(n) = (\alpha \circ \beta)(n) = \epsilon(n)$ for each positive integer n, then

$$\alpha \circ \beta = \beta \circ \alpha = \epsilon$$

Thus, $\beta = \alpha^{-1}$.

The proof of the converse is left for the reader (Exercise 4).

■ **THEOREM 5 /** If α is a multiplicative function, not identically zero, then α^{-1} exists and is multiplicative.

PROOF: Since α is not identically zero, then $\alpha(1) = 1$. Thus, from Theorem 4 [using (7.3)], it follows that α^{-1} exists, that

$$\alpha^{-1}(1) = 1$$

and

$$\alpha^{-1}(n) = - \sum_{\substack{d|n \\ d<n}} \alpha^{-1}(d)\alpha\left(\frac{n}{d}\right) \qquad \text{if } n > 1 \tag{7.4}$$

We must now prove that if a and b are relatively prime positive integers, $\alpha^{-1}(ab) = \alpha^{-1}(a)\alpha^{-1}(b)$. Suppose there is a pair of relatively prime positive integers a and b such that $\alpha^{-1}(ab) \neq \alpha^{-1}(a)\alpha^{-1}(b)$. From the well-ordering principle we know that there exists a pair of relatively prime positive integers with this property such that their product is the smallest element in the set of all such products. Let m, n be this pair. Then

$$(m, n) = 1, \quad \alpha^{-1}(mn) \neq \alpha^{-1}(m)\alpha^{-1}(n)$$

and if c and d are relatively prime positive integers such that $cd < mn$, then $\alpha^{-1}(cd) = \alpha^{-1}(c)\,\alpha^{-1}(d)$. It is obvious that neither m nor n is equal to 1. Consider the quantity $\alpha^{-1}(m)\,\alpha^{-1}(n) - \alpha^{-1}(mn)$. From (7.4) we obtain

$$\alpha^{-1}(m)\alpha^{-1}(n) - \alpha^{-1}(mn) = \alpha^{-1}(m)\alpha^{-1}(n) + \sum_{\substack{d|mn \\ d<mn}} \alpha^{-1}(d)\alpha\left(\frac{mn}{d}\right)$$

If $d|mn$, we can write $d = st$ where $s|m$ and $s|n$. We can now rewrite the above equation as

$$\alpha^{-1}(m)\alpha^{-1}(n) - \alpha^{-1}(mn) = a^{-1}(m)\alpha^{-1}(n) + \sum_{\substack{s|m \\ t|n \\ st < mn}} \alpha^{-1}(st)\alpha\left(\frac{m}{s} \cdot \frac{n}{t}\right)$$

Because $st < mn$, then $\alpha^{-1}(st) = \alpha^{-1}(s)\,\alpha^{-1}(t)$. Using the fact that $\alpha(1) = 1$, we obtain

$$\alpha^{-1}(m)\alpha^{-1}(n) - \alpha^{-1}(mn) = \alpha^{-1}(m)\alpha^{-1}(n) + \sum_{\substack{s|m \\ t|n \\ st < mn}} \alpha^{-1}(s)\alpha^{-1}(t)\alpha\left(\frac{m}{s}\right)\alpha\left(\frac{n}{t}\right)$$

$$= \alpha^{-1}(m)\alpha(1)\alpha^{-1}(n)\alpha(1)$$

$$+ \sum_{\substack{s|m \\ t|n \\ st < mn}} \alpha^{-1}(s)\alpha\left(\frac{m}{s}\right)\alpha^{-1}(t)\alpha\left(\frac{n}{t}\right)$$

$$= \sum_{\substack{s|m \\ t|n}} \alpha^{-1}(s)\alpha\left(\frac{m}{s}\right)\alpha^{-1}(t)\alpha\left(\frac{n}{t}\right)$$

$$= \left(\sum_{s|m} \alpha^{-1}(s)\alpha\left(\frac{m}{s}\right)\right)\left(\sum_{t|n} \alpha^{-1}(t)\alpha\left(\frac{n}{t}\right)\right)$$

$$= (\alpha^{-1} \circ \alpha)(m) \cdot (\alpha^{-1} \circ \alpha)(n)$$

$$= \epsilon(m) \cdot \epsilon(n) = 0$$

since m and n are not both equal to 1.

Thus, $\alpha^{-1}(mn) = \alpha^{-1}(m)\alpha^{-1}(n)$, which contradicts the choice of m and n. Thus, $\alpha^{-1}(ab) = \alpha^{-1}(a)\alpha^{-1}(b)$ for any pair of relatively prime positive integers, a, b; that is, α^{-1} is multiplicative.

EXERCISES

1. Let $\alpha(n) = n^2$. Calculate $\alpha^{-1}(n)$ for $n = 1, 2, \cdots, 10$.

2. (a) Show that $\epsilon \circ \alpha = \alpha \circ \epsilon = \alpha$ for any arithmetic function α.
   (b) Show that $\epsilon^{-1} = \epsilon$ and $(\alpha^{-1})^{-1} = \alpha$.

3. Suppose α and β have inverses. Show that $\alpha \circ \beta$ also has an inverse and that

$$(\alpha \circ \beta)^{-1} = \alpha^{-1} \circ \beta^{-1}$$

4. Complete the proof of Theorem 4 by proving:
   If $\alpha(1) = 0$, then no function β exists such that $\alpha \circ \beta = \epsilon$.

PROBLEMS

1. Prove that the inverse of a function is unique; that is, if $\alpha \circ \beta = \epsilon$ and $\alpha \circ \gamma = \epsilon$, then $\beta = \gamma$.

2. (*Requires knowledge of elementary modern algebra.*) Let G be the set of all arithmetic functions α such that $\alpha(1) \neq 0$. Let H be the set of all elements of G which are multiplicative. Show that G is a group under the operation "$\circ$" and that H is a subgroup of G.

3. Define the binary operation "$*$" on the arithmetic functions by

$$(\alpha * \beta)(n) = \sum_{d \mid n} \alpha(d)\beta(d)$$

(*a*) Prove: $\alpha * \beta = \beta * \alpha$.
(*b*) Prove: If α and β are multiplicative, so is $\alpha * \beta$.
(*c*) Show by an example that the operation "$*$" is not associative.
(*d*) If α and $\alpha * \beta$ are multiplicative, does it follow that β is multiplicative?

4. Use Problem 3 to prove: If $n = p_1^{\alpha_1} \cdot p_2^{\alpha_2} \cdots p_k^{\alpha_k}$, where the p_i are distinct primes, then

$$\sum_{d \mid n} d\varphi(d) = \frac{p_1^{2\alpha_1 + 1} + 1}{p_1 + 1} \cdot \frac{p_2^{2\alpha_2 + 1} + 1}{p_2 + 1} \cdots \frac{p_k^{2\alpha_k + 1} + 1}{p_k + 1}$$

[Elementary Problem E1725, *American Mathematical Monthly*, Vol. 71 (1964), p. 912.]

7.4 / THE MÖBIUS INVERSION FORMULA

The following problem was solved by A. F. Möbius (1790–1868), a student of Gauss.

Suppose the arithmetic functions α and β are related by the following formula: For each positive integer n,

$$\alpha(n) = \sum_{d \mid n} \beta(d)$$

Is it possible to "invert" the series and express β as a function of α?

In order to solve this problem we introduce several basic functions that can be used to construct more complicated ones.

■ DEFINITION / The functions v, ι, and μ are defined as follows:

$v(n) = 1$ for each positive integer n,
$\iota(n) = n$ for each positive integer n,
$\mu = v^{-1}$.

Thus, for example, $\tau = v \circ v$ and $\sigma = \iota \circ v$.

The problem of Möbius can now be restated as follows: *Given that* $\alpha = \beta \circ v$, *express* β *in terms of* α. Using the theory developed in this chapter, it is trivial that

$$\beta = \alpha \circ v^{-1} = \alpha \circ \mu$$

Thus,

$$\beta(n) = \sum_{d \mid n} \alpha(d) \mu\left(\frac{n}{d}\right)$$

for each positive integer n. (The Möbius Inversion Formula.)

The function μ, called the *Möbius function*, plays a role in the solution of many advanced problems in number theory. In the next theorem we obtain a formula for the exact value of this function.

■ THEOREM 6 / $\mu(1) = 1$,

$\mu(n) = 0$, if n is divisible by a square,

$\mu(p_1 p_2 \cdots p_k) = (-1)^k$, if the primes

$p_1, p_2, \cdots, p_k$ are distinct.

PROOF: From (7.4) it follows that $\mu(1) = 1$ and

$$\mu(n) = -\sum_{\substack{d \mid n \\ d < n}} \mu(d) v\left(\frac{n}{d}\right) = -\sum_{\substack{d \mid n \\ d < n}} \mu(d) \qquad (7.5)$$

Thus, if p is a prime number,

$$\mu(p) = -\sum_{\substack{d \mid p \\ d < p}} \mu(d) = -\mu(1) = -1$$

Because μ is multiplicative (it is the inverse of a multiplicative function), then if $p_1, p_2, \cdots, p_k$ are distinct primes,

$$\mu(p_1 p_2 \cdots p_k) = \mu(p_1) \mu(p_2) \cdots \mu(p_k) = (-1)^k$$

From (7.5) it follows that

$$\mu(p^2) = -\{\mu(1) + \mu(p)\} = 0$$

$$\mu(p^3) = -\{\mu(1) + \mu(p) + \mu(p^2)\} = 0$$

If we continue by induction on n, we see that $\mu(p^n) = 0$ $(n = 2, 3, \cdots)$. (The details are left to the reader.) Since μ is multiplicative, it follows that if n is divisible by a square, then $\mu(n) = 0$.

The following theorem establishes a connection between certain sums involving $\alpha \circ \beta$ and sums involving α and β. From this theorem a number of interesting relationships between arithmetic functions can be derived. We state two of these relationships in the corollaries, some others are in the exercises.

■ **THEOREM 7** / Let α and β be arithmetic functions. Then

$$\sum_{m=1}^{n} (\alpha \circ \beta)(m) = \sum_{d=1}^{n} \left(\alpha(d) \sum_{k=1}^{[n/d]} \beta(k) \right) = \sum_{d=1}^{n} \sum_{k=1}^{[n/d]} \alpha(d)\beta(k)$$

PROOF:
$$\sum_{m=1}^{n} (\alpha \circ \beta)(m) = \sum_{m=1}^{n} \sum_{d \mid m} \alpha(d)\beta\left(\frac{m}{d}\right)$$

Each integer d in the second sum is in the range from 1 to n, and each integer in that range occurs as such a d at least once. If we fix d, we will obtain a term $\alpha(d)\,\beta(m/d)$ for every multiple m of d, $1 \le m \le n$; that is, a term $\alpha(d)\beta(kd/d)$ for every k between 1 and n/d (inclusive). If we sum over all such d, and, for fixed d, all such k, we obtain the desired result.

■ **COROLLARY 7.1** / $\displaystyle\sum_{m=1}^{n} \mu(m)\left[\frac{n}{m}\right] = 1$

PROOF: Let $\alpha = \mu$, $\beta = v$ in Theorem 7.

■ **COROLLARY 7.2** / $\displaystyle\sum_{m=1}^{n} \tau(m) = \sum_{m=1}^{n} \left[\frac{n}{m}\right]$.

PROOF: Let $\alpha = \beta = v$ in Theorem 7.

Corollary 7.2 can be used to establish that

$$\sum_{m=1}^{n} \tau(m)$$

is "approximately equal" to $n \cdot \log n$. Consequently, for large values of n, the sum behaves quite regularly although τ is itself rather irregular. This approximation is a consequence of the fact that the second sum in the statement of Corollary 7.2 is an exact count of the lattice points in the first quadrant that lie on or under the curve $y = n/x$. It can be proved that in this case, the number of lattice points is approximately equal to the area under the curve for $1 \le x \le n$. The proof is comparatively difficult and is omitted in this book.

EXERCISES

1. *Prove:*

$$\sum_{d|n} \mu(d) = 0, \qquad \text{if } n > 1.$$

2. *Prove:*

$$\sum_{d|n} d\mu\left(\frac{n}{d}\right) = \varphi(n).$$

(See Theorem 7 of Chapter 4.)

3. Use Exercise 2 to prove that $\varphi \circ \tau = \sigma$. (See Problem 1 of Section 7.2.)

4. *Prove:*

$$\prod_{d|n} d = n^{\tau(n)/2}.$$

5. Use Theorem 7 to prove that

$$\sum_{m=1}^{n} \sigma(m) = \sum_{m=1}^{n} m[n/m].$$

PROBLEMS

1. Let α be a totally multiplicative function, $\alpha(1) \neq 0$. Prove that $\alpha^{-1}(n) = \alpha(n)\mu(n)$ for each positive integer n.

2. *Prove:* If $f(n) > 0$ for each positive integer n and

$$g(n) = \prod_{d|n} f(d)$$

then

$$f(n) = \prod_{d|n} g(d)^{\mu(n/d)}$$

[*Hint:* Use logarithms.]

7.5* / THE RING OF ARITHMETIC FUNCTIONS

This section has as prerequisite: a knowledge of elementary modern algebra.

We have previously defined the "product" of two arithmetic functions. We now define the "sum" of two functions.

■ **DEFINITION** / Let α and β be arithmetic functions. The function $\alpha \oplus \beta$ is defined by

$$(\alpha \oplus \beta)(n) = \alpha(n) + \beta(n)$$

■ THEOREM 8 / The arithmetic functions form an integral domain under the operations $\oplus$ and $\circ$.

PROOF: We must show that the functions have the following properties under the two operations:

(1) $(\alpha \oplus \beta) \oplus \gamma = \alpha \oplus (\beta \oplus \gamma)$.

(2) $\alpha \oplus \beta = \beta \oplus \alpha$.

(3) There is a "zero" function, denoted by θ, such that $\alpha \oplus \theta = \alpha$ for each function α.

(4) If α is an arithmetic function, then α has an "additive inverse" β such that $\alpha \oplus \beta = \beta \oplus \alpha = \theta$.

(5) $\alpha \circ (\beta \circ \gamma) = (\alpha \circ \beta) \circ \gamma$ (proved in Theorem 2).

(6) $\alpha \circ \beta = \beta \circ \alpha$ (proved in Theorem 1).

(7) $\alpha \circ (\beta \oplus \gamma) = \alpha \circ \beta \oplus \alpha \circ \gamma$ (distributive property).

(8) There is a "multiplicative identity" (the function ϵ).

(9) If $\alpha \circ \beta = \alpha \circ \gamma$ and $\alpha \neq \theta$, then $\beta = \gamma$ (the cancellation law).

If we define θ by

$$\theta(n) = 0 \qquad (n = 1, 2, \cdots)$$

then θ has property (3). For (4) we define the function β by

$$\beta(n) = -\alpha(n) \qquad (n = 1, 2, \cdots)$$

Except for (9) the proofs of the other properties only involve manipulation.

PROOF OF (9): Proving the cancellation law is equivalent to proving that if $\alpha \circ \beta = \theta$, then $\alpha = \theta$ or $\beta = \theta$. Suppose that $\alpha \neq \theta$ and $\beta \neq \theta$. Let m and n be the smallest positive integers such that $\alpha(m) \neq 0$ and $\beta(n) \neq 0$. Let d be a positive divisor of mn. If $1 \leq d < m$, then $\alpha(d) = 0$, and, if $m < d \leq mn$, $\beta(mn/d) = 0$. Therefore,

$$(\alpha \circ \beta)(mn) = \sum_{d \mid mn} \alpha(d)\beta\left(\frac{mn}{d}\right) = \alpha(m)\beta(n) \neq 0$$

It follows that if $\alpha \circ \beta = \theta$, then either α or β must be θ.

EXERCISES

1. *Prove:* $(\alpha \oplus \beta) \oplus \gamma = \alpha \oplus (\beta \oplus \gamma)$.

2. *Prove:* $\alpha \oplus \beta = \beta \oplus \alpha$.

3. *Prove:* If α and β are multiplicative functions, neither equal to θ, then $\alpha \oplus \beta$ is not multiplicative.

4. *Prove:* $\theta \circ \alpha = \theta$ for each α.

5. Use the cancellation law to prove: If $\alpha \circ \alpha = \epsilon$, then $\alpha = \pm \epsilon$.

PROBLEMS

1. We define $\dfrac{\alpha}{\beta}$ to be the arithmetic function γ if γ is the *unique* solution of $\beta \circ \gamma = \alpha$.

(a) Prove that if γ is a solution of $\beta \circ \gamma = \alpha$, then it is the only solution, provided $\beta \neq \theta$.

(b) Prove that if $\beta(1) \neq 0$, then $\dfrac{\alpha}{\beta}$ exists.

2. Prove the following "laws of fractions":

(a) $\dfrac{\alpha}{\alpha} = \epsilon$;

(b) $\dfrac{\alpha}{\beta} \circ \dfrac{\delta}{\gamma} = \dfrac{\alpha \circ \delta}{\beta \circ \gamma}$;

(c) $\dfrac{\alpha}{\beta} \oplus \dfrac{\delta}{\gamma} = \dfrac{\alpha \circ \gamma \oplus \beta \circ \delta}{\beta \circ \gamma}$.

ELEMENTARY RESULTS ON THE DISTRIBUTION OF PRIME NUMBERS / **8**

8.1 / INTRODUCTION

Some of the deepest investigations in number theory are concerned with the distribution of prime numbers. Most of these researches are in the realm of *analytic number theory* (the applications of real and complex analysis to problems in number theory) and are thus outside the scope of this book.

In this chapter a few of the elementary results on the distribution of prime numbers are proved and some of the deeper results are stated without proof. In the appendix some techniques of factorization are discussed.

8.2 / THE INFINITY OF PRIME NUMBERS

One of the oldest surviving proofs in number theory is the following proof of an infinity of prime numbers, due to Euclid.

■ THEOREM 1 / There is an infinity of prime numbers.

PROOF: Suppose the set of primes is finite. Let $p_1, p_2, \cdots, p_n$ be all of the primes. Form the number

$$m = p_1 p_2 \cdots p_n - 1$$

Since m is not divisible by any of the prime numbers in the above list, then m is a composite number that is not divisible by a prime number, which contradicts the unique factorization theorem. Thus, the number of primes is infinite.

Several modifications can be made in the above proof that enable us to prove related results. One such modification proves that if p_k is the kth prime in the natural ordering (that is, $p_1 = 2, p_2 = 3, p_3 = 5, \cdots$), then

$$p_{k+1} \le p_1 p_2 \cdots p_k - 1$$

(Problem 2).

We can prove a second modification: the residue class $\mathcal{R}_3$ (mod 4) contains an infinity of primes. Before proving this result, we observe that since 2 is the only even prime, all other primes are in $\mathcal{R}_1$ (mod 4) or $\mathcal{R}_3$ (mod 4).

■ THEOREM 2 / There is an infinity of prime numbers that are congruent to 3 (mod 4).

PROOF: Suppose the number of such primes is finite. Let

$$p_1, p_2, \cdots, p_n$$

be the prime numbers in $\mathcal{R}_3$ (mod 4). Form the number

$$m = 4\, p_1\, p_2 \cdots p_n - 1$$

Then m is odd and is not divisible by any of the primes in our list. Since m is congruent to 3 (mod 4), then m is composite. Thus, m has prime factors, all of which are congruent to 1 (mod 4). But the product of numbers congruent to 1 (mod 4) is also congruent to 1 (mod 4), and so

$$1 \equiv m \equiv 3 \ (\text{mod } 4)$$

which is impossible. Thus, $\mathcal{R}_3$ (mod 4) contains an infinite number of primes.

Does the residue class $\mathcal{R}_1$ (mod 4) also contain an infinity of prime numbers? The answer is affirmative, but unfortunately, the proof is not as simple as that of Theorem 2 (see Section 9.6).

A more general problem is the following: *Let a and m be relatively prime positive integers. Does the residue class $\mathcal{R}_a$ (mod m) contain an infinity of primes?* The following theorem answers this question completely. The proof is beyond the scope of this book.

■ THEOREM OF DIRICHLET / *Let a and m be relatively prime positive integers. There is an infinity of prime numbers in the arithmetic progression*

$$\{a, a + m, a + 2m, a + 3m, \cdots\}$$

Given the theorem of Dirichlet, we might suppose that the prime numbers are distributed among the integers in a regular pattern. It is easy to see, however, that this is not the case. Suppose n is a positive integer. Then

$$\{(n + 1)! + 2, (n + 1)! + 3, (n + 1)! + 4, \cdots, (n + 1)! + (n + 1)\}$$

is a set of n consecutive composite numbers. Thus, the prime numbers are not distributed in a regular pattern.

EXERCISE

1. Prove that there is an infinity of prime numbers in the residue class $\mathscr{R}_5$ (mod 6).

PROBLEMS

1. Where does the proof break down if we try to modify the proof of Theorem 2 to prove an infinity of primes congruent to 1 (mod 4)?

2. Modify the proof of Theorem 1 to prove that if the kth prime is p_k then

$$p_{k+1} \leq p_1 p_2 \cdots p_k - 1$$

8.3 / THE SIEVE OF ERATOSTHENES

One of the most efficient methods of constructing tables of prime numbers is the *sieving process*, invented by the Greek mathematician Eratosthenes (276–194 B.C.). The work involved in the process is simplified if we make the following observation:

If the integer n is composite, it must have a prime factor that is less than or equal to $\sqrt{n}$. If this were not the case, we could write $n = ab$ where $a > \sqrt{n}$ and $b > \sqrt{n}$. This would imply that $n = ab > \sqrt{n}\sqrt{n} = n$, which is impossible.

To illustrate the method we will construct a table containing all primes less than 130.

We begin by listing all of the numbers from 2 to 129. See Table 8.1. (Since 1 is not a prime it is omitted.)

The first number in our list, 2, must be a prime and no multiple of 2 except 2 itself can be a prime. We remove all multiples of 2 (except $2 \cdot 1$) from our list and place the symbol "—" above the position. The next remaining number, 3, must be a prime so we delete the multiples of 3, placing the symbol "~" above the position. We now delete the multiples of 5(" · "), the multiples of 7 (" = "), and the multiples of 11 ("≈"). (Our work is simplified if we notice that the first multiple of 5 to be removed is 25, the first multiple of 7 is 49 and the first multiple of 11 is 121.)

Because the largest prime less than $\sqrt{130}$ is 11, it follows from the observation preceding the example that the remaining numbers must be primes. Thus, the primes less than 130 are 2, 3, 5, 7, 11, 13, 17, 19, 23, 29, 31, 37, 41, 43, 47, 53, 59, 61, 67, 71, 73, 79, 83, 89, 97, 101, 103, 107, 109, 113, 127.

Observe that we have constructed a factor table as well as a table of primes. For example, we see that the smallest prime factor of 119 is 7.

The sieve of Eratosthenes can be used to derive a formula for the number of primes less than or equal to n if the primes less than or equal to $\sqrt{n}$ are known. In order to use the standard notation we define the function π.

■ DEFINITION / Let x be a real number. $\pi(x)$ is the number of prime numbers less than or equal to x.

Table 8.1*

	2	3	4	5	6	7	8	9
10	11	12	13	14	15	16	17	18	19
20	21	22	23	24	25	26	27	28	29
30	31	32	33	34	35	36	37	38	39
40	41	42	43	44	45	46	47	48	49
50	51	52	53	54	55	56	57	58	59
60	61	62	63	64	65	66	67	68	69
70	71	72	73	74	75	76	77	78	79
80	81	82	83	84	85	86	87	88	89
90	91	92	93	94	95	96	97	98	99
100	101	102	103	104	105	106	107	108	109
110	111	112	113	114	115	116	117	118	119
120	121	122	123	124	125	126	127	128	129

*The symbol — indicates that the number is a multiple of 2; ~, a multiple of 3; ·, a multiple of 5; =, a multiple of 7; ≈, a multiple of 11.

Example.

$$\pi(-5) = \pi(1\tfrac{1}{2}) = 0,$$
$$\pi(2) \quad = \pi(2.7) = 1,$$
$$\pi(12) \quad = \pi(11) \quad = 5.$$

If $p_1, p_2, \cdots, p_k$ are the primes less than or equal to n, the formula for $\pi(n)$ is

$$\pi(n) = n - 1 + \pi(\sqrt{n}) - \left\{ \left[\frac{n}{p_1}\right] + \left[\frac{n}{p_2}\right] + \cdots + \left[\frac{n}{p_k}\right] \right\}$$

$$+ \left\{ \left[\frac{n}{p_1 p_2}\right] + \left[\frac{n}{p_1 p_3}\right] + \cdots + \left[\frac{n}{p_1 p_k}\right] + \left[\frac{n}{p_2 p_3}\right] + \cdots \right.$$ (8.1)

$$\left. + \left[\frac{n}{p_{k-1} p_k}\right] \right\} - \left\{ \left[\frac{n}{p_1 p_2 p_3}\right] + \cdots + \left[\frac{n}{p_{k-2} p_{k-1} p_k}\right] \right\} + \cdots$$

$$+ (-1)^k \left[\frac{n}{p_1 p_2 \cdots p_k}\right]$$

To prove this formula, we recall the steps in the sieve of Eratosthenes. The number of elements in the original set is $n - 1$. The number divisible by p_1 is $[n/p_1]$, the number divisible by p_2 is $[n/p_2]$, and so on. If we delete all numbers divisible by p_1 (including p_1 itself) and then all numbers divisible by p_2, we have deleted $[n/p_1] + ([n/p_2] - [n/p_1p_2])$ numbers. (The $[n/p_1p_2]$ numbers are those divisible by both p_1 and p_2 and were thus deleted at the first stage.) If we continue this line of reasoning, we obtain $(n - 1)$ plus the complicated expression involving the greatest integer function for the number of elements remaining in the set. In the process we have removed the prime numbers p_1, ..., p_k from the list as well as all of their multiples. When we replace these numbers, we obtain (8.1).

As a check on the formula we calculate the number of primes less than or equal to 129. In this case

$$\pi(\sqrt{n}) = \pi(\sqrt{129}) = 5$$

The primes less than or equal to $\sqrt{129}$ are

$$2, 3, 5, 7, \text{ and } 11$$

From the formula we obtain

$$\pi(129) = 129 - 1 + 5 - \left[\frac{129}{2}\right] - \left[\frac{129}{3}\right] - \left[\frac{129}{5}\right] - \left[\frac{129}{7}\right]$$

$$- \left[\frac{129}{11}\right] + \left[\frac{129}{2 \cdot 3}\right] + \left[\frac{129}{2 \cdot 5}\right] + \left[\frac{129}{2 \cdot 7}\right] + \left[\frac{129}{2 \cdot 11}\right]$$

$$+ \left[\frac{129}{3 \cdot 5}\right] + \left[\frac{129}{3 \cdot 7}\right] + \left[\frac{129}{3 \cdot 11}\right] + \left[\frac{129}{5 \cdot 7}\right] + \left[\frac{129}{5 \cdot 11}\right]$$

$$+ \left[\frac{129}{7 \cdot 11}\right] - \left[\frac{129}{2 \cdot 3 \cdot 5}\right] - \left[\frac{129}{2 \cdot 3 \cdot 7}\right] - \left[\frac{129}{2 \cdot 3 \cdot 11}\right] - \left[\frac{129}{2 \cdot 5 \cdot 7}\right]$$

$$- \left[\frac{129}{2 \cdot 5 \cdot 11}\right] - \left[\frac{129}{2 \cdot 7 \cdot 11}\right] - \left[\frac{129}{3 \cdot 5 \cdot 7}\right] - \left[\frac{129}{3 \cdot 5 \cdot 11}\right] - \left[\frac{129}{3 \cdot 7 \cdot 11}\right]$$

$$- \left[\frac{129}{5 \cdot 7 \cdot 11}\right] + \left[\frac{129}{2 \cdot 3 \cdot 5 \cdot 7}\right] + \left[\frac{129}{2 \cdot 3 \cdot 5 \cdot 11}\right] + \left[\frac{129}{2 \cdot 3 \cdot 7 \cdot 11}\right]$$

$$+ \left[\frac{129}{2 \cdot 5 \cdot 7 \cdot 11}\right] + \left[\frac{129}{3 \cdot 5 \cdot 7 \cdot 11}\right] - \left[\frac{129}{2 \cdot 3 \cdot 5 \cdot 7 \cdot 11}\right]$$

$$= 129 - 1 + 5 - 64 - 43 - 25 - 18 - 11 + 21 + 12$$

$$+ 9 + 5 + 8 + 6 + 3 + 3 + 2 + 1 - 4 - 3 - 1 - 1$$

$$- 1 - 0 - 1 - 0 - 0 - 0 + 0 + 0 + 0 + 0 + 0 - 0$$

$$= 31$$

We can verify that this is correct by counting the primes in our table.

Although the formula is very awkward to use, it is the only formula for the exact value of $\pi(n)$. In actual computation there are a number of shortcuts that may be used but the process remains cumbersome. By use of the formula it has been established that

$$\pi(100,000,000) = 5,761,455$$

and

$$\pi(1,000,000,000) = 50,847,478$$

EXERCISES

1. Use the sieve of Eratosthenes to calculate all prime numbers less than 200.

2. Use formula (8.1) to calculate $\pi(200)$.

3. *Prove:* If $\pi(\sqrt{n}) = k$, then formula (8.1) has $2^k + 2$ terms.

8.4* | REMARKS ON THE DISTRIBUTION OF PRIME NUMBERS

Until the problem was considered by Gauss, little of significance was determined about the distribution of prime numbers. Much of the effort before that time had been wasted on attempts to find polynomials that generate all of the primes or take on only prime values.[1] For example, it was believed by certain mathematicians in the Middle Ages that the polynomial

$$f(x) = x^2 - x + 41$$

takes on only prime values as x varies over the nonnegative integers. Although this is the case for $x = 0, 1, 2, \cdots, 40$, it is easy to see that

$$f(41) = 41^2$$

which is composite. It is now relatively simple for us to prove that any integral polynomial must take on composite values (see Problem 4, Section 3.6). Thus, the attempts mentioned above were doomed to failure.

---

[1] It has been proved theoretically that prime-generating functions (not polynomials) do exist, but to date no one has exhibited a nontrivial function of this type. As an example, W. H. Mills (*Bulletin, American Mathematical Society*, June, 1940) proved that there is a real number α such that $[\alpha^{3^n}]$ takes on only prime values.

Even Fermat attempted to find a prime-generating function. He believed that any number of form

$$f_n = 2^{2^n} + 1 \ (n = 0, 1, 2, \cdots)$$

is a prime, but had to admit that he could not prove it. The proposition is correct for $n = 0, 1, 2, 3, 4$, but by factoring f_5, Euler showed that the general proposition is false. In this case, Fermat's intuition was quite wrong, because no additional primes of this type have ever been found, even after extensive searches with electronic computers.

THE PRIME NUMBER THEOREM

Gauss changed the direction of research on prime numbers by instituting a study of $\pi(x)$, the number of primes not exceeding x. While studying prime tables, he noticed that as x becomes large, $\pi(x)$ behaves similarly to $x/\log x$ (the logarithm to the base e), and he later conjectured that

$$\lim_{x \to \infty} \frac{\pi(x)}{x/\log x} = 1$$

This proposition, known as the *prime number theorem*, is usually written using the abbreviated notation

$$\pi(x) \sim \frac{x}{\log x}$$

[We say that $\pi(x)$ is asymptotically equal to $x/\log x$.] Note that this does not imply that the difference $\pi(x) - x/\log x$ ever becomes small, but only that it comes small compared to $x/\log x$.

The first major step towards a proof of this theorem was made by the Russian mathematician Chebychev, who, in 1850, proved that positive constants a and b exist such that

$$a \frac{x}{\log x} < \pi(x) < b \frac{x}{\log x} \qquad (x \geq 2)$$

In 1896, Hardamard and Vallee-Poussin independently proved the prime number theorem. The proofs depended on deep investigations in complex analysis, starting with Riemann's zeta function[2]

$$\zeta(s) = 1 + \frac{1}{2^s} + \frac{1}{3^s} + \frac{1}{4^s} + \cdots \qquad (s > 1)$$

---

[2]The zeta function is intimately connected with prime numbers because

$$\zeta(s) = \left(1 + \frac{1}{2^s} + \frac{1}{2^{2s}} + \cdots\right)\left(1 + \frac{1}{3^s} + \frac{1}{3^{2s}} + \cdots\right)\cdots$$

the product extending over all prime numbers.

For years it was believed that no elementary proof of the prime number existed, but in 1950 P. Erdös and A. Selberg were able to prove this theorem using nothing more advanced than elementary calculus.

PRIMES IN ARITHMETIC PROGRESSION

As mentioned in Section 8.2, Direchlet proved that if $(a, m) = 1$, the residue class $\mathcal{R}_a$ (mod m) contains an infinity of prime numbers. It is natural to inquire whether certain residue classes are "richer" in primes than are others. Vallee-Poussin established that this is not the case by proving a "prime number theorem for primes in arithmetic progression." He proved that if $(a, m) = 1$ and $\pi_{a,m}(x)$ denotes the number of primes of form $a + km$, which do not exceed x, then

$$\pi_{a,m}(x) \sim \frac{1}{\varphi(m)} \cdot \frac{x}{\log x}$$

In other words, over a large finite interval, all of the residue classes relatively prime to m contain "approximately" the same number of primes.

BERTRAND'S CONJECTURE

On the basis of tables J. Bertrand conjectured in 1845 that if $n > 3$, there is a prime number between n and $2n - 2$. It is easy to verify this for small values of n. For example,

5 is between n and $2n - 2$, if $n = 4$
7 is between n and $2n - 2$, if $n = 5$ or 6
11 is between n and $2n - 2$, if $n = 7, 8, 9, 10$
19 is between n and $2n - 2$, if $n = 11, 12, \cdots, 18$
31 is between n and $2n - 2$, if $n = 19, 20, \cdots, 30$.

This conjecture was proved soon afterwards by Chebychev, who also proved the following stronger statement:

If $\epsilon > \frac{1}{5}$, there is an integer N (which depends on ϵ) such that if x is any integer greater than N, there is a prime number between x and $x(1 + \epsilon)$.

Chebychev's result has since been improved so as to remove the restriction that $\epsilon > \frac{1}{5}$. We now know that the proposition is true for any positive number ϵ.

If $\epsilon \geq 1$, we obtain from Bertrand's conjecture and direct verification that there is a prime number between x (exclusive) and $2x$ (inclusive).[3]

PRIME TWINS

Two consecutive odd primes are called *prime twins*. For example, the first few prime twins are 3 and 5, 5 and 7, 11 and 13, 17 and 19, 29 and 31, 41 and 43.

---

[3]The bound $2x$ is needed only for $x = 1$.

Is there an infinity of prime twins? This is one of the oldest problems in mathematics. We have some information about the distribution of prime twins, but the above question is still unsolved. It has been proved that the series

$$\frac{1}{p_1} + \frac{1}{p_2} + \frac{1}{p_3} + \cdots$$

is divergent when summed over all prime numbers, while the series

$$\frac{1}{q_1} + \frac{1}{q_2} + \frac{1}{q_3} + \cdots$$

is convergent when summed over all prime twins. Thus, the prime twins are comparatively rare in the sequence of all prime numbers.

Many results in number theory were first conjectured on the basis of plausible arguments that could not be developed into rigorous proofs. There is an argument of this type that seems to indicate that the number of prime twins is infinite and that a "prime number theorem" holds for prime twins. If we let $\alpha(x)$ denote the number of prime twins that do not exceed x, the argument leads to the conjecture that

$$\alpha(x) \sim \frac{cx}{\log^2 x}$$

where c is a certain positive constant. The conjecture is obtained from theoretical considerations and agrees quite well with actual counts made by electronic computers.

GOLDBACH'S CONJECTURE

In a letter to Euler (in 1742), Christian Goldbach stated that from empirical observations he believed that every even integer could be expressed as a sum of two odd primes (at that time the number 1 was counted as a prime number).

It has since been verified that every even integer n in the range $6 \le n \le$ 100,000 is the sum of two odd primes (excluding 1). This is easy to check for small even integers. For example,

$$\begin{array}{ll}
6 = 3 + 3 & 22 = 3 + 19 \\
8 = 3 + 5 & 24 = 5 + 19 \\
10 = 5 + 5 & 26 = 7 + 19 \\
12 = 7 + 5 & 28 = 5 + 23 \\
14 = 7 + 7 & 30 = 7 + 23 \\
16 = 5 + 11 & 32 = 3 + 29 \\
18 = 7 + 11 & 24 = 5 + 29 \\
20 = 7 + 13 & 36 = 7 + 29
\end{array}$$

Although many mathematicians have worked on this conjecture, it has never been proved or disproved. The first significant advance was made by the Russian mathematician Vinogradov, who, in 1937, obtained a partial solution to a consequence of Goldbach's conjecture. Note that the conjecture implies that every odd integer greater than 9 is a sum of three odd primes. Vinogradov proved that every *sufficiently large* odd integer is the sum of three odd primes; that is, there is a number N such that any odd integer greater than N is the sum of three odd primes. Theorems of this type are useful if we can get a reasonable upper bound on N, because we can check the remaining numbers and see if the proposition holds for them. Unfortunately, the value obtained for N is so large that the remaining numbers can not be checked even on an electronic computer.

APPENDIX / FACTORIZATION METHODS OF FERMAT AND EULER

A. INTRODUCTION

Many problems in number theory require the factorization of some given integer. The only efficient factorization method is by the use of factor tables, but, unfortunately, it is not possible to include all of the integers in these tables. Consequently, we must rely on other, less efficient, methods.

The most obvious technique is to divide the primes less than $\sqrt{N}$ into N and see which, if any, leave no remainder. This works well if N is small, but is impractical if N is large, since we probably will not know which of the numbers less than $\sqrt{N}$ are primes. It is also obvious that the labor is prohibitive.

There are a number of methods for factoring large numbers. Because many of them are variations on two basic methods, each of which having a comparatively simple proof, we will restrict ourselves to these two methods—one due to Fermat and one to Euler.

As we shall see, each of the methods involves recognizing when certain numbers are squares. In order to facilitate our work, we construct a table that can be used to eliminate many nonsquares from consideration.

If we compute the squares of 0, 1, 2, $\cdots$, 9, modulo 10, we see that

$$
\begin{aligned}
0^2 &\equiv 0 \\
1^2 &\equiv 9^2 \equiv 1 \\
2^2 &\equiv 8^2 \equiv 4 \qquad (\text{mod } 10) \\
3^2 &\equiv 7^2 \equiv 9 \\
4^2 &\equiv 6^2 \equiv 6 \\
5^2 &\equiv 5
\end{aligned}
$$

Thus, if an integer ends in one of the digits 2, 3, 7, or 8, we see that it is not a square. Consequently, we can eliminate approximately 40 percent of the numbers from consideration.

If we repeat this process for the modulus 100, we find that a square must end in one of the pairs of digits listed in Table 8.2.

Table 8.2 Table of last two digits of squares.

00	16	21	36	41	56	61	76	81
01		24		44		64		84
04		25		49		69		89
09		29						

By checking the last two digits against the 22 entries in the table, we see that we can eliminate approximately 78 percent of the numbers from consideration.

B. FERMAT'S METHOD

Fermat's factorization method starts from the observation that if N is a difference of two squares, say $N = x^2 - y^2$, then N can be factored as

$$N = (x - y)(x + y)$$

The method depends on the fact that if N is odd,[4] the converse is also true.

▪ THEOREM 3 / Let N be an odd integer. If N can be factored as

$$N = ab \ (1 \leq a \leq b)$$

then N can be written as a difference of two squares x^2 and y^2, where

$$x = \frac{b + a}{2} \quad \text{and} \quad y = \frac{b - a}{2}$$

The proof follows immediately from the expansion of

$$\left(\frac{b + a}{2}\right)^2 - \left(\frac{b - a}{2}\right)^2$$

and is left for the reader.

In order to apply the theorem we note that if N is the difference of two squares, we can write

$$x^2 - N = y^2$$

---

[4]The factors of 2 are obvious, so we may assume that N is odd.

We now substitute values of x starting with $x = [\sqrt{N}] + 1$. If N is composite, we will eventually find a value of x for which $x^2 - N$ is a square.

Rather than compute x^2, $(x + 1)^2$, $(x + 2)^2$, $\cdots$, separately, Fermat noted that the method is easier to apply if we use the following scheme:

$$(x + 1)^2 - N = (x^2 - N) + (2x + 1)$$
$$(x + 2)^2 - N = [(x + 1)^2 - N] + (2x + 3)$$
$$(x + 3)^2 - N = [(x + 2)^2 - N] + (2x + 5)$$
$$\cdots$$

The following example is the one used by Fermat to illustrate his method:

Example 1.

Factor $N = 2{,}027{,}651{,}281$.

SOLUTION: Since $[\sqrt{N}] = 45{,}029$ we start our calculations with $x = 45{,}030$.

x	$x^2 - N$
45,030	49,619
	$2 \cdot 45{,}030 + 1 =$ 90,061
45,031	139,680
	$2 \cdot 45{,}030 + 3 =$ 90,063
45,032	229,743
	$2 \cdot 45{,}030 + 5 =$ 90,065
45,033	319,808
	$2 \cdot 45{,}030 + 7 =$ 90,067
45,034	409,875
	90,069
45,035	499,944
	90,071
45,036	590,015
	90,073
45,037	680,088
	90,075
45,038	770,163
	90,077
45,039	820,240
	90,079
45,040	950,319
	90,081
45,041	$1{,}040{,}400 = 1020^2$

Thus,

$$N = 45,041^2 - 1020^2 = (45,041 - 1020)(45,041 + 1020)$$
$$= 44,021 \cdot 46,061$$

In the above list we can eliminate all values of $x^2 - N$ except 499,944 and 1,040,400 by checking our table of last digits of squares.

Several short cuts are available. For example, it is easy to eliminate the factors 3, 5, and 11 by inspection.[5] If we eliminate all of the primes less than the prime p as factors, we must only check

$$x^2 - N \quad \text{for } x = [\sqrt{N}] + 1, \cdots, \left[\frac{N + p^2}{2p}\right]$$

(see Exercise 2). If we check the last two digits of N against the table of squares, we can eliminate many values of x from consideration. In the above example, because N ends in 81, we see that x^2 must end in 81 and y^2 in 00, or x^2 in 25 and y^2 in 44. Thus, x must end in 09, 41, 59, 91, 05, 15, 25, 35, 45, 55, 65, 75, 85, or 95.

EXERCISES

1. Use Fermat's method to factor
   (*a*) 3,085,811;
   (*b*) 3,642,517.

2. *Prove:* If the smallest prime factor of N is greater than or equal to c, then in Fermat's method we do not need to check $x^2 - N$ for x greater than $(N + c^2)/2c$.

C. EULER'S METHOD

In Chapter 10 we will prove the following theorem (Theorem 4):

Let the positive integer N be written in the form $N = m^2 n$, where n does not contain a square factor. N can be written as a sum of two squares (one may be 0^2) if, and only if, each odd prime factor of n is of form $4k + 1$.

Using this theorem we can prove a factorization method commonly ascribed to Euler.[6] The method is more limited than Fermat's, because it can

---

[5]N has 3 as a factor if and only if the sum of the digits is congruent to zero (mod 3), and has 11 as a factor if and only if the alternating sum of the digits is congruent to zero (mod 11).

[6]The method was apparently known to both Mersenne and de Bessy, but Euler was the first person to use it extensively.

be applied only to numbers of form $4k + 1$. Furthermore, in certain cases we cannot factor the number in question, but we are merely informed that the number is composite, with an even number of factors of form $4k + 3$.

An immediate consequence of the above theorem is:

If N is a positive integer of form $4k + 1$ that cannot be written as a sum of two squares, then N is composite and has an even number of prime factors of form $4k + 3$, at least two of which are distinct.

We now turn our attention to those integers of form $4k + 1$ that can be written as sums of two squares. [*Note: If $N = a^2 + b^2$, where a and b are not relatively prime, then (a^2, b^2) is a factor of N. Thus, in the sequel, we need only consider the case $N = a^2 + b^2$, where a and b are relatively prime.*]

∎ **THEOREM 4** / Let N be a positive integer of form $4k + 1$ which can be written as a sum of two relatively prime squares. Then N is composite if, and only if, N can be written as a sum of two squares in two distinct ways.

PROOF: (Part I) Suppose N is composite. If N is a square the proof is trivial. If N is not a square, we can write $N = ab$ $(1 < a, 1 < b)$, where we may assume that a has all of the prime factors of form $4k + 3$. Then b has only prime factors of form $4k + 1$, and so we can write b as a sum of two squares:

$$b = x^2 + y^2$$

We now distinguish two cases.

Case I. If a is a square, say $a = t^2$, then

$$N = ab = (tx)^2 + (ty)^2$$

Because N can also be written as a sum of two relatively prime squares, there are two ways of writing N as a sum of two squares.

Case II. If a is not a square, it follows from the theorem quoted above that

$$a = m^2 a'$$

where a' has only prime factors of form $4k + 1$. Thus, a can be written as a sum of two nonzero squares,

$$a = s^2 + t^2$$

If either x or y is zero the proof is as in Case I. If neither x nor y is zero, on substituting, we obtain

$$N = ab = (s^2 + t^2)(x^2 + y^2)$$
$$= (sx + ty)^2 + (sy - tx)^2$$
$$= (sx - ty)^2 + (sy + tx)^2$$

Since N is odd, it follows that $|sx - ty| \neq |sy - tx|$, and so N can be written in two ways as a sum of two squares.

(Part II) Suppose N can be written in two distinct ways as a sum of two squares:

$$N = a^2 + b^2 = c^2 + d^2$$

In each sum one of the squares must be even and the other odd. Suppose a and c are even. Then

$$a^2 - c^2 = d^2 - b^2$$

and so

$$(a - c)(a + c) = (d - b)(d + b) \tag{8.2}$$

If $D = (a - c, d - b)$, D is even, since $a - c$ and $d - b$ are even. We now write

$$a - c = Ds \qquad d - b = Dt \qquad (s, t) = 1$$

Substituting into (8.2) and cancelling D, we obtain

$$s(a + c) = t(d + b) \tag{8.3}$$

which implies that

$$s \mid (d + b)$$

since $(s, t) = 1$. We can now write

$$d + b = su$$

and substitute into (8.3) obtaining

$$a + c = tu$$

Because s and t are relatively prime,

$$u = (a + c, d + b)$$

and so u is even. It now follows that N is composite since

$$
\begin{aligned}
N &= \tfrac{1}{4}(2N + 2N) = \tfrac{1}{4}(2a^2 + 2b^2 + 2c^2 + 2d^2) \\
&= \tfrac{1}{4}[(a - c)^2 + (a + c)^2 + (d - b)^2 + (d + b)^2] \\
&= \tfrac{1}{4}(D^2 s^2 + t^2 u^2 + D^2 t^2 + s^2 u^2) \\
&= \tfrac{1}{4}(D^2 + u^2)(s^2 + t^2) \\
&= \left[\left(\frac{D}{2}\right)^2 + \left(\frac{u}{2}\right)^2 \right](s^2 + t^2)
\end{aligned}
$$

In the last part of the proof we did not use the fact that N can be written as a sum of two relatively prime squares. Thus, we obtain the following corollary to the proof:

■ **COROLLARY 4.1** / Let N be an odd integer that can be written as a sum of two squares in two distinct ways:

$$N = a^2 + b^2 = c^2 + d^2 \quad (a \text{ and } c \text{ even})$$

Then N is composite and can be factored as

$$N = \left(\left[\frac{D}{2} \right]^2 + \left(\frac{u}{2} \right)^2 \right)(s^2 + t^2)$$

where

$$D = (a - c, d - b) \qquad s = \frac{a - c}{D} \qquad t = \frac{d - b}{D}$$

$$u = \frac{d + b}{s}$$

In summary, if N is a positive integer of form $4k + 1$, then
1. If N cannot be written as a sum of two squares, N is composite, with an even number of prime factors of form $4k + 3$, at least two of which are distinct.
2. If N can be written as a sum of two squares that are not relatively prime, N is composite and has the greatest common divisor of the two squares as a factor.
3. If N can be written as a sum of two relatively prime squares in just one way, N is a prime number.
4. If N can be written as a sum of two squares in two distinct ways, Corollary 4.1 can be used to factor N.

To apply the method, we observe that if N is a sum of two squares, one of the squares must be less than or equal to $N/2$. Thus, we must check whether $N - a^2$ is a square for $a = 1, 2, \cdots, [\sqrt{N/2}]$. The work is expedited if we note that

$$N - (a - 1)^2 = (N - a^2) + (2a - 1)$$

$$N - (a - 2)^2 = [N - (a - 1)^2] + (2a - 3)$$

$$N - (a - 3)^2 = [N - (a - 2)^2] + (2a - 5)$$

$$\cdots$$

Example 2.

Use Euler's method to factor $N = 493$.

SOLUTION: Since N is of form $4k + 1$, the method can be used. We must check $N - a^2$ for $a = 1, 2, \cdots, [\sqrt{N/2}] = 15$.

a	$N - a^2$
15	268
	$2 \cdot 15 - 1 = 29$
14	297
	$2 \cdot 15 - 3 = 27$
13	$324 = 18^2$
	$2 \cdot 15 - 5 = 25$
12	349
	23
11	372
	21
10	393
	19
9	412
	17
8	429
	15
7	444
	13
6	457
	11
5	468
	9
4	477
	7
3	$484 = 22^2$

Since $N = 13^2 + 18^2 = 3^2 + 22^2$, then

$$D = (13 - 3, 22 - 18) = 2$$

$$s = \frac{13 - 3}{2} = 5$$

$$t = \frac{22 - 18}{2} = 2$$

$$u = \frac{22 + 18}{5} = 8$$

$$493 = \left[\left(\frac{2}{2}\right)^2 + \left(\frac{8}{2}\right)^2 \right](5^2 + 2^2) = 17 \cdot 29$$

EXERCISE

1. Use Euler's method to decide if the following numbers are primes. If possible, use Corollary 4.1 to factor the numbers.
   (*a*) 1357;
   (*b*) 1423.

QUADRATIC RESIDUES / 9

9.1 / INTRODUCTION

Some general theorems about polynomial congruences were proved in Chapters 3 and 4. In this chapter we will consider the simplest nonlinear polynomial congruence—the quadratic congruence

$$x^2 \equiv a \pmod{m} \tag{9.1}$$

where a and m are relatively prime.

In most cases it is sufficient to study this congruence rather than the more general quadratic congruence

$$a_0 x^2 + b_0 x + c_0 \equiv 0 \pmod{m} \tag{9.2}$$

for if a_0 is relatively prime to m and b_0 is *even* (or m is odd), then the congruence (9.2) can be easily reduced to a congruence of type (9.1) (see Problems 3 and 4). The problem of solving (9.1) can be further reduced, because by Theorem 7 of Chapter 3, solving,

$$x^2 \equiv a \pmod{p_1^{\alpha_1} p_2^{\alpha_2} \cdots p_k^{\alpha_k}}$$

is equivalent to solving the system of congruences

$$x^2 \equiv a \pmod{p_1^{\alpha_1}}$$
$$x^2 \equiv a \pmod{p_2^{\alpha_2}}$$
$$\cdots$$
$$x^2 \equiv a \pmod{p_k^{\alpha_k}}$$

As we shall see later solving

$$x^2 \equiv a \pmod{p^\alpha}$$

can be accomplished easily if we can solve

$$x^2 \equiv a \pmod{p}$$

134

Most of this chapter, therefore, will be concerned with the congruence

$$x^2 \equiv a \pmod{p}$$

where p is an odd prime and $a \not\equiv 0 \pmod{p}$.

■ DEFINITION / Let a be relatively prime to m. We say that a is a *quadratic residue* (*mod m*) if the congruence

$$x^2 \equiv a \pmod{m}$$

has a solution. If the congruence has no solution, we say that a is a *quadratic nonresidue* (*mod m*).

Example 1.

By considering the squares of $1^2, 2^2, \cdots, 10^2 \pmod{11}$, we see that

$$1^2 \equiv 10^2 \equiv 1 \pmod{11}$$
$$2^2 \equiv \ \ 9^2 \equiv 4 \pmod{11}$$
$$3^2 \equiv \ \ 8^2 \equiv 9 \pmod{11}$$
$$4^2 \equiv \ \ 7^2 \equiv 5 \pmod{11}$$
$$5^2 \equiv \ \ 6^2 \equiv 3 \pmod{11}$$

Thus, the quadratic residues (mod 11) are 1, 3, 4, 5, and 9, and the quadratic nonresidues are 2, 6, 7, 8, and 10.

Example 2.

By considering the squares of 1, 5, 7, and 11, we see that, modulo 12, the only quadratic residue is 1, while the quadratic nonresidues are 5, 7, and 11.

EXERCISE

1. List the quadratic residues and quadratic nonresidues (mod m) for:
   (a) $m = 17$;
   (b) $m = 18$;
   (c) $m = 19$.

PROBLEMS

1. *Prove:* If a and b are quadratic residues (mod m), then ab is also a quadratic residue (mod m).

2. *Prove:* If a is a quadratic residue and b is a quadratic nonresidue (mod m), then ab is a quadratic nonresidue (mod m).

3. Show that solving the quadratic congruence

$$x^2 + 2bx + c \equiv 0 \pmod{m}$$

is equivalent to solving

$$y^2 \equiv b^2 - c \pmod{m}$$

4. Let $m = p_1^{\alpha_1} p_2^{\alpha_2} \cdots p_k^{\alpha_k}$ (distinct odd primes). Let a be relatively prime to m. Show that solving

$$ax^2 + bx + c \equiv 0 \pmod{m}$$

is equivalent to solving a system of congruences

$$y^2 \equiv A \pmod{p_1^{\alpha_1}}$$

$$y^2 \equiv A \pmod{p_2^{\alpha_2}}$$

$$\cdots$$

$$y^2 \equiv A \pmod{p_k^{\alpha_k}}$$

[*Hint:* See Problem 3.]

9.2 / EULER'S CRITERION

It is not difficult to prove that the product of two quadratic residues is a quadratic residue and that the product of a quadratic residue and a non-residue is a nonresidue (Problems 1 and 2 of Section 9.1). If we study the examples in Section 9.1, we see that the situation is more complicated when we have the product of two quadratic nonresidues. Modulo 11, the quadratic nonresidues are 2, 6, 7, 8, and 10, and the product of any two numbers in this set is a quadratic residue. Modulo 12, the quadratic nonresidues are 5, 7, and 11 and the product of any two distinct nonresidues is a nonresidue. If we considered a few more examples, we would be led to conjecture that the product of two quadratic nonresidues is a quadratic residue, provided the modulus is a prime number.

Euler discovered a criterion for deciding when a given number is a quadratic residue, modulo an odd prime number. This criterion provides us with the simplest proof of the quadratic character of the product of two integers.

■ THEOREM 1 / (Euler's Criterion) If a is relatively prime to the odd prime, p, then a is a quadratic residue or a quadratic nonresidue (mod p), according to whether $a^{(p-1)/2} \equiv 1 \pmod{p}$ or $a^{(p-1)/2} \equiv -1 \pmod{p}$.

PROOF: Using Fermat's theorem we find that

$$(a^{(p-1)/2} - 1)(a^{(p-1)/2} + 1) \equiv a^{p-1} - 1 \equiv 0 \pmod{p}$$

and thus

$$a^{(p-1)/2} \equiv 1 \quad \text{or} \quad a^{(p-1)/2} \equiv -1 \pmod{p}$$

If a is a quadratic residue (mod p), there exists an integer x_0 such that $x_0^2 \equiv a$ (mod p). By Fermat's theorem,

$$a^{(p-1)/2} \equiv (x_0^2)^{(p-1)/2} \equiv x_0^{p-1} \equiv 1 \pmod{p}$$

To prove the converse, we assume that $a^{(p-1)/2} \equiv 1 \pmod{p}$. If g is a primitive root (mod p), there exists a positive integer t such that

$$g^t \equiv a \pmod{p}$$

Then

$$g^{t \cdot (p-1)/2} \equiv a^{(p-1)/2} \equiv 1 \pmod{p}$$

which (by Theorem 8 of Chapter 4) implies that

$$t \cdot \frac{p-1}{2} \equiv 0 \pmod{p-1}$$

Thus, t is even, and so

$$(g^{t/2})^2 \equiv g^t \equiv a \pmod{p}$$

which implies that a is a quadratic residue (mod p).

■ **COROLLARY** 1.1 / Let p be a prime number, let a and b be relatively prime to p.

(a) If a and b are quadratic residues (mod p), so is ab.

(b) If a and b are quadratic nonresidues, ab is a quadratic residue.

(c) If a is a quadratic residue and b is a quadratic nonresidue, then ab is a quadratic nonresidue.

PROOF OF (b): Since a and b are relatively prime to p, then so is ab. If $p = 2$, there are no quadratic nonresidues. Thus, we need only consider the case in which p is an odd prime. Since a and b are quadratic nonresidues, then by Euler's criterion

$$(ab)^{(p-1)/2} \equiv a^{(p-1)/2} b^{(p-1)/2} \equiv (-1)(-1) \equiv 1 \pmod{p}$$

Therefore, ab is a quadratic residue (mod p).

Much of the work in quadratic residues is simplified if we use the following notation, due to A. M. Legendre (1752–1833).

■ DEFINITION / Let a be relatively prime to the prime number p. The *Legendre symbol* $(a|p)$ is defined to be the number 1 if a is a quadratic residue (mod p), and the number -1 if a is a quadratic nonresidue (mod p).

We can now summarize the results of Theorem 1 and Corollary 1.1 as follows:

■ COROLLARY 1.2 / Let a and b be relatively prime to the prime number p. Then
(a) $a \equiv b$ (mod p) implies that $(a|p) = (b|p)$;
(b) $(ab|p) = (a|p)(b|p)$;
(c) if p is greater than 2, then $(a|p) \equiv a^{(p-1)/2}$ (mod p).

The following definition will be needed for the problems.

■ DEFINITION / We say that the integers a and b are *associates, modulo m*, if $ab \equiv 1$ (mod m).

PROBLEMS

1. Let a be relatively prime to the prime number p. Prove that a has an associate (mod p) and that this associate of a is not equal to a unless $a \equiv \pm 1$ (mod p).

2. (Wilson's theorem). If p is an odd prime number, then

$$(p-1)! \equiv -1 \text{ (mod } p)$$

[*Hint:* Group the numbers $1, 2, \cdots, p-1$ in pairs that are associates.]

3. (Generalized version of Wilson's theorem.) If p is an odd prime number, then

$$\left(\frac{p-1}{2}\right)!^2 (-1)^{(p-1)/2} \equiv -1 \text{ (mod } p)$$

[*Hint:* In the product $(p-1)!$, note that

$$\frac{p-1}{2} + 1 \equiv -\left(\frac{p-1}{2}\right) \text{ (mod } p)$$

$$\frac{p-1}{2} + 2 \equiv -\left(\frac{p-1}{2} - 1\right) \text{ (mod } p)$$

and so on.]

4. Use Problem 3 to prove that if p is of form $4n + 1$, then -1 is a quadratic residue (mod p).

9.3 / ELEMENTARY REMARKS ON THE DISTRIBUTION OF QUADRATIC RESIDUES

There are a number of interesting problems concerning the distribution of quadratic residues, modulo the odd prime number p. In this section we will consider the following questions:

1. Are the number 1, 2, 3, $\cdots$, $p - 1$ equally divided among quadratic residues and nonresidues?

2. Can we obtain an upper bound (which depends only on p) for the size of the smallest quadratic nonresidue?

3. Is there an upper bound for the maximum length of a sequence of consecutive quadratic residues?

4. How does the quadratic character of a affect the quadratic character of $p - a$?

We will answer questions 1 and 4. Bounds for 2 and 3 are considered in the problem section.

■ **THEOREM 2** / Let a be relatively prime to the odd prime number p. If p is of form $4n + 1$, then $-a$ is a quadratic residue (mod p) if, and only if, a is a quadratic residue. If p is of form $4n + 3$, then $-a$ is a quadratic nonresidue (mod p) if, and only if, a is a quadratic residue.

PROOF: From Theorem 1 we see that
$$(-a|p) \equiv (-a)^{(p-1)/2} \equiv (-1)^{(p-1)/2}a^{(p-1)/2} \equiv (-1)^{(p-1)/2}(a|p) \pmod{p}.$$
Since the quantities $(-a|p)$ and $(-1)^{(p-1)/2}$ $(a|p)$ are equal to either $+1$ or -1, this congruence implies that
$$(-a|p) = (-1)^{(p-1)/2}(a|p)$$
If p is of form $4n + 1$, then $(p-1)/2$ is even, and so
$$(-a|p) = (a|p)$$
If p is of form $4n + 3$, then $(p - 1)/2$ is odd, and so
$$(-a|p) = -(a|p)$$

■ **COROLLARY 2.1** / If p is of form $4n + 1$, then -1 is a quadratic residue (mod p). If p is of form $4n + 3$, then -1 is a quadratic nonresidue (mod p).

As a simple consequence of Theorem 2 we find that if p is of form $4n + 3$, then half of the numbers
$$1, 2, \cdots, p - 1$$
are quadratic residues and half are quadratic nonresidues. We will now prove that this is always the case. Obviously, this is equivalent to proving that
$$\sum_{a=1}^{p-1} (a|p) = 0.$$

■ THEOREM 3 / If p is an odd prime number then

$$\sum_{a=1}^{p-1} (a|p) = 0$$

PROOF: Let g be a primitive root (mod p). From Theorem 11 of Chapter 4 we know that g^t ranges over the numbers $1, 2, \cdots, p-1$ (mod p), in some order, as t ranges over the numbers $1, 2, \cdots, p-1$. Because g belongs to the exponent $p-1$ (mod p) then

$$g^{(p-1)/2} \equiv -1 \pmod{p}$$

Thus, if $a \equiv g^t$ (mod p), then

$$(a|p) = (g^t|p) \equiv (g^t)^{(p-1)/2} \equiv (g^{(p-1)/2})^t \equiv (-1)^t \pmod{p}$$

and so $$(a|p) = (g^t|p) = (-1)^t$$

If we now sum the Legendre symbols, we obtain

$$\sum_{a=1}^{p-1} (a|p) = \sum_{t=1}^{p-1} (g^t|p) = \sum_{t=1}^{p-1} (-1)^t = 0$$

Example.

Which of the numbers, $1, 2, \cdots, 18$ are quadratic residues, and which are non-residues (mod 19)?

SOLUTION: Write the numbers in the following pattern:

+	−	−	+	+	+	+	−	+
1	2	3	4	5	6	7	8	9
−	+	+	−	−	−	−	+	−
18	17	16	15	14	13	12	11	10

Because 1, 4, 9, and 16 are squares, they are obviously quadratic residues. By Theorem 2 the numbers 18, 15, 10, and 3 are quadratic nonresidues. Because 3 and 18 are nonresidues and $3 \cdot 6 = 18$, Corollary 1.1 implies that 6 is a quadratic residue (and thus 13 is a nonresidue). Because 3 is a nonresidue and 6 is a residue, then 2 is a nonresidue (and so 17 is a residue). Continuing in this manner, we find that the quadratic residues are 1, 4, 5, 6, 7, 9, 11, 16, 17, and the quadratic nonresidues are 2, 3, 8, 10, 12, 13, 14, 15, and 18.

EXERCISES

1. Find the quadratic residues (mod 43).

2. Find the quadratic residues (mod 41). [*Hint:* Find 20 quadratic residues. The other numbers must be nonresidues.]

PROBLEMS

In the following problems p is an odd prime number.

1. If q is the smallest positive quadratic nonresidue (mod p), show that q is a prime number.

2. If q is the smallest positive quadratic nonresidue (mod p), prove that $q < \sqrt{p} + 1$. [Hint: Show that the numbers q, $2q$, $\cdots$, $(q-1)q$, are all less than p.]

3. Prove that there exist two consecutive quadratic residues and two consecutive quadratic nonresidues if $p \geq 7$.

4. Let m be greater than 1. If m, $m + 1$, $\cdots$, $m + k - 1$ all have the same quadratic character, and if $m - 1$ does not have the same quadratic character as m, show that $k \leq m$.

5. Let k be a quadratic nonresidue which is greater than $\sqrt{p}$. Prove that no sequence of k consecutive quadratic residues or k consecutive quadratic non-residues exists.

9.4 / THE LEMMA OF GAUSS

Two basic questions concerning quadratic residues are:

1. Given a prime number p, which numbers are quadratic residues and which are quadratic nonresidues?

2. Given an integer a, for which primes is a a quadratic residue and for which primes is a a quadratic nonresidue?

The second question is obviously more difficult than the first, since it involves an infinite set of prime numbers, rather than a finite set of residue classes. The preceding material in this chapter has been along the lines indicated by the first question. We now turn our attention to the second.

Gauss devised a criterion for determining when a number is a quadratic residue (mod p), which can sometimes be used to answer the second question.

■ THEOREM 4 / (The Lemma of Gauss) Let a be relatively prime to the odd prime number p. Reduce each of the numbers a, $2a$, $\cdots$, $(p-1)/2 \cdot a$ (mod p) to a number between 1 and $p - 1$, inclusive. Let u be the number of these elements that exceed $p/2$. Then $(a|p) = (-1)^u$.

PROOF: Let s_1, s_2, $\cdots$, s_u be the numbers that exceed $p/2$, and let t_1, t_2, $\cdots$, t_v be the remaining numbers. Obviously, these numbers are distinct and so

$$u + v = \frac{p-1}{2}$$

We will now establish that $p - s_i$ is not one of the t's $(i = 1, 2, \cdots, u)$. Suppose that

$$p - s_i = t_j$$

There exist integers k_i and k_j between 1 and $(p - 1)/2$, inclusive, such that $ak_i \equiv s_i$ and $ak_j \equiv t_j \pmod{p}$. Thus,

$$p - ak_i \equiv p - s_i \equiv t_j \equiv ak_j \pmod{p}$$

which implies that

$$a(k_i + k_j) \equiv 0 \pmod{p}$$

Since $(a, p) = 1$, then

$$k_i + k_j \equiv 0 \pmod{p}$$

which is impossible, due to the fact that

$$0 < k_j + k_i < p - 1$$

Thus, the numbers

$$p - s_1, p - s_2, \cdots, p - s_u, t_1, t_2, \cdots, t_v$$

are the numbers $1, 2, \cdots, (p - 1)/2$ in some order. Taking the product of these numbers we obtain

$$(p - s_1)(p - s_2) \cdots (p - s_u) \cdot t_1 \cdots t_v = \left(\frac{p - 1}{2}\right)!$$

$$(-s_1)(-s_2) \cdots (-s_u) \cdot t_1 \cdots t_v \equiv \left(\frac{p - 1}{2}\right)! \pmod{p}$$

$$(-1)^u s_1 s_2 \cdots s_u t_1 \cdots t_v \equiv \left(\frac{p - 1}{2}\right)! \pmod{p}$$

Because $s_1, s_2, \cdots, s_u, t_1, \cdots, t_v$ are congruent $\pmod p$, in some order, to the numbers

$$a, 2a, \cdots, \frac{p - 1}{2} \cdot a$$

then

$$(-1)^u a^{(p - 1)/2} \left(\frac{p - 1}{2}\right)! \equiv (-1)^u a \cdot 2a \cdot 3a \cdots \frac{p - 1}{2} a$$

$$\equiv (-1)^u s_1 s_2 \cdots s_u t_1 t_2 \cdots t_v \equiv \left(\frac{p - 1}{2}\right)! \pmod{p}$$

If we now cancel $(p - 1)/2\,!$, we obtain

$$(-1)^u a^{(p - 1)/2} \equiv 1 \pmod{p}$$

and so

$$(-1)^u \equiv a^{(p - 1)/2} \pmod{p}$$

Using Euler's criterion, this implies that

$$(a|p) \equiv a^{(p - 1)/2} \equiv (-1)^u \pmod{p}$$

and since $p > 2$, that

$$(a|p) = (-1)^u$$

As an application we determine which primes have 2 as a quadratic residue.

■ THEOREM 5 / If the prime number p is of form $8n \pm 1$, then 2 is a quadratic residue (mod p). If p is of form $8n \pm 3$, then 2 is a quadratic nonresidue (mod p).

PROOF: To apply the lemma of Gauss, we must consider the numbers

$$2, 4, 6, \cdots, \frac{p - 1}{2} \cdot 2$$

Since these numbers are in the proper range, we must count the number that exceed $p/2$. Noting that $2k < p/2$ if, and only if, $k < p/4$, we see that $[p/4]$ of these numbers are less than $p/2$. Thus, the number of those that exceed $p/2$ is

$$u = \frac{p - 1}{2} - \left[\frac{p}{4}\right]$$

Case I. If $p = 8n + 1$, then $[p/4] = 2n$. Thus,

$$(2|p) = (-1)^u = (-1)^{(p - 1)/2 - [p/4]} = (-1)^{4n - 2n} = 1$$

The other three cases are left for the reader (Exercise 1).

We now use Theorem 4 to prove another criterion for quadratic residues. The main use of this result is as a lemma for the quadratic reciprocity law, to be proved in Section 9.5.

■ THEOREM 6 / If a is an odd positive integer, relatively prime to the odd prime p, then

$$(a|p) = (-1)^{\sum_{j=1}^{(p-1)/2} [ja/p]}$$

PROOF: We will use the same notation as in Theorem 4. We divide each term ja $(j = 1, 2, \cdots, (p - 1)/2)$ by p, obtaining

$$ja = qp + r, \qquad 0 < r < p$$

The quotient q is equal to $[ja/p]$ and the remainder r is one of the numbers s_1, $s_2, \cdots, s_u, t_1, \cdots, t_v$. Thus

$$\sum_{j=1}^{(p-1)/2} ja = \sum_{j=1}^{(p-1)/2} p\left[\frac{ja}{p}\right] + \sum_{j=1}^{u} s_j + \sum_{j=1}^{v} t_j \qquad (9.3)$$

In the proof of Theorem 4 we established that the numbers

$$p - s_1, p - s_2, \cdots, p - s_u, t_1, \cdots, t_v$$

are just the numbers $1, 2, \cdots, (p-1)/2$, in some order. Therefore,

$$\sum_{j=1}^{(p-1)/2} j = \sum_{j=1}^{u} (p - s_j) + \sum_{j=1}^{v} t_j = pu - \sum_{j=1}^{u} s_j + \sum_{j=1}^{v} t_j \qquad (9.4)$$

Subtracting (9.4) from (9.3), we obtain

$$(a-1)\sum_{j=1}^{(p-1)/2} j = p\left\{ \sum_{j=1}^{(p-1)/2}\left[\frac{ja}{p}\right] - u \right\} + 2\sum_{j=1}^{u} s_j \qquad (9.5)$$

If we now reduce (9.5) modulo 2, recalling that a and p are congruent to 1, we obtain

$$0 \equiv 1\left\{ \sum_{j=1}^{(p-1)/2}\left[\frac{ja}{p}\right] - u \right\} + 0 \pmod 2$$

and so

$$\sum_{j=1}^{(p-1)/2}\left[\frac{ja}{p}\right] \equiv u \pmod 2$$

Applying Theorem 4, we see that

$$(a|p) = (-1)^u = (-1)^{\sum\limits_{j=1}^{(p-1)/2}[ja/p]}$$

EXERCISES

1. Complete the proof of Theorem 5.

2. Prove that $(2|p) = (-1)^{(p^2-1)/8} = (-1)^{[(p+1)/4]}$

PROBLEM

1. Use Theorem 4 to prove that 3 is a quadratic residue, modulo the odd prime p, if, and only if, $p \equiv \pm 1 \pmod{12}$.

9.5 / THE QUADRATIC RECIPROCITY LAW

Let p and q be odd prime numbers. It is natural to inquire whether the quadratic character of p (mod q) affects that of q (mod p). On empirical grounds, Euler stated that there is a connection between them. Two years later, Legendre stated his famous *quadratic reciprocity law:*

$$(p|q)(q|p) = (-1)^{(p-1)/2 \cdot (q-1)/2}$$

Legendre was able to prove his conjecture for certain cases, but was not able to extend his proof. At the age of 18, with no knowledge of the work of his predecessors, Gauss conjectured that the quadratic reciprocity law holds, and one year later was able to prove it. Gauss felt a personal attachment to this theorem and during his lifetime he was able to prove it in seven different ways. The proof we shall give is due to Eisenstein, one of Gauss' students, and is based on a geometrical interpretation of Theorem 6.

Using Theorem 6, we see that

$$(p|q) \cdot (q|p) = (-1)^{\sum_{j=1}^{(p-1)/2}[jq/p]} (-1)^{\sum_{k=1}^{(q-1)/2}[kp/q]}$$

$$= (-1)^{\sum_{j=1}^{(p-1)/2}[jq/p] + \sum_{k=1}^{(q-1)/2}[kp/q]}$$

Thus, if we can establish that

$$\sum_{j=1}^{(p-1)/2}\left[\frac{jq}{p}\right] + \sum_{k=1}^{(q-1)/2}\left[\frac{kp}{q}\right] = \frac{p-1}{2} \cdot \frac{q-1}{2} \qquad (9.6)$$

the reciprocity law will be proved. To prove (9.6) we count the lattice points in a portion of the XY-plane in two different ways.

■ THEOREM 7 / (The Quadratic Reciprocity Law) If p and q are distinct odd prime numbers, then

$$(p|q)(q|p) = (-1)^{(p-1)/2 \cdot (q-1)/2}.$$

PROOF: Consider the rectangle in the XY-plane bounded by the lines $x = 0$, $x = p/2$, $y = 0$, and $y = q/2$. We bisect this rectangle by the line $y = qx/p$ (see Figure 9.1). Let T_1 be the portion of the rectangle below the line and T_2 be the portion of the rectangle above the line.

Because p and q are prime numbers, none of the lattice points interior to the rectangle lies on the line $y = qx/p$. Hence, the lattice points all lie in T_1 or in T_2. To count the lattice points interior to T_1, we observe that if $1 \le j < p/2$, the number of lattice points in T_1 that are directly above the point $(j, 0)$ is $[jq/p]$. Thus, the number of lattice points in T_1 is

$$\sum_{j=1}^{(p-1)/2} \left[\frac{jq}{p}\right]$$

In a similar way, if $1 \le k < q/2$, the number of lattice points in T_2, directly to the right of the point $(0, k)$, is $[kp/q]$, and so T_2 contains

$$\sum_{j=1}^{(q-1)/2} \left[\frac{kp}{q}\right]$$

lattice points. Thus, the number of lattice points in the rectangle is

$$\sum_{j=1}^{(p-1)/2} \left[\frac{jq}{p}\right] + \sum_{k=1}^{(q-1)/2} \left[\frac{kp}{q}\right]$$

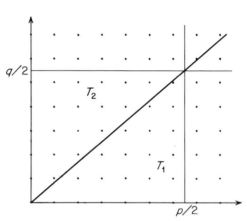

Figure 9.1 $p = 13, q = 11$.

It is obvious that the rectangle contains a total of

$$\frac{p-1}{2} \cdot \frac{q-1}{2}$$

lattice points. It follows that

$$(p|q)(q|p) = (-1)^{\sum\limits_{j=1}^{(p-1)/2}[jq/p] + \sum\limits_{k=1}^{(q-1)/2}[kp/q]} = (-1)^{(p-1)/2 \cdot (q-1)/2}$$

▪ **COROLLARY** 7.1 / Let p and q be distinct odd prime numbers. If both p and q are of form $4n + 3$, then p is a quadratic residue (mod q) if, and only if, q is a quadratic nonresidue (mod p). If at least one of the primes is of form $4n + 1$, then p is a quadratic residue (mod q) if, and only if, q is a quadratic residue (mod p).

Example 1.

Show that 43 is a quadratic nonresidue (mod 1093).

SOLUTION: Since 1093 is a prime of form $4n + 1$, then

$$(43|1093) = (1093|43)$$

Since $1093 \equiv 18 \pmod{43}$, then

$$(1093|43) = (18|43) = (2|43)(9|43)$$

From Theorem 5 we see that $(2|43) = -1$, and, since $9 = 3^2$, $(9|43) = +1$. Thus,

$$(43|1093) = (2|43)(9|43) = (-1)(+1) = -1$$

and so 43 is a quadratic nonresidue (mod 1093).

Example 2.

Find all odd prime numbers for which 3 is a quadratic residue.

SOLUTION: Since 3 is of form $4n + 3$ we must consider two cases.

Case I. Let p be a prime of form $4n + 3$. Then $(3|p) = -(p|3)$, and so 3 is a quadratic residue (mod p) if, and only if, p is a quadratic nonresidue (mod 3); that is, if, and only if, $p \equiv 2 \pmod 3$. This requirement, together with the condition $p \equiv 3 \pmod 4$, implies that 3 is a quadratic residue (mod p) if, and only if, $p \equiv 11 \pmod{12}$ (by the Chinese remainder theorem).

Case II. Suppose p is a prime of form $4n + 1$. Then $(3|p) = (p|3)$, and 3 is a quadratic residue (mod p) if, and only if, $p \equiv 1 \pmod 3$. The two restrictions imply that 3 is a quadratic residue (mod p) if, and only if, $p \equiv 1 \pmod{12}$.

Combining the results of the two cases, we see that 3 is a quadratic residue, modulo the odd prime p, if, and only if, $p \equiv \pm 1 \pmod{12}$.

Example 3.

Find all odd prime numbers for which -3 is a quadratic residue.

SOLUTION: *Case I.* Let p be a prime of form $4n + 1$. Then

$$(-3|p) = (-1|p) \cdot (3|p) = (3|p)$$

Therefore, by Example 2, -3 is a quadratic residue (mod p) if, and only if, $p \equiv \pm 1 \pmod{12}$. Since $p \equiv 1 \pmod 4$, this implies that p must be congruent to 1 (mod 12).

Case II. Let p be a prime of form $4n + 3$. Then -3 is a quadratic residue (mod p) if, and only if, 3 is a quadratic nonresidue (mod p), which, by Example 2, implies that $p \equiv \pm 5 \pmod{12}$. Since $p \equiv 3 \pmod 4$, then p must be congruent to 7 (mod 12).

Combining the results of the two cases we find that -3 is a quadratic residue, modulo the odd prime p, if, and only if,

$$p \equiv 1 \pmod 6$$

EXERCISES

1. Use the quadratic reciprocity law to evaluate the Legendre symbols:
   (a) $(61|1217)$;
   (b) $(67|1987)$;
   (c) $(67|1997)$.

2. Prove that if (x, y) is a lattice point interior to the rectangle described in the proof of Theorem 7, then (x, y) does not lie on the line $y = qx/p$.

3. Find all odd primes p for which 2 and 3 are quadratic residues.

PROBLEM

1. Determine all odd prime numbers p for which q is a quadratic residue for $q = 5, 7, 11$.

9.6* / APPLICATION TO PRIMES IN ARITHMETIC PROGRESSION

In Section 8.2 we established that the arithmetic progressions $\{4n - 1\}$ and $\{6n - 1\}$ contain an infinity of prime numbers, and observed that the proofs of the corresponding theorems for $\{4n + 1\}$ and $\{6n + 1\}$ are more difficult. Using results on quadratic residues we can now dispose of those cases as well.

■ THEOREM 8 / There is an infinity of prime numbers of form $4n + 1$.

PROOF: Assume the set of such primes is finite and let $\{5, 11, \cdots, p\}$ be all of them. Consider the number

$$N = (2 \cdot 5 \cdot 11 \cdots p)^2 + 1$$

Since N is larger than p and is of form $4n + 1$, then N must be composite. Furthermore, if q is a prime factor of N, then q is of form $4n + 3$. But then $(2 \cdot 5 \cdot 11 \cdots p)^2 \equiv -1 \pmod{q}$, which, by Theorem 2, is impossible.

Using Example 3 of Section 9.5, we can prove a similar result for primes of form $6n + 1$. The proof is left for the reader.

■ THEOREM 9 / There is an infinity of prime numbers of form $6n + 1$.

9.7* / QUADRATIC RESIDUES FOR A COMPOSITE MODULUS. THE JACOBI SYMBOL

By use of the following theorem we can determine all quadratic residues for an odd composite modulus. The proof is left for the reader (Problems 1, 2, and 3). The more general case (quadratic residues for an even modulus) is considered in Problems 4 and 5.

■ THEOREM 10 / Let $q_1, q_2, \cdots, q_n$ be distinct odd primes and let

$$Q = q_1^{\alpha_1} q_2^{\alpha_2} \cdots q_n^{\alpha_n} \qquad \alpha_j \geq 1$$

The integer P is a quadratic residue (mod Q) if, and only if, P is a quadratic residue (mod q_j) ($j = 1, 2, \cdots, n$).

For example, since $(30|7) = 1$ and $(30|11) = -1$, then 30 is a quadratic nonresidue (mod $7 \cdot 11^2$).

We now extend the definition of the Legendre symbol to cover the case where the modulus is an odd composite number. The most natural way to do this is to define $(P|Q) = 1$ if P is a quadratic residue (mod Q), and $(P|Q) = -1$ if P is a quadratic nonresidue. Unfortunately, if we do this, we lose the quadratic reciprocity law. This property is of such convenience that we choose a different, less natural, way of defining $(P|Q)$, which preserves the quadratic reciprocity law. The extended symbol is due to C. G. J. Jacobi (1804–1851).

■ DEFINITION / Factor the odd integer Q as a product of prime numbers: $Q = q_1 q_2 \cdots q_n$ (not necessarily distinct). Let P be relatively prime to Q. The *Jacobi symbol* $(P|Q)$ is defined by

$$(P|Q) = (P|q_1)(P|q_2) \cdots (P|q_n)$$

where the symbols on the right are Legendre symbols.

The fact that the Jacobi symbol $(P|Q)$ is equal to $+1$ does not imply that P is a quadratic residue (mod Q). For example,

$$(30|7 \cdot 11^2) = (30|7) \cdot (30|11) \cdot (30|11) = +1$$

even though 30 is a quadratic nonresidue (mod $7 \cdot 11^2$). On the other hand, we get the following corollary to Theorem 10.

■ COROLLARY 10.1 / If P and Q are relatively prime and $(P|Q) = -1$, then P is a quadratic nonresidue (mod Q).

Before proving the extended quadratic reciprocity law, we establish some simple properties of the Jacobi symbol. In the statement of the theorem we assume that the Q's are odd and the respective P's are relatively prime to the Q's.

■ THEOREM 11 /
(a) $(P|Q_1Q_2) = (P|Q_1)(P|Q_2)$;
(b) $(P_1P_2|Q) = (P_1|Q)(P_2|Q)$;
(c) if $P_1 \equiv P_2 \pmod{Q}$, then $(P_1|Q) = (P_2|Q)$.

SKETCH OF THE PROOF: (a) follows immediately from the definition of the Jacobi symbol. (b) and (c) are consequences of the fact that the Jacobi symbol is a product of Legendre symbols, and the respective properties hold for Legendre symbols.

■ LEMMA / If $a_1, a_2, \cdots, a_n$ are odd integers, then

$$\frac{a_1 - 1}{2} + \frac{a_2 - 1}{2} + \cdots + \frac{a_n - 1}{2} \equiv \frac{a_1 a_2 \cdots a_n - 1}{2} \pmod{2}$$

PROOF: If $n = 2$, then, since $(a_1 - 1)$ and $(a_2 - 1)$ are even,

$$\frac{a_1 a_2 - 1}{2} - \left(\frac{a_1 - 1}{2} + \frac{a_2 - 1}{2}\right) = \frac{a_1 a_2 - a_1 - a_2 + 1}{2}$$

$$= \frac{(a_1 - 1)(a_2 - 1)}{2} \equiv 0 \pmod{2}$$

Thus,

$$\frac{a_1 - 1}{2} + \frac{a_2 - 1}{2} \equiv \frac{a_1 a_2 - 1}{2} \pmod{2}$$

The rest of the proof follows easily by mathematical induction and is left for the reader.

■ THEOREM 12 / (The Extended Quadratic Reciprocity Law.) If P and Q are relatively prime odd positive integers, each greater than 1, then

$$(P|Q)(Q|P) = (-1)^{(P-1)/2 \cdot (Q-1)/2}$$

PROOF: Let $P = p_1 p_2 \cdots p_m$ and $Q = q_1 q_2 \cdots q_n$ be the factorizations into prime numbers. Applying Theorem 11 several times, we obtain

$$(P|Q) \cdot (Q|P) = \prod_{i=1}^{m} \prod_{j=1}^{n} (p_i|q_j) \cdot \prod_{i=1}^{m} \prod_{j=1}^{n} (q_j|p_i)$$

$$= \prod_{i=1}^{m} \prod_{j=1}^{n} (p_i|q_j)(q_j|p_i)$$

From the quadratic reciprocity law for Legendre symbols it follows that

$$(P|Q)(Q|P) = \prod_{i=1}^{m} \prod_{j=1}^{n} (-1)^{[(p_i - 1)/2][(q_j - 1)/2]}$$

$$= (-1)^{\sum_{i=1}^{m} \sum_{j=1}^{n} (p_i - 1)/2 \cdot (q_j - 1)/2}$$

$$= (-1)^{\left\{ \sum_{i=1}^{m} (p_i - 1)/2 \right\} \left\{ \sum_{j=1}^{n} (q_j - 1)/2 \right\}}$$

From the lemma we see that

$$\sum_{i=1}^{m} \frac{p_i - 1}{2} \equiv \frac{p_1 p_2 \cdots p_m - 1}{2} \equiv \frac{P - 1}{2} \ (\text{mod } 2)$$

and

$$\sum_{j=1}^{n} \frac{q_j - 1}{2} \equiv \frac{Q - 1}{2} \ (\text{mod } 2)$$

which implies that

$$(P|Q)(Q|P) = (-1)^{\left\{ \sum_{i=1}^{m} (p_i - 1)/2 \right\} \left\{ \sum_{j=1}^{n} (q_j - 1)/2 \right\}}$$

$$= (-1)^{(P - 1)/2 \cdot (Q - 1)/2}$$

With the quadratic reciprocity law we can invert the Legendre symbol when both of the numbers involved are primes. The extended quadratic reciprocity law allows us to invert them when one of the numbers is composite. This is one reason for defining the Jacobi symbol as we did. Its connection with quadratic residues is rather incidental.

Example.

Show that the congruence $x^2 \equiv 15 \ (\text{mod } 1093)$ has no solution.

SOLUTION: The prime number 1093 is of form $4n + 1$. Thus,

$$(15|1093) = (1093|15) = (-2|15) = (-2|3)(-2|5)$$
$$= (1|3)(3|5) = (+1-)(1) = -1$$

Because the Legendre symbol $(15|1093)$ is negative, 15 is a quadratic nonresidue $(\text{mod } 1093)$.

EXERCISES

1. Which of the following congruences have solutions?

(a) $x^2 \equiv 39 \ (\text{mod } 131)$;

(b) $x^2 \equiv 78 \ (\text{mod } 131)$;

(c) $2x^2 + 5x - 7 \equiv 0 \pmod{79}$;

(d) $x^2 \equiv 20 \pmod{117}$ (composite modulus).

2. By an example, show that if we define the symbol (a/b) equal to $+1$ or -1 according to whether a is a quadratic residue or nonresidue, modulo b, then the quadratic reciprocity law does not hold for composite b.

PROBLEMS

1. Let m and n be relatively prime positive integers. If a is relatively prime to mn, prove that a is a quadratic residue $\pmod{mn}$ if, and only if, a is a quadratic residue $\pmod{m}$ and $\pmod{n}$. [*Hint:* If $x_0^2 \equiv a \pmod{m}$ and $y_0^2 \equiv a \pmod{n}$, we wish to find a solution to

$$\begin{cases} z^2 \equiv x_0^2 \pmod{m} \\ z^2 \equiv y_0^2 \pmod{n} \end{cases}$$

2. Let p be an odd prime number and let n be a positive integer. Prove that a is a quadratic residue $\pmod{p^n}$ if, and only if, a is a quadratic residue $\pmod{p}$. [*Hint:* If $x_0^2 = a + mp$, show that one of the numbers

$$x_0, \ x_0 + p, \ x_0 + 2p, \ x_0 + 3p, \cdots$$

is a solution of $z^2 \equiv a \pmod{p^2}$.]

3. Prove Theorem 10.

4. Let k be an odd integer.

(a) Find all solutions of $x^2 \equiv k \pmod 2$.

(b) Find all solutions of $x^2 \equiv k \pmod 4$.

(c) If $\beta \geq 3$, prove that

$$x^2 \equiv k \pmod{2^\beta}$$

has a solution if, and only if, $k \equiv 1 \pmod 8$.

5. Use Problems 1, 2, and 4 to generalize Theorem 10.

THE TWO- AND FOUR-SQUARE PROBLEMS / 10

10.1 / INTRODUCTION

In his correspondence with Fermat, Bachet mentioned that Diophantus had assumed that each positive integer can be written as a sum of four squares. Bachet verified this assumption for all integers up to 325, but was unable to devise a proof. A few years later, Fermat stated that he had a proof of this result, but, since he was more interested in proposing problems for other mathematicians than in exhibiting his methods of proof, this proof (if he had one) was lost to posterity.

The difficulty of the problem is evidenced by the fact that even Euler could not solve it. He did, however, make significant progress towards a solution. In 1770, over a hundred years after Fermat's death, J. L. Lagrange used a result of Euler (Lemma 4 of Section 10.3) to prove the assumption made by Diophantus.

We can never know if Fermat had a valid proof. Most authorities believe that he did have one, since several of the known proofs of the "four-square theorem" rely on the "method of descent," one of Fermat's favorite techniques.[1]

Let us examine the first few positive integers and see how many squares are needed to represent them.

$$1 = 1^2 \qquad \text{(one square needed)}$$
$$2 = 1^2 + 1^2 \qquad \text{(two squares needed)}$$
$$3 = 1^2 + 1^2 + 1^2 \qquad \text{(three squares needed)}$$
$$4 = 2^2 \qquad \text{(one square needed)}$$
$$5 = 2^2 + 1^2 \qquad \text{(two squares needed)}$$
$$6 = 2^2 + 1^2 + 1^2 \qquad \text{(three squares needed)}$$
$$7 = 2^2 + 1^2 + 1^2 + 1^2 \qquad \text{(four squares needed)}$$
$$8 = 2^2 + 2^2 \qquad \text{(two squares needed)}$$
$$9 = 3^2 \qquad \text{(one square needed)}$$
$$10 = 3^2 + 1^2 \qquad \text{(two squares needed)}$$

---

[1]The method of descent is a variation on the well-ordering principle. An illustration of the technique is in Section 11.3.

We see from our small table that the first ten positive integers can be written as sums of four squares (counting 0^2) and that one of them cannot be written as a sum of less than four squares. What is more interesting is the fact that most of these numbers can be written as sums of two squares.

Diophantus studied the problem of representing numbers as sums of two squares and sums of three squares and gave necessary conditions that these representations exist. Unfortunately, the surviving texts are unclear and we do not know if he had a correct criterion.

In the following section we will study the problem of representing positive integers as sums of two squares.

10.2 / THE TWO-SQUARE PROBLEM

In this section we will establish necessary and sufficient conditions which insure that a positive integer can be written as a sum of two squares.

If we examine the brief table in Section 10.1, we see that (allowing one of the squares to be 0^2) the following positive integers can be written as sums of two squares: 1, 2, 4, 5, 8, 9, 10. If we consider the products of these numbers, we see that they can also be represented in this manner. If we can prove that this is always the case, we will have achieved an important first step in solving the two-square problem.

■ THEOREM 1 / If each of a and b can be written as a sum of two squares, then the product ab can also be written as a sum of two squares.

SKETCH OF THE PROOF: The proof follows from the algebraic identity:

$$(s^2 + t^2)(u^2 + v^2) = (su + tv)^2 + (sv - tu)^2$$

The next problem we will consider is that of deciding which prime numbers can be written as sums of two squares. Because it is obvious that the prime number 2 can be written in this form, we may restrict ourselves to odd primes. The following lemma, due to the Norwegian mathematician Axel Thue, provides an essential step in the proof.

■ LEMMA / Let p be a prime number and let a be relatively prime to p. The congruence

$$x \equiv ay \pmod{p}$$

has a solution x_0, y_0 such that

$$0 < |x_0| < \sqrt{p} \quad \text{and} \quad 0 < |y_0| < \sqrt{p}$$

PROOF: Let $m = [\sqrt{p}]$. Consider the set of numbers

$$1 + a, \ 1 + 2a, \cdots, \ 1 + (m + 1)a$$
$$2 + a, \ 2 + 2a, \ \cdots, \ 2 + (m + 1)a$$
$$\cdots$$
$$(m + 1) \ + a, \ (m + 1) + 2a, \ \cdots, \ (m + 1) + (m + 1)a$$

This set contains $(m + 1)^2$ numbers (not necessarily distinct). Since $(m + 1)^2 > p$, at least two of the numbers, say $x_1 + y_1 a$ and $x_2 + y_2 a$, must lie in the same residue class (mod p), where $x_1 \neq x_2$ or $y_1 \neq y_2$. Thus,

$$(x_1 - x_2) \equiv (y_2 - y_1)a \ (\text{mod } p)$$

Because one of the terms $(x_1 - x_2)$ and $(y_2 - y_1)$ is not zero, it follows that neither is zero. Since x_1, x_2, y_1, y_2 are all greater than zero and less than or equal to $m + 1$, then

$$0 < |x_1 - x_2| \leq m < \sqrt{p} \quad \text{and} \quad 0 < |y_2 - y_1| \leq m < \sqrt{p}$$

If we let $x_0 = x_1 - x_2$ and $y_0 = y_2 - y_1$, the proof is complete.

■ THEOREM 2 / The odd prime p can be written as a sum of two squares if, and only if, -1 is a quadratic residue (mod p).

PROOF: (Part I) Suppose p is the sum of two squares, say $p = a^2 + b^2$. Since p is a prime number, then $b \neq 0$. This implies that there is an integer c such that

$$cb \equiv 1 \ (\text{mod } p)$$

Thus, $\qquad\qquad (ca)^2 + (cb)^2 \equiv (ca)^2 + 1 \equiv 0 \ (\text{mod } p)$

Since $\qquad\qquad\qquad (ca)^2 \equiv -1 \ (\text{mod } p)$

then -1 is a quadratic residue (mod p).

(Part II) If -1 is a quadratic residue (mod p), there exists an integer a such that

$$a^2 + 1 \equiv 0 \ (\text{mod } p) \tag{10.1}$$

Because the integer a must be relatively prime to p, then by the lemma, there exist integers x_0 and y_0,

$$0 < |x_0| < \sqrt{p}, \qquad 0 < |y_0| < \sqrt{p}$$

such that $\qquad\qquad\qquad x_0 \equiv y_0 a \ (\text{mod } p)$

If we now multiply (10.1) by $y_0{}^2$, we obtain

$$y_0{}^2(a^2 + 1) \equiv (y_0 a)^2 + y_0{}^2 \equiv x_0{}^2 + y_0{}^2 \equiv 0 \ (\text{mod } p)$$

The restrictions on the size of x_0 and y_0 insure us that

$$0 < x_0{}^2 + y_0{}^2 < 2p$$

and so $$x_0{}^2 + y_0{}^2 = p$$

The following theorem now follows easily from Theorem 2 and Corollary 2.1 of Chapter 9.

■ **THEOREM 3** / The odd prime number p can be written as a sum of two squares, if, and only if, p is of form $4n + 1$.

It follows from Theorems 1 and 3 that any number of form m^2k, where k has no prime factors of form $4n + 3$, is a sum of two squares. We will now prove that these are the only numbers that can be represented in this manner.

■ **THEOREM 4** / Write the positive integer N in the form $N = m^2k$, where k does not contain a square factor. Then N can be written as a sum of two squares if, and only if, k has no prime factor of form $4n + 3$.

PROOF: If k has no prime factors of form $4n + 3$, it follows from Theorem 1 that k can be written as a sum of two squares, say $k = a^2 + b^2$. Therefore, $m^2k = (ma)^2 + (mb)^2$, a sum of two squares.

To prove the converse, suppose that $N = a^2 + b^2$. Let $d = (a, b)$. Then $d^2 | N$, so that $d^2 | m^2$. If we write $a = a'd$, $b = b'd$, then

$$\frac{N}{d^2} = \frac{a^2 + b^2}{d^2} = a'^2 + b'^2 \equiv 0 \ (\text{mod k}) \tag{10.2}$$

Let p be an odd prime factor of k. Since a' and b' are relatively prime, then one of them, say a', is relatively prime to p. Pick an integer c such that

$$ca' \equiv 1 \ (\text{mod } p)$$

From (10.2) we see that

$$(ca')^2 + (cb')^2 \equiv 1 + (cb')^2 \equiv 0 \ (\text{mod } p)$$

which implies that -1 is a quadratic residue, modulo p. Thus, p is of form $4n + 1$.

EXERCISES

1. Express all of the primes of form $4n + 1$ between 100 and 150 as sums of two squares.

2. Which of the following can be written as a sum of two squares?
   (a) $2 \cdot 3^4 \cdot 5 \cdot 7^2$;
   (b) 819.

3. Let $N = m^2 k = a^2 + b^2$, where k does not have a square factor. Let $d = (a, b)$. Prove that $d^2 | m^2$.

10.3 / THE FOUR-SQUARE PROBLEM

We have determined which numbers can be written as sums of two squares. Certain numbers (for example, 3 and 11) can be written as sums of three squares, while others (such as 7 and 23) require four squares. In this section we will prove the four-square theorem. In the problem section the three-square problem will be considered briefly.

■ **LEMMA 1** / If a and b can be written as sums of four squares, so can the product ab.

SKETCH OF THE PROOF: The proof follows from the following algebraic identity, first noticed by Euler:

$$(x_1^2 + x_2^2 + x_3^2 + x_4^2)(y_1^2 + y_2^2 + y_3^2 + y_4^2)$$
$$= (x_1 y_1 + x_2 y_2 + x_3 y_3 + x_4 y_4)^2 + (x_1 y_2 - x_2 y_1 + x_3 y_4 - x_4 y_3)^2$$
$$+ (x_1 y_3 - x_3 y_1 + x_4 y_2 - x_2 y_4)^2 + (x_1 y_4 - x_4 y_1 + x_2 y_3 - x_3 y_2)^2$$

It follows by mathematical induction that if $a_1, a_2, \cdots, a_n$ can be written as sums of four squares, then the product $a_1 a_2 \cdots a_n$ can be written as a sum of four squares. Thus, it is sufficient to prove that each prime number can be written in this manner.

In the following lemma we consider a proposition for ordered pairs of integers that is similar to a property of residue classes. A matter of notation: We say that the ordered pairs of integers (a, b) and (c, d) are *congruent* $(mod\, m)$ if $a \equiv c$ and $b \equiv d$ (mod m).

■ **LEMMA 2** / A set of ordered pairs of integers, containing more than m^2 elements, must have two elements that are congruent (mod m).

PROOF: Each ordered pair of integers is congruent (mod m) to one of the following m^2 ordered pairs:

$$(1, 1), (1, 2), \cdots, (1, m)$$
$$(2, 1), (2, 2), \cdots, (2, m)$$
$$\cdots$$
$$(m, 1), (m, 2), \cdots, (m, m)$$

If a set contains more than m^2 ordered pairs, at least two of them must be congruent (mod m) to one of the ordered pairs in the above list. Obviously, these two ordered pairs are congruent (mod m).

■ **LEMMA 3** / Let a, b, c, and d be given integers, let p be a prime number. The system of congruences

$$\begin{cases} ax + by - z \equiv 0 \ (\mathrm{mod}\ p) \\ cx + dy - u \equiv 0 \ (\mathrm{mod}\ p) \end{cases}$$

has a nontrivial solution x_0, y_0, z_0, u_0 such that each number in the solution is less than $\sqrt{p}$ in absolute value.

PROOF: Let x, y, z, and u be independent variables. Define α and β as functions of x, y, z, u by

$$\alpha = \alpha(x, y, z, u) = ax + by - z$$
$$\beta = \beta(x, y, z, u) = cx + dy - u$$

As x, y, z, and u vary over the domain $\{0, 1, \cdots, m = [\sqrt{p}]\}$, we obtain $(m + 1)^4$ values of α (not necessarily distinct) and $(m + 1)^4$ corresponding values of β. Thus, we have $(m + 1)^4$ ordered pairs (α, β) with α and β corresponding to the same values of x, y, z, u. Since $(m + 1)^4 > p^2$, it follows from Lemma 2 that at least two ordered pairs, (α_1, β_1) and (α_2, β_2), have corresponding components that are congruent (mod p). Thus,

$$\alpha_1 \equiv ax_1 + by_1 - z_1 \equiv \alpha_2 \equiv ax_2 + by_2 - z_2 \ (\mathrm{mod}\ p)$$

and

$$\beta_1 \equiv cx_1 + dy_1 - u_1 \equiv \beta_2 \equiv cx_2 + dy_2 - u_2 \ (\mathrm{mod}\ p)$$

which implies that

$$a(x_1 - x_2) + b(y_1 - y_2) - (z_1 - z_2) \equiv 0 \ (\mathrm{mod}\ p)$$

and

$$c(x_1 - x_2) + d(y_1 - y_2) - (u_1 - u_2) \equiv 0 \ (\mathrm{mod}\ p)$$

Since (α_1, β_1) and (α_2, β_2) correspond to different values of x, y, z, and u, then at least one of the numbers $x_1 - x_2, y_1 - y_2, z_1 - z_2, u_1 - u_2$ is not zero. If we recall the range of values for x, y, z, and u, we see that $x_1 - x_2, y_1 - y_2$, $z_1 - z_2$, and $u_1 - u_2$ and all less than $\sqrt{p}$ in absolute value. If we now let $x_0 = x_1 - x_2$, $y_0 = y_1 - y_2$, $z_0 = z_1 - z_2$, and $u_0 = u_1 - u_2$, the proof is complete.

The following lemma is the one proved by Euler and later used by Lagrange in his proof of the four-square theorem.

■ LEMMA 4 / If p is an odd prime number, there exist integers a and b such that

$$a^2 + b^2 \equiv -1 \pmod{p}$$

PROOF: Consider the following two sets:

$$A = \left\{ 0^2, 1^2, 2^2, \cdots, \left(\frac{p-1}{2}\right)^2 \right\}$$

$$B = \left\{ -0^2 - 1, -1^2 - 1, -2^2 - 1, \cdots, -\left(\frac{p-1}{2}\right)^2 - 1 \right\}$$

Obviously, the elements of A are incongruent (mod p) as are the elements of B. Since the union of A and B contains more than p elements, at least two numbers in the union are congruent (mod p). One of these numbers, say a^2, must be in A and the other, say $-b^2 - 1$, in B. Thus,

$$a^2 + b^2 \equiv -1 \pmod{p}$$

■ THEOREM 5 / Each prime number can be written as a sum of four squares.

PROOF: We have verified that the theorem is correct if $p = 2$ or $p = 3$. Thus, we may restrict ourselves to proving the theorem for primes greater than 3. By Lemma 4, there exist integers a and b such that

$$a^2 + b^2 \equiv -1 \pmod{p}$$

As a special case of Lemma 3 we find a nontrivial solution x_0, y_0, z_0, u_0 of

$$\begin{cases} ax + by \equiv z \pmod{p} \\ bx - ay \equiv u \pmod{p} \end{cases}$$

such that each of the numbers is less than $\sqrt{p}$ in absolute value. Thus,

$$\begin{aligned} z_0^2 + u_0^2 &\equiv (ax_0 + by_0)^2 + (bx_0 - ay_0)^2 \\ &\equiv (a^2 + b^2)(x_0^2 + y_0^2) \\ &\equiv -(x_0^2 + y_0^2) \pmod{p} \end{aligned}$$

and so

$$x_0^2 + y_0^2 + z_0^2 + u_0^2 \equiv 0 \pmod{p}$$

Using the restrictions on the size of x_0, y_0, z_0, u_0, we find that

$$0 < x_0^2 + y_0^2 + z_0^2 + u_0^2 < 4p$$

and so

$$x_0^2 + y_0^2 + z_0^2 + u_0^2$$

is one of the numbers p, $2p$, or $3p$.

Case I. If $x_0^2 + y_0^2 + z_0^2 + u_0^2 = p$, we are through.

Case II. If $x_0^2 + y_0^2 + z_0^2 + u_0^2 = 2p$, then two of the four numbers, say x_0 and y_0, must be even and the other two odd. If we now expand

$$\left(\frac{x_0 + y_0}{2}\right)^2 + \left(\frac{x_0 - y_0}{2}\right)^2 + \left(\frac{z_0 + u_0}{2}\right)^2 + \left(\frac{z_0 - u_0}{2}\right)^2$$

we find that this number is equal to p, and so p is a sum of four squares.

Case III. If $x_0^2 + y_0^2 + z_0^2 + u_0^2 = 3p$, then exactly one of the numbers, say x_0, is divisible by 3. If we allow negative values for some of the other numbers, we may assume that $y_0 \equiv z_0 \equiv u_0 \pmod 3$. If we now expand

$$\left(\frac{y_0 + z_0 + u_0}{3}\right)^2 + \left(\frac{x_0 + z_0 - u_0}{3}\right)^2 + \left(\frac{x_0 - y_0 + u_0}{3}\right)^2$$
$$+ \left(\frac{x_0 + y_0 - z_0}{3}\right)^2$$

we find it is equal to p.

Thus, in all three cases, p is a sum of four squares.

■ **COROLLARY 5.1** / Each positive integer can be written as a sum of four squares.

EXERCISES

1. Write the following numbers as sums of four squares. Which of these numbers can be written as sums of three squares?
   (a) 31;
   (b) 47;
   (c) 94.

2. Prove that in Case II of the proof of Theorem 5, two of the numbers x_0, y_0, z_0, u_0 are even and two are odd. Prove that in Case III exactly one of the numbers is divisible by 3.

PROBLEMS

1. Prove that there is an infinity of positive integers that cannot be written as sums of three squares. [*Hint:* Show that no integer of form $8k + 7$ can be written as a sum of three squares.]

2. Prove that no integer of form $4^n(8k + 7)$, $n \geq 0$, can be written as a sum of three squares. [It can be proved that these are the only integers that cannot be written as sums of three squares, but the proof is beyond the scope of this book.]

10.4* / REMARKS ON WARING'S PROBLEM

About the time that Lagrange proved the four-square theorem, the English mathematician Edward Waring stated that each positive integer can be written as a sum of nine cubes, nineteen fourth powers, "and so on." Waring probably arrived at this conjecture by studying tables; it is unlikely that he could prove it for any of the cases involved.

In the nineteenth century, a number of mathematicians worked on this problem. They proved that for $k = 3$, 4, 5, 6, 7, 8, and 10, each positive integer can be written as a sum of a fixed number of kth powers. The major advance in this direction was made by the great German analyst David Hilbert, who, in 1906, proved:

If k is a positive integer, there is a number $g(k)$ such that each positive integer can be written as a sum of $g(k)$ kth powers.

Unfortunately, Hilbert's proof was not constructive. It established the existence of $g(k)$, but could not be used to determine the value of this number. [From Corollary 5.1 we know that $g(2) = 4$.] Since Hilbert's time many outstanding mathematicians have worked on this problem.[2] The exact value of $g(k)$ is now known for all values of k except $k = 4$ and $k = 5$. The known results for small values of k are: $g(2) = 4$, $g(3) = 9$, $19 \leq g(4) \leq 35$, $37 \leq g(5) \leq 54$, $g(6) = 73$.

If we examine tables for the representations of integers as sums of cubes, we find that the first integer requiring nine cubes in 23 and the next is 239. The surprising fact is that these are the only integers that are known to require nine cubes. Every other integer that has been checked has been written as a sum of eight cubes. If we pursue this line of investigation further, we find that apparently only fifteen other numbers require as many as eight cubes, the largest being 454.

With this in mind, it is natural to define $G(k)$ to be the minimum number of kth powers needed for the representation of all *sufficiently large* numbers; that is, all numbers above some bound, which of course, also depends on k.

In Problem 2 of Section 10.3 it was established that there is an infinity of numbers that cannot be written as sums of three squares. Thus, $G(2) = g(2) = 4$.

In general, we would expect to find that $G(k)$ is smaller than $g(k)$. The heuristic argument is as follows: We know that all positive integers can be written as sums of $g(k)$ kth powers. For the small positive integers there are

---

[2]Many of the important results were obtained by the English analysts G. H. Hardy and J. E. Littlewood and by the Russian mathematician I. M. Vinogradov.

few kth powers available for the representations and the number of different representations for a fixed integer is very limited. As we go further in the sequence of integers, we have many more kth powers at our disposal and, consequently, we would expect to have several representations for each sufficiently large integer. Among these representations, it is likely that at least one will require fewer than $g(k)$ kth powers. The small integers that require $g(k)$ kth powers are thus seen to be oddities—consequences of the scarcity of kth powers at the beginning of the sequence of integers.

The above argument seems to be justified by the known results. It has been proved, for instance, that for most values of k, $g(k)$ is larger than $k \cdot 2^{k-1}$, but that, in general, $G(k)$ is no larger than approximately $k \cdot \log k$. Thus, for most values of k, $G(k)$ is much smaller than $g(k)$.

The exact value of $G(k)$ is only known for $k = 2$ and $k = 4$. As mentioned above, we have proved that $G(2) = 4$. In 1939, H. Davenport proved that $G(4) = 16$. It is known that $G(3)$ is one of the numbers 4, 5, 6, or 7. We do not know which, but examination of extensive tables indicates that it is probably either 4 or 5.

SOME NONLINEAR DIOPHANTINE PROBLEMS / 11

There is no simple technique for the solution of nonlinear diophantine equations such as Euler discovered for linear diophantine equations (Section 2.3). In this chapter we will consider some isolated examples of nonlinear diophantine equations, chosen primarily for historical reasons.

11.1 / THE PYTHAGOREAN PROBLEM

The Pythagorean identity $a^2 + b^2 = c^2$ (where a and b are the lengths of the sides of a right triangle and c is the length of the hypotenuse) has been known since antiquity. The ancient Greeks were very interested in finding right triangles such that a, b, and c are positive integers. Such a triple of integers a, b, c, is called a *Pythagorean triple*. The associated triangle is called a *Pythagorean triangle*. Common examples are 3, 4, 5 and 5, 12, 13.

Two natural questions arise:

1. *Is there an infinity of Pythagorean triples?*

2. *Is there a formula that can be used to generate all Pythagorean triples?*

To answer the first question we observe that if a, b, c is a Pythagorean triple and k is a positive integer, ka, kb, kc is also a Pythagorean triple. Thus, the answer is obviously affirmative. For example, we obtain the Pythagorean triples 6, 8, 10; 9, 12, 15; 12, 16, 20; and so on, from the triple 3, 4, 5.

Suppose now that a, b, c is a Pythagorean triple and that $d = (a, b)$. Then obviously, $d^2 | c^2$, and so $d | c$. It follows by a similar argument that

$$d = (a, b) = (a, c) = (b, c)$$

If we factor $a = a'd$, $b = b'd$, $c = c'd$, then

$$a'^2 + b'^2 = \frac{a^2 + b^2}{d^2} = \frac{c^2}{d^2} = c'^2$$

which means that a', b', c' is a Pythagorean triple in which the numbers are pairwise relatively prime.

■ **DEFINITION** / A set of pairwise relatively prime positive integers, a, b, c is called a *primitive Pythagorean triple* if $a^2 + b^2 = c^2$.

Question 1 becomes more interesting if we rephrase it as:

1'. *Is there an infinity of primitive Pythagorean triples?*

If we can find all primitive Pythagorean triples, we obviously can use them to generate all Pythagorean triples. Therefore, in this section we will concentrate on solving the diophantine equation

$$x^2 + y^2 = z^2$$

in positive integers, subject to the side condition $(x, y) = 1$ [which, of course, implies that $(x, z) = (y, z) = 1$].

In order to keep the proof of the main theorem relatively simple, we will establish several of the needed results in a series of lemmas

■ **LEMMA 1** / If x, y, z is a primitive Pythagorean triple, then one of the numbers x, y is even and one is odd.

PROOF: Because the triple is primitive, x and y are obviously not both even. Suppose that both are odd. Then

$$x^2 \equiv y^2 \equiv 1 \ (\text{mod } 4)$$

and so $\qquad\qquad z^2 \equiv x^2 + y^2 \equiv 2 \ (\text{mod } 4)$

which is impossible since the square of an even integer is congruent to zero (mod 4). Thus, one of the numbers x, y is even and one is odd.

In order to have a standard notation, we will assume in the sequel that x is odd and y is even. Obviously, z is odd.

■ **LEMMA 2** / If x, y, z is a primitive Pythagorean triple, then the integers

$$\frac{z - x}{2} \qquad \text{and} \qquad \frac{z + x}{2}$$

are relatively prime.

PROOF: Any common divisor of

$$\frac{z - x}{2} \quad \text{and} \quad \frac{z + x}{2}$$

must divide their sum and difference—the numbers x and z. Since $(x, z) = 1$, this means that

$$\left(\frac{z - x}{2}, \frac{z + x}{2}\right) = 1$$

■ LEMMA 3 / If a and b are relatively prime positive integers having a square as their product, then a and b are also squares.

The proof is left for the reader (Exercise 2).

We are now able to prove that there is a formula (in two parameters) that can be used to generate all primitive Pythagorean triples.

■ THEOREM 1 / The positive integers x, y, z constitute a primitive Pythagorean triple if, and only if, there exist two relatively prime positive integers s and t, $s > t$, one even and one odd, such that

$$x = s^2 - t^2$$
$$y = 2st$$
$$z = s^2 + t^2$$

PROOF: (Part I) Let x, y, z be a primitive Pythagorean triple. Then

$$y^2 = z^2 - x^2 = (z + x)(z - x)$$

and so

$$\left(\frac{y}{2}\right)^2 = \frac{z + x}{2} \cdot \frac{z - x}{2} \qquad (11.1)$$

By Lemma 2 the factors on the right are relatively prime, and by Lemma 3 each of them is a square, say

$$\frac{z + x}{2} = s^2 \qquad \frac{z - x}{2} = t^2$$

where s and t are positive integers. By adding and subtracting these quantities, we obtain

$$x = s^2 - t^2, z = s^2 + t^2$$

From (11.1) we obtain

$$\left(\frac{y}{2}\right)^2 = \frac{z + x}{2} \cdot \frac{z - x}{2} = s^2 t^2$$

and so

$$y = 2st$$

Obviously, any common divisor of s and t will divide both x and z, meaning that $(s, t) = 1$. In particular, we see that s and t are not both even. If they are both odd, then x, y, and z are all even, which is impossible. Thus, one of the numbers s, t is even and the other is odd.

(Part II) The "only if" part of the proof is left for the reader (Problem 1).

■ COROLLARY 1.1 / There is an infinity of primitive Pythagorean triples.

A few of the primitive Pythagorean triples are listed in Table 11.1.

Table 11.1

s	t	x $(s^2 - t^2)$	y $(2st)$	z $(s^2 + t^2)$
2	1	3	4	5
4	1	15	8	17
6	1	35	12	37
3	2	5	12	13
5	2	21	20	29

EXERCISES

1. Construct a table of all primitive Pythagorean triples with z less than 100.

2. Prove Lemma 3.

PROBLEMS

1. Complete the proof of Theorem 1.

2. (*a*) Observe that if $s = t + 1$, the conditions of Theorem 1 are satisfied. Derive the parametric form of x, y, z in terms of t for this special case.
(*b*) Let x_t, y_t, z_t be the values of x, y, z in part (*a*). Obtain a recursive formula for $x_{t+1}, y_{t+1}, z_{t+1}$ in terms of x_t, y_t, z_t. (This special case of Theorem 1 was known to the ancient Greeks.)

3. If n is an odd integer greater than 1, prove that there is a primitive Pythagorean triple with $x = n$. If n is a prime, prove that only one such Pythagorean triple exists.

4. By a method similar to the proof of Theorem 1 obtain all "primitive" solutions of

$$x^2 + 2y^2 = z^2$$

5. Find all "primitive" solutions of

$$x^2 + y^2 = z^4$$

11.2 / HISTORICAL NOTE: FERMAT'S LAST THEOREM

Fermat made a practice of annotating his copy of the works of Diophantus with marginal notes. With one exception, the theorems mentioned in the margins have since been proved correct.

One of Diophantus' problems is closely related to Pythagorean triples (see Problem 1). In the margin next to this problem Fermat wrote the following comment:

However, it is impossible to write a cube as a sum of two cubes, a fourth power as a sum of two fourth powers, and, in general, any power beyond the second as a sum of two similar powers. For this I have discovered a truly wonderful proof, but the margin is too small to contain it.

In other words, the diophantine equation

$$x^n + y^n = z^n \qquad n \geq 3$$

has no positive solutions.

This problem, now called *Fermat's Last Theorem*, has been attacked from every conceivable standpoint by the best mathematicians of the last 300 years. Many interesting results have been established, but the "theorem" has never been proved.

E. Kummer (1810–1893) made the greatest advances toward a solution. Instead of confining himself to the field of rational numbers, he extended his concept of number theory to include the algebraic numbers (those complex numbers that are roots of polynomials with rational coefficients). In 1843 he submitted what he thought was a proof, but Dirichlet pointed out a flaw in the argument. Kummer had assumed that factorization into "primes" is unique in a certain subring of the algebraic numbers, when, in fact, this factorization is *not* unique. Because this assumption was essential, the proof was not valid.

Kummer returned to the problem and, by using the theory of ideals, he was able to salvage parts of his proof and to establish very general conditions for the insolvability of Fermat's equation. Most of the progress made on the problem in the last century has been along the lines of Kummer's theory.

With the advent of the high-speed electronic computer, it has become possible to check Kummer's criteria for large exponents. At the time of this writing it has been proved that the diophantine equation

$$x^n + y^n = z^n$$

has no positive solutions if $3 \leq n < 25,000$.

Fermat's conjecture has received much attention from nonmathematicians in this century. This is partially due to the fact that in 1908 the German mathematician Wolfskehl left a bequest of 100,000 marks to the person who first solved it. The immediate consequence of the bequest was that the referees were swamped with "solutions" from amateurs, many of whom did not even understand the problem. Interest among amateurs has declined since the value of the prize was wiped out in the post-World War I inflation.

We can be fairly safe in assuming that Fermat never had a valid proof. Since the problem has been attacked from every conceivable angle for 300 years, it is unlikely that he had a method of proof that has not been rediscovered.

EXERCISE

1. Inkeri has proved that if Fermat's equation does have a solution x_0, y_0, z_0 for some positive integer n (with $x_0 < y_0 < z_0$), then

(i) $$x_0 > \left(\frac{2n^3 + 1}{\log 3n} \right)^n \qquad \text{if } x_0 y_0 z_0 \not\equiv 0 \pmod{n}$$

and

(ii) $$x_0 > n^{3n-4} \qquad \text{if } x_0 y_0 z_0 \equiv 0 \pmod{n}$$

Use the bound on n mentioned in the text to show that x_0 would have more than 320,000 digits.

PROBLEM

The following is the problem of Diophantus mentioned in the text:

1. If a is a fixed positive integer, the equation $x^2 + y^2 = a^2$ has an infinity of *rational* solutions. [*Hint:* If x and y are rational, the number m defined by $x = my - a$ is also rational. Show that x and y can be expressed in terms of the parameter m.]

11.3* / SOME ELEMENTARY RESULTS ON FERMAT'S LAST THEOREM

One of Fermat's favorite methods of proof was the "method of descent." This is a variation on the well-ordering principle in which we show that if there exists a positive integer with a certain property, there must exist a smaller positive integer that has the same property. Thus, we obtain an infinite decreasing sequence of positive integers all having the specified property, which is clearly an impossibility. We will illustrate this method of proof by proving a special case of Fermat's last theorem—a case which Fermat himself probably proved.

■ THEOREM 2 / The diophantine equation $x^4 + y^4 = z^2$ has no positive solutions.

PROOF: Suppose the diophantine equation $x^4 + y^4 = z^2$ has a solution x_0, y_0, z_0. By an argument similar to that in Section 11.1, we may assume that x_0, y_0, z_0 are pairwise relatively prime, x_0 is odd, and y_0 is even. Since $(x_0^2)^2 + (y_0^2)^2 = z_0^2$ then x_0^2, y_0^2, z_0 is a primitive Pythagorean triple. Thus, there exist relatively prime positive integers s and t, $s > t$, one even and one odd, such that

$$x_0^2 = s^2 - t^2$$
$$y_0^2 = 2st \qquad\qquad (11.2)$$
$$z_0 = s^2 + t^2$$

From the first equation in (11.2) we see that x_0, t, s is a primitive Pythagorean triple with x_0 odd and t even. Using Theorem 1 again we find that relatively prime positive integers a and b exist, $a > b$, one even and one odd, such that

$$x_0 = a^2 - b^2 \qquad t = 2ab \qquad s = a^2 + b^2$$

On substituting this into the second equation in (11.2), we obtain

$$y_0^2 = 2(a^2 + b^2) \cdot 2ab$$

so that

$$\left(\frac{y_0}{2}\right)^2 = (a^2 + b^2)ab$$

Since a and b are relatively prime, then $a^2 + b^2$, a and b are pairwise relatively prime. Applying Lemma 3 of Section 11.1 twice, we find that a, b and $a^2 + b^2$ are all squares, say

$$a = a_0^2 \qquad b = b_0^2 \qquad s = a^2 + b^2 = s_0^2$$

Thus,

$$s_0^2 = a^2 + b^2 = a_0^4 + b_0^4$$

Since

$$s_0 \le s < s^2 + t^2 = z_0$$

we see that if a positive solution x_0, y_0, z_0 exists, there must exist another positive solution a_0, b_0, s_0 with $s_0 < z_0$. It follows from the method of descent that no positive solutions can exist.

■ COROLLARY 2.1 / The diophantine equation $x^4 + y^4 = z^4$ has no positive solution.

We can now use Corollary 2.1 to show that Fermat's equation has no solution in an infinity of cases:

■ COROLLARY 2.2 / The diophantine equation $x^n + y^n = z^n$ has no positive solution if $n \equiv 0 \pmod 4$.

PROOF: If $n = 4m$ and x_0, y_0, z_0 is a positive solution of $x^n + y^n = z^n$, then $x_0{}^m$, $y_0{}^m$, $z_0{}^m$ is a positive solution of $x^4 + y^4 = z^4$, which contradicts Corollary 2.1.

By a simple modification of the proof of Corollary 2.2 we can show that it is sufficient to prove Fermat's last theorem for the special case in which the exponent is an odd prime number. The proof is left for the reader.

■ THEOREM 3 / If there exists a positive integer n $(n \geq 3)$ such that $x^n + y^n = z^n$ has a positive solution, there exists an odd prime number p (which divides n) such that $x^p + y^p = z^p$ has a positive solution.

EXERCISE

1. Prove Theorem 3.

PROBLEMS

1. If there exists a right triangle with rational sides such that the area is the square of an integer, show that there exists a primitive Pythagorean triple such that the area of the associated triangle is also a square of an integer.

2. Use the method of descent to prove: There exists no primitive Pythagorean triple such that the area of the associated triangle is a square. Combine this result with that of Problem 1 to obtain a more general theorem.

11.4* / THREE DIOPHANTINE PROBLEMS

In this section we will propose three diophantine problems (two of a classical nature). The solutions are left for the reader.

A PROBLEM OF DIOPHANTUS

The following problem was proposed by Diophantus (Problem 18, Book VI of *Arithmetic*): "Find a Pythagorean triangle in which the bisector of one of the acute angles is rational."

Let us make some preliminary observations: (1) The triangle with sides ka, kb, kc has this property if and only if the triangle with sides a, b, c has it. Thus, we need only consider primitive Pythagorean triangles. (2) If a is the odd number in the primitive Pythagorean triple, a, b, c, then (using the standard notation) the bisector of angle A is irrational.

Problem 1. (*a*) Prove the above statements. (*b*) Prove that there exists an infinity of primitive Pythagorean triangles such that the bisector of the angle opposite the even side is rational. (*c*) Derive a parametric form for the primitive Pythagorean triples in (*b*).

THE CONGRUUM

A positive integer h was called a *congruent number* [not to be confused with "congruence (mod m)"] in the Middle Ages if there exists a rational number x such that $x^2 + h$ and $x^2 - h$ are both rational squares. Because the problem of determining all congruent numbers is very difficult, we will consider a related problem.

We will call the positive integer k a *congruum* if the system of diophantine equations

$$x^2 + k = y^2$$
$$x^2 - k = z^2$$

has a nontrivial solution.

Problem 2. (*a*) If a, b, c is a Pythagorean triple, show that the number $2ab$ is a congruum. (This result was known to the Arabs in the tenth century.) (*b*) Prove that each congruum is of the type found in (*a*); that is, if k is a congruum, there exists a Pythagorean triple a, b, c, such that $k = 2ab$. (*c*) If k is a congruum, prove that $k \equiv 0 \pmod{24}$. Find the first few congrua.

THE MAGIC HEXAGON

A hexagonal array of the numbers 1 through k into k cells, such that all of the rows sum to the same number, is called a *magic hexagon*. The number of cells in a shortest row is called the *order* of the hexagon. A magic hexagon of order three is shown in Figure 11.1.

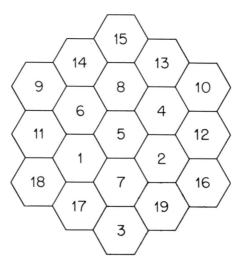

Figure 11.1 Magic hexagon of order 3. (Copyright 1963, *Scientific American.*)

In 1910 a railroad clerk, Clifford Adams, began searching for a magic hexagon of order 3. He found one only after a 47-year search and then, unfortunately, lost the paper on which the solution was written. After 5 years spent trying to rediscover the solution, he located the lost paper and sent it to Martin Gardner, editor of the "Mathematical Games" section of *Scientific American.* Gardner sent the solution to the mathematician C. W. Trigg, who was able to prove a rather astonishing fact: The hexagon found by Adams is the only magic hexagon of any order that exists (except for rotations and reflections of itself). It is, of course, the one shown in Figure 11.1.

Trigg first reduced the problem to a diophantine equation involving the order which he proved had only the solutions 1 and 3. For order 3 he examined all logical possibilities and found no other magic hexagons.

Problem 3. (*a*) Prove: If n is the order of a magic hexagon, the largest rows contain $2n - 1$ cells each, the total number of cells is $3n^2 - 3n + 1$, and the sum of the numbers in all of the cells is

$$\frac{9n^4 - 18n^3 + 18n^2 - 9n + 2}{2}$$

(*b*) Show that the row sum *r* satisfies the diophantine equation

$$r = \frac{9n^4 - 18n^3 + 18n^2 - 9n + 2}{2(2n - 1)}$$

Prove that this equation has only the solutions $n = 1, r = 1$ and $n = 3, r = 38$.

CONTINUED FRACTIONS AND PELL'S EQUATION / 12

12.1 / INTRODUCTION

In this chapter we consider the diophantine equation

$$x^2 - Dy^2 = 1 \; (D \neq 0)$$

Commonly called *Pell's equation* after the seventeenth century mathematician John Pell, it probably should be called *Fermat's equation* after the man who initiated its comparatively recent study. In one of his works, Euler mistakenly attributed the equation to Pell (who had no connection with it).

Our plan of attack is based on the following considerations: If $\sqrt{D}$ is an irrational number and a/b is a rational approximation to $\sqrt{D}$, then a^2/b^2 is an approximation to D, say

$$\frac{a^2}{b^2} - D = \frac{c}{b^2} \neq 0$$

Multiplying by b^2, we obtain

$$a^2 - Db^2 = c \neq 0$$

If a/b is a "good" approximation to $\sqrt{D}$ (in some sense), we would expect c to be a small integer. If, in particular, c happens to be 1, we have a solution of Pell's equation, and a/b is a "very good" approximation to $\sqrt{D}$. Thus, the problem of solving Pell's equation is closely associated with the problem of approximating $\sqrt{D}$ by rational numbers.

As we will see later the best way to approximate $\sqrt{D}$ is by use of continued fractions.

EXERCISES

1. If we consider the decimal approximation of $\sqrt{2}$ ($\sqrt{2} \approx 1.4142$), we obtain the following sequence of rational approximations

$$\frac{a}{b} = \frac{1}{1}, \frac{7}{5}, \frac{141}{100}, \frac{707}{500}, \frac{7071}{5000}$$

Which of these are " good " in the sense that $a^2 - 2b^2 = \pm 1$?

2. Show that the following rational approximations to $\sqrt{2}$ are all " good " in the sense of Exercise 1:

$$\frac{a}{b} = \frac{1}{1}, \frac{3}{2}, \frac{7}{5}, \frac{17}{12}, \frac{41}{29}, \frac{99}{70}$$

12.2 / PRELIMINARY RESULTS ON PELL'S EQUATION

Observe that if x, y is a solution of Pell's equation, then so are $x, -y; -x, y$; and $-x, -y$. Because one of these pairs must contain nonnegative numbers, we may restrict our investigation to nonnegative solutions. Observe also that if $y = 0$, then $x = \pm 1$; and if $x = 0$, we have no solutions except in the trivial case $D = -1$ when we have $y = \pm 1$. These trivial solutions will not be considered further.

Two other cases can be ruled out at once: If $D < 0$, Pell's equation obviously has no positive solution. If D is a square, say $D = d^2$, the equation is

$$x^2 - (dy)^2 = 1$$

If there is a positive solution, then 1 is the difference of two positive squares, which is clearly impossible. Thus, in this case we can have no positive solutions.

In the remainder of this chapter we will consider Pell's equation for the case where D is positive and not a square. We will obtain only the positive solutions of the equation.

If Pell's equation has a positive solution, it has a positive solution x_1, y_1 for which $x_1 + y_1 \sqrt{D}$ is a minimum. This solution is called the *fundamental solution*. The following theorem shows that this solution is well-named, for it can be used to generate all other positive solutions.

■ **THEOREM 1** / If x_1, y_1 is the fundamental solution of Pell's equation, all positive solutions are of form x_n, y_n where

$$x_n + y_n\sqrt{D} = (x_1 + y_1\sqrt{D})^n$$

The solution x_n, y_n can also be computed from the formulas

$$\begin{cases} x_n = \tfrac{1}{2}\{(x_1 + y_1\sqrt{D})^n + (x_1 - y_1\sqrt{D})^n\} \\ y_n = \dfrac{1}{2\sqrt{D}}\{(x_1 + y_1\sqrt{D})^n - (x_1 - y_1\sqrt{D})^n\} \end{cases}$$

or from the recursive formulas

$$\begin{cases} x_{n+1} = x_1 x_n + D y_1 y_n \\ y_{n+1} = x_1 y_n + x_n y_1 \end{cases}$$

[When using the formula $x_n + y_n\sqrt{D} = (x_1 + y_1\sqrt{D})^n$, we find x_n and y_n by expanding $(x_1 + y_1\sqrt{D})^n$ and equating rational and irrational parts with x_n and y_n.]

PROOF: (Part I) Let x_n and y_n be defined as above. Observe that

$$x_n - y_n\sqrt{D} = (x_1 - y_1\sqrt{D})^n$$

[this follows easily from the expansions of $(x_1 + y_1\sqrt{D})^n$ and $(x_1 - y_1\sqrt{D})^n$ by the binomial theorem]. Thus,

$$\begin{aligned} x_n{}^2 - y_n{}^2 D &= (x_n - y_n\sqrt{D})(x_n + y_n\sqrt{D}) \\ &= (x_1 - y_1\sqrt{D})^n (x_1 + y_1\sqrt{D})^n \\ &= (x_1{}^2 - y_1{}^2 D)^n = 1^n = 1 \end{aligned}$$

and so x_n, y_n is a solution.

(Part II) Let x', y' be a positive solution of Pell's equation. We must show that there is a positive integer n such that $(x_1 + y_1\sqrt{D})^n = x' + y'\sqrt{D}$. Suppose that no such n exists. Since $x_1 + y_1\sqrt{D}$ is the fundamental solution, there exists a positive integer m such that

$$(x_1 + y_1\sqrt{D})^m < x' + y'\sqrt{D} < (x_1 + y_1\sqrt{D})^{m+1} \tag{12.1}$$

Since

$$(x_1 - y_1\sqrt{D})^m (x_1 + y_1\sqrt{D})^m = 1$$

then

$$(x_1 - y_1\sqrt{D})^m > 0$$

Multiplying (12.1) by $(x_1 - y_1\sqrt{D})^m$ and combining terms, we obtain

$$1 < (x' + y'\sqrt{D})(x_1 - y_1\sqrt{D})^m = (x' + y'\sqrt{D})(x_m - y_m\sqrt{D})$$

$$= (x'x_m - Dy'y_m) + (x_my' - x'y_m)\sqrt{D} < x_1 + y_1\sqrt{D} \qquad (12.2)$$

It follows by direct computation that

$$x_0 = x'x_m - Dy'y_m, \ y_0 = x_my' - x'y_m$$

is a solution of Pell's equation. If we can show that it is a positive solution, we will contradict the fact that x_1, y_1 is the fundamental solution. Since x_0, y_0 is a solution, then

$$x_0{}^2 - y_0{}^2 D = (x_0 - y_0\sqrt{D})(x_0 + y_0\sqrt{D}) = 1$$

From (12.2) we know that

$$x_0 + y_0\sqrt{D} > 0$$

and so

$$x_0 - y_0\sqrt{D} > 0$$

If we add these two inequalities, we obtain

$$2x_0 > 0$$

Since

$$x_0 + y_0\sqrt{D} > 1$$

then

$$x_0 - y_0\sqrt{D} < 1$$

Subtracting these inequalities, we obtain

$$2y_0\sqrt{D} > 0$$

Thus, x_0, y_0 is a positive solution, which is a contradiction. Therefore, each positive solution is of form x_n, y_n.

The other formulas for x_n, y_n are left for the reader (Exercises 3 and 4).

■ **COROLLARY 1.1** / If $x^2 - Dy^2 = 1$ has a positive solution, then it has an infinity of solutions.

The recursive formulas for x_n, y_n stated in Theorem 1 were known to the Hindu mathematician Bhascara (about A.D. 1140).

In the following sections the theory of continued fractions will be developed as a means of solving Pell's equation.

EXERCISES

1. Show that the fundamental solution of $x^2 - 15y^2 = 1$ is $x_1 = 4$, $y_1 = 1$. Calculate x_n, y_n for $n = 2, 3, 4$.

2. Prove that if Pell's equation has a positive solution, then the fundamental solution exists.

3. *Prove:*
$$\begin{cases} x_n = \tfrac{1}{2}\{(x_1 + y_1\sqrt{D})^n + (x_1 - y_1\sqrt{D})^n\} \\[2mm] y_n = \dfrac{1}{2\sqrt{D}}\{(x_1 + y_1\sqrt{D})^n - (x_1 - y_1\sqrt{D})^n\} \end{cases}$$

4. *Prove:*
$$\begin{cases} x_{n+1} = x_1 x_n + D y_1 y_n \\[2mm] y_{n+1} = x_1 y_n + x_n y_1 \end{cases}$$

5. *Prove:* If D is a positive integer which is not a square, then $\sqrt{D}$ is irrational.

6. Verify that the pair x_0, y_0, defined in the proof of Theorem 1, is a solution of Pell's equation.

PROBLEM

1. Suppose that $x^2 - Dy^2 = -1$ has a positive solution and x_1, y_1 is the positive solution such that $x_1 + y_1\sqrt{D}$ is a minimum. Define x_n, y_n $(n = 1, 2, \cdots)$ by

$$x_n + y_n\sqrt{D} = (x_1 + y_1\sqrt{D})^n$$

Prove that x_2, y_2 is the fundamental solution of Pell's equation, that all solutions of

$$x^2 - Dy^2 = -1$$

are given by x_n, y_n $(n = 1, 3, 5, \cdots)$, and all solutions of

$$x^2 - Dy^2 = 1$$

are given by x_n, y_n $(n = 2, 4, 6, 8, \cdots)$.

12.3 / FINITE CONTINUED FRACTIONS

■ DEFINITION / An expression of form

$$a_1 + \cfrac{1}{a_2 + \cfrac{1}{a_3 + \cfrac{1}{a_4 + \cfrac{\cdots}{\cdots + \cfrac{1}{a_n}}}}}$$

where each a_i ($i \geq 2$) is a nonzero complex number, is called a *finite continued fraction.* If all of the *a*'s are integers and all except possibly a_1 are positive, the continued fraction is called a *finite simple continued fraction.*

Rather than use the cumbersome fraction notation, we will designate the above continued fraction by the symbol[1]

$$\langle a_1, a_2, \cdots, a_n \rangle$$

For example,

$$\langle -1, 1, 2, 3, 4 \rangle = -1 + \cfrac{1}{1 + \cfrac{1}{2 + \cfrac{1}{3 + \cfrac{1}{4}}}} = -\frac{13}{43}$$

Obviously, any finite simple continued fraction represents a rational number. We will now prove that the converse of this statement is also true.

■ THEOREM 2 / Any rational number can be written as a finite simple continued fraction.

---

[1]Other notations in common usage are $[a_1, a_2, \cdots, a_n]$ and

$$a_1 + \frac{1}{a_2+} \frac{1}{a_3+} \frac{1}{a_4+} \cdots \frac{1}{a_n}$$

PROOF: Let a/b be a rational number. We may assume that $b > 0$. From the Euclidean algorithm we obtain the following chain of equations:

$$a = a_1 b + b_1 \qquad 0 < b_1 < b$$
$$b = a_2 b_1 + b_2 \qquad 0 < b_2 < b_1$$
$$b_1 = a_3 b_2 + b_3 \qquad 0 < b_3 < b_2$$
$$\cdots$$
$$b_{n-3} = a_{n-1} b_{n-2} + b_{n-1} \qquad 0 < b_{n-1} < b_{n-2}$$
$$b_{n-2} = a_n b_{n-1}$$

Because the b's are positive integers, it follows that $a_2, a_3, \cdots, a_n$ are also positive integers. Rewriting these expressions, we obtain

$$\frac{a}{b} = a_1 + \frac{b_1}{b}$$

$$\frac{b}{b_1} = a_2 + \frac{b_2}{b_1}$$

$$\frac{b_1}{b_2} = a_3 + \frac{b_3}{b_2}$$

$$\cdots$$

$$\frac{b_{n-2}}{b_{n-1}} = a_n$$

By successive substitution

$$\frac{a}{b} = a_1 + \cfrac{1}{\cfrac{b}{b_1}} = a_1 + \cfrac{1}{a_2 + \cfrac{1}{\cfrac{b_1}{b_2}}} =$$

$$\cdots$$

$$= a_1 + \cfrac{1}{a_2 + \cfrac{1}{a_3 + \cfrac{\cdot}{\cdot\cdot \cfrac{1}{a_n}}}} = \langle a_1, a_2, \cdots, a_n \rangle$$

It is natural to inquire at this point whether the simple continued fraction expansion of a rational number is unique. It is easy to see that it is not, for if $a_n > 1$, then

$$\langle a_1, a_2, \cdots, a_n \rangle = \langle a_1, a_2, \cdots, a_n - 1, 1 \rangle$$

while if $a_n = 1$, then

$$\langle a_1, a_2, \cdots, a_n \rangle = \langle a_1, a_2, \cdots, a_{n-1} + 1 \rangle$$

It follows from this argument that a rational number can be expressed as a simple continued fraction in at least two different ways. It turns out that if we require the expansion to terminate with the number 1, the expansion is unique. The proof of this is left for the reader (Problem 1). We summarize these results in the following theorem.

■ **THEOREM 3 / A** rational number can be written as a finite simple continued fraction in exactly two ways, one with an odd number of terms and one with an even number of terms.

■ **DEFINITION / A** continued fraction formed from $\langle a_1, a_2, \cdots, a_n \rangle$ by neglecting all of the terms after a given term is called a *convergent* to the original continued fractions.\ The *first convergent* is $\langle a_1 \rangle$, the *second convergent* is $\langle a_1, a_2 \rangle$, $\cdots$, the *n*th *convergent* is $\langle a_1, a_2, \cdots, a_n \rangle$. We will denote the *k*th convergent by the symbol C_k.

Therefore,

$$C_1 = \langle a_1 \rangle = \frac{a_1}{1}$$

$$C_2 = \langle a_1, a_2 \rangle = a_1 + \frac{1}{a_2} = \frac{a_1 a_2 + 1}{a_2}$$

$$C_3 = \langle a_1, a_2, a_3 \rangle = a_1 + \frac{1}{a_2 + \dfrac{1}{a_3}} = \frac{(a_1 a_2 + 1)a_3 + a_1}{a_2 a_3 + 1} \tag{12.3}$$

$$C_4 = \langle a_1, a_2, a_3, a_4 \rangle = \frac{\{(a_1 a_2 + 1)a_3 + a_1\} \cdot a_4 + (a_1 a_2 + 1)}{(a_2 a_3 + 1) \cdot a_4 + a_2}$$

To simplify the above expression, we define two sequences inductively. (The sequences depend on the continued fraction $\langle a_1, a_2, \cdots, a_n \rangle$.)

$P_0 = 1$	$Q_0 = 0$
$P_1 = a_1$	$Q_1 = 1$
$P_2 = a_2 P_1 + P_0$	$Q_2 = a_2 Q_1 + Q_0 = a_2$
$P_3 = a_3 P_2 + P_1$	$Q_3 = a_3 Q_2 + Q_1$
$P_4 = a_4 P_3 + P_2$	$Q_4 = a_4 Q_3 + Q_2$
$\cdots$	$\cdots$
$P_k = a_k P_{k-1} + P_{k-2}$	$Q_k = a_k Q_{k-1} + Q_{k-2}$
$\cdots$	$\cdots$
$P_n = a_n P_{n-1} + P_{n-2}$	$Q_n = a_n Q_{n-1} + Q_{n-2}$

If we substitute these values in (12.3), we obtain

$$C_1 = \langle a_1 \rangle = \frac{P_1}{Q_1}$$

$$C_2 = \langle a_1, a_2 \rangle = \frac{P_2}{Q_2}$$

$$C_3 = \langle a_1, a_2, a_3 \rangle = \frac{P_3}{Q_3}$$

$$C_4 = \langle a_1, a_2, a_3, a_4 \rangle = \frac{P_4}{Q_4}$$

We will now prove that this relationship always holds.

■ THEOREM 4 / If C_k is the kth convergent to $\langle a_1, a_2, \cdots, a_n \rangle$, then

$$C_k = \frac{P_k}{Q_k}$$

PROOF: We have shown the proposition to be true when $k = 1$ (and 2, 3, 4 as well). Assume it is true for the integer $k < n$. The $k + 1$st convergent is

$$C_{k+1} = \langle a_1, a_2, \cdots, a_{k-1}, a_k, a_{k+1} \rangle$$

$$= \left\langle a_1, a_2, \cdots, a_{k-1}, a_k + \frac{1}{a_{k+1}} \right\rangle$$

This expression for C_{k+1} is the kth convergent to a *different* continued fraction, call it C'_k. We will denote the numerators and denominators of the convergents to this new continued fraction by P'_i and Q'_i, respectively. By our inductive assumption we see that

$$C_{k+1} = C'_k = \frac{P'_k}{Q'_k} = \frac{\left(a_k + \dfrac{1}{a_{k+1}} \right) \cdot P'_{k-1} + P'_{k-2}}{\left(a_k + \dfrac{1}{a_{k+1}} \right) \cdot Q'_{k-1} + Q'_{k-2}}$$

$$= \frac{a_k P'_{k-1} + P'_{k-2} + \dfrac{1}{a_{k+1}} \cdot P'_{k-1}}{a_k Q'_{k-1} + Q'_{k-2} + \dfrac{1}{a_{k+1}} \cdot Q'_{k-1}}$$

If we compare the convergents of the two continued fractions we see that

$$P_j = P'_j \quad \text{and} \quad Q_j = Q'_j \quad (j = 0, 1, 2, \cdots, k-1)$$

Thus

$$C_{k+1} = \frac{(a_k P_{k-1} + P_{k-2}) + \dfrac{1}{a_{k+1}} P_{k-1}}{(a_k Q_{k-1} + Q_{k-2}) + \dfrac{1}{a_{k+1}} Q_{k-1}} = \frac{P_k + \dfrac{1}{a_{k+1}} P_{k-1}}{Q_k + \dfrac{1}{a_{k+1}} Q_{k-1}}$$

$$= \frac{a_{k+1} P_k + P_{k-1}}{a_{k+1} Q_k + Q_{k-1}} = \frac{P_{k+1}}{Q_{k+1}}$$

Therefore,
$$C_k = \frac{P_k}{Q_k} \qquad (k = 1, 2, \cdots, n).$$

EXERCISES

1. Calculate P_j, Q_j, C_j ($j = 1, 2, \cdots, 6$) for the continued fraction $\langle 1, 2, 2, 2, 2, 2 \rangle$. Note that the sequence $C_1, C_2, \cdots, C_6$ is the sequence of approximations to $\sqrt{2}$ given in Exercise 2 of Section 12.1.

2. Express $179/127$ as a continued fraction with 6 terms.

3. Express $179/127$ as a continued fraction with 7 terms.

4.(a) Calculate P_5 and Q_5 for the continued fraction in Exercise 2. Show that $x = Q_5$, $y = -P_5$ is a solution of $179x + 127y = 1$.

(b) Calculate P_6 and Q_6 for the continued fraction in Exercise 3. Show that $x = Q_6$, $y = -P_6$ is a solution of $179x + 127y = -1$.

PROBLEM

1.(a) Prove that the representation of a rational number as a simple continued fraction is unique if we require the last term to be 1. [*Hint:* Use mathematical induction.]

(b) Use (a) to prove that a rational number can be written as a simple continued fraction in only two ways.

12.4 / PROPERTIES OF P_n AND Q_n

The reader has probably noticed that in the exercises of the preceding section the following pairs of numbers are relatively prime: P_n and Q_n, P_n and P_{n+1}, Q_n and Q_{n+1}. In this section we will prove a basic theorem. As corollaries we will show that the above pairs of numbers are always relatively prime, and that if $(a, b) = 1$, the convergents to a/b can be used to solve the linear diophantine equations

$$ax + by = 1 \quad \text{and} \quad ax + by = -1$$

(see Exercise 4 of Section 12.3). The most important use of the theorem will be in establishing an order relationship among the convergents.

■ **THEOREM 5** / If $k \geq 1$, then $P_k Q_{k-1} - Q_k P_{k-1} = (-1)^k$.

PROOF: The proposition can be verified directly from the definitions of the sequences $\{P_j\}$ and $\{Q_j\}$ for the case $k = 1$. Assume that the proposition is true for the integer K. Then

$$P_{K+1} Q_K - Q_{K+1} P_K = (a_{K+1} P_K + P_{K-1}) Q_K - (a_{K+1} Q_K + Q_{K-1}) P_K$$

$$= -(P_K Q_{K-1} - Q_K P_{K-1}) = -(-1)^K = (-1)^{K+1}$$

From the principle of mathematical induction it follows that the proposition is true for each positive integer k.

■ **COROLLARY 5.1** / If $n \geq 0$, the following pairs of integers are relatively prime: P_n and P_{n+1}, Q_n and Q_{n+1}, P_n and Q_n.

PROOF: The greatest common divisor of P_n and P_{n+1} is the smallest positive integer that can be written as a sum of multiples of P_n and P_{n+1}. From Theorem 5 we see that

$$P_{n+1}(-1)^{n+1} Q_n + P_n(-1)^{n+2} Q_{n+1} = 1$$

Thus, $$(P_{n+1}, P_n) = 1$$

The other two proofs are similar.

■ **COROLLARY 5.2** / Let a and b be relatively prime integers, $b > 0$. If the simple continued fraction expansion of a/b has n terms, then

$$x = Q_{n-1}, y = -P_{n-1}$$

is a solution of the linear diophantine equation

$$ax + by = (-1)^n$$

PROOF: $C_n = P_n/Q_n = a/b$. Since both a/b and P_n/Q_n are reduced to lowest terms, then $a = P_n$ and $b = Q_n$. By Theorem 5,

$$aQ_{n-1} + b(-P_{n-1}) = (-1)^n$$

We have established that a/b can be written in two ways as a continued fraction: One with an odd number of terms and one with an even number of terms. Thus, Corollary 5.1 provides us with solutions to both

$$ax + by = 1 \quad \text{and} \quad ax + by = -1$$

We will now use Theorem 5 to establish an order relationship among the convergents. This relationship is of basic importance in the theory of infinite continued fractions.

■ **THEOREM 6** / If C_k is the kth convergent to the simple continued fraction $\langle a_1, a_2, \cdots, a_n \rangle$, then

$$C_1 < C_3 < C_5 < \cdots < C_6 < C_4 < C_2$$

PROOF: Using Theorems 4 and 5 we obtain

$$C_{k+2} - C_k = (C_{k+2} - C_{k+1}) + (C_{k+1} - C_k)$$

$$= \left(\frac{P_{k+2}}{Q_{k+2}} - \frac{P_{k+1}}{Q_{k+1}} \right) + \left(\frac{P_{k+1}}{Q_{k+1}} - \frac{P_k}{Q_k} \right)$$

$$= \frac{(-1)^{k+2}}{Q_{k+2}Q_{k+1}} + \frac{(-1)^{k+1}}{Q_{k+1}Q_k}$$

$$= \frac{(-1)^{k+1}(Q_{k+2} - Q_k)}{Q_k Q_{k+1} Q_{k+2}}$$

Since $Q_{k+2} - Q_k > 0$ (see Exercise 1), the sign of $C_{k+2} - C_k$ is the same as that of $(-1)^{k+1}$; that is, $C_{k+2} > C_k$ if k is odd, and $C_{k+2} < C_k$ if k is even. Thus,

$$C_1 < C_3 < C_5 < \cdots$$

and

$$C_2 > C_4 > C_6 > \cdots$$

We now must prove that if m is odd and n is even, $C_m < C_n$. Since $C_2 > C_4 > C_6 > \cdots > C_n$, it is obviously no restriction to assume that $n > m$. Using Theorem 5 we obtain

$$C_n - C_{n-1} = \frac{(-1)^n}{Q_n Q_{n+1}} > 0$$

Because m and $n - 1$ are both odd,

$$C_m \le C_{n-1} < C_n$$

EXERCISES

1. Prove that $Q_{k+1} > Q_k > 0$ if $k \geq 1$.

2. Generalize Corollary 5.2 by removing the restriction that a and b are relatively prime.

12.5 / INFINITE CONTINUED FRACTIONS

Let $a_1, a_2, a_3, \cdots$ be an infinite sequence of real numbers. We would like to define the expression $\langle a_1, a_2, \cdots \rangle$ in a meaningful manner. Note that each of the finite continued fractions $\langle a_1 \rangle, \langle a_1, a_2 \rangle, \cdots, \langle a_1, a_2, \cdots, a_n \rangle \cdots$, is defined, provided $a_i \neq 0$ ($i = 2, 3, \cdots$). Thus, the natural way to define $\langle a_1, a_2, \cdots \rangle$ is as $\lim_{n \to \infty} \langle a_1, a_2, \cdots, a_n \rangle$, *provided the limit exists.*

We will now prove that in an important special case the above limit does exist.

■ THEOREM 7 / Let $a_1, a_2, \cdots$ be an infinite sequence of integers, all positive except possibly a_1. Let $C_n = \langle a_1, a_2, \cdots, a_n \rangle$. Then $\lim_{n \to \infty} C_n$ exists and is finite.

PROOF: We may consider each C_n as one of the convergents to a finite simple continued fraction. By Theorem 6,

$$C_1 < C_3 < C_5 < \cdots < C_6 < C_4 < C_2$$

The sequence C_{2n} is a bounded, decreasing sequence and thus has a limit α. Since each C_{2n} is greater than each C_{2k+1} then α is greater than or equal to each C_{2k+1}. Therefore, since $\lim_{k \to \infty} Q_k = \infty$ (see Exercise 4),

$$0 \leq \lim_{k \to \infty} (\alpha - C_{2k+1}) \leq \lim_{k \to \infty} (C_{2k} - C_{2k+1}) = \lim_{k \to \infty} \frac{(-1)^{2k}}{Q_{2k}Q_{2k+1}} = 0$$

Thus,

$$\lim_{k \to \infty} C_{2k+1} = \alpha = \lim_{k \to \infty} C_{2k}$$

and the sequence C_n converges to the real number α.

■ DEFINITION / Let $a_1, a_2, \cdots$ be a sequence of integers, all positive except possibly a_1. The expression

$$\langle a_1, a_2, \cdots \rangle$$

is called an *infinite simple continued fraction* and is defined to be equal to the number

$$\lim_{n \to \infty} \langle a_1, a_2, \cdots, a_n \rangle$$

Let $\alpha = \langle a_1, a_2, \cdots \rangle$. Since α is between C_n and C_{n+1} for any two consecutive convergents, we obtain the following theorem:

■ THEOREM 8 / If C_n is the nth convergent to the irrational number α, then

$$|\alpha - C_n| < \frac{1}{Q_n Q_{n+1}}$$

Example 1.

Evaluate $\alpha = \langle 1, 2, 2, 2, \cdots \rangle$. How close is the approximation C_6?

SOLUTION: We write

$$\alpha = 1 + \frac{1}{1 + \langle 1, 2, 2, \cdots \rangle} = 1 + \frac{1}{1 + \alpha}$$

Thus, $\qquad\qquad \alpha^2 = 2$

so that $\qquad\qquad \alpha = \sqrt{2} \quad\text{ or }\quad \alpha = -\sqrt{2}$

Since $\qquad\qquad \alpha > C_1 > 0$

then $\qquad\qquad \alpha = \sqrt{2}$

Since $C_6 = 99/70$, $Q_6 = 70$, $Q_7 = 169$, then

$$\left| \sqrt{2} - \frac{99}{70} \right| < \frac{1}{70 \cdot 169} < 0.00009$$

■ NOTATION / It is customary to write continued fractions of the type considered in Example 1 with a bar to indicate the repeating block. Thus,

$$\langle 1, 2, 2, 2, \cdots \rangle = \langle 1, \overline{2} \rangle$$
$$\langle 1, 2, 3, 4, 1, 2, 3, 4, 1, 2, 3, 4, \cdots \rangle = \langle \overline{1, 2, 3, 4} \rangle,$$

and so on.

Example 2.

Write $\sqrt{3}$ and $-\sqrt{3}$ as infinite simple continued fractions.

SOLUTION:

(a)
$$\sqrt{3} = 1 + (\sqrt{3} - 1) = 1 + \cfrac{1}{\cfrac{1}{\sqrt{3} - 1}}$$

$$\frac{1}{\sqrt{3} - 1} = \frac{\sqrt{3} + 1}{3 - 1} = \frac{1 + \sqrt{3}}{2} = \frac{2 + (\sqrt{3} - 1)}{2} = 1 + \cfrac{1}{\cfrac{2}{\sqrt{3} - 1}}$$

$$\frac{2}{\sqrt{3} - 1} = \frac{2(\sqrt{3} + 1)}{3 - 1} = \sqrt{3} + 1 = 2 + (\sqrt{3} - 1) = 2 + \cfrac{1}{\cfrac{1}{\sqrt{3} - 1}}$$

From the last two equations, it follows that

$$\frac{1}{\sqrt{3} - 1} = \left\langle 1, \frac{2}{\sqrt{3} - 1} \right\rangle = \left\langle 1, 2, \frac{1}{\sqrt{3} - 1} \right\rangle = \left\langle 1, 2, 1, \frac{2}{\sqrt{3} - 1} \right\rangle$$

$$= \cdots = \langle 1, 2, 1, 2, 1, 2, \cdots \rangle = \langle \overline{1, 2} \rangle$$

Therefore,

$$\sqrt{3} = \left\langle 1, \frac{1}{\sqrt{3} - 1} \right\rangle = \langle 1, \overline{1, 2} \rangle$$

(b)
$$-\sqrt{3} = -2 + (2 - \sqrt{3}) = -2 + \cfrac{1}{\cfrac{1}{2 - \sqrt{3}}}$$

$$\frac{1}{2 - \sqrt{3}} = \frac{2 + \sqrt{3}}{4 - 3} = 2 + \sqrt{3} = 3 + (\sqrt{3} - 1) = 3 + \cfrac{1}{\cfrac{1}{\sqrt{3} - 1}}$$

In (a) we established that

$$\frac{1}{\sqrt{3} - 1} = \langle \overline{1, 2} \rangle$$

Thus,

$$-\sqrt{3} = -2 + \cfrac{1}{3 + \cfrac{1}{\cfrac{1}{\sqrt{3} - 1}}} = -2 + \cfrac{1}{3 + \cfrac{1}{\langle \overline{1, 2} \rangle}} = \langle -2, 3, \overline{1, 2} \rangle$$

In the above examples we made the implicit assumption that

$$\langle a_1, a_2, a_3, \cdots \rangle = a_1 + \frac{1}{\langle a_2, a_3, \cdots \rangle}$$

This important fact, which is trivial for finite continued fractions, must be proved for the infinite case (see Problem 1).

■ THEOREM 9 / Any irrational number can be written as an infinite continued fraction. Furthermore, the representation is unique.

PROOF: Let α be an irrational number. We write

$$\alpha = [\alpha] + \{\alpha\} = [\alpha] + \cfrac{1}{\cfrac{1}{\{\alpha\}}}$$

where $\{\alpha\}$ represents the fractional part of α. Because α is irrational, then $1/\{\alpha\}$ is irrational and greater than 1. Let

$$a_1 = [\alpha] \quad \text{and} \quad \alpha_1 = \frac{1}{\{\alpha\}}$$

We now write

$$\alpha_1 = [\alpha_1] + \{\alpha_1\} = [\alpha_1] + \cfrac{1}{\cfrac{1}{\{\alpha_1\}}}$$

where $1/\{\alpha_1\}$ is irrational and greater than 1. Let

$$a_2 = [\alpha_1], \alpha_2 = \frac{1}{\{\alpha_1\}}$$

We continue inductively:

$$a_3 = [\alpha_2], \alpha_3 = \frac{1}{\{\alpha_2\}} > 1 \quad (\alpha_3 \text{ irrational})$$

$$a_4 = [\alpha_3], \alpha_4 = \frac{1}{\{\alpha_3\}} > 1 \quad (\alpha_4 \text{ irrational})$$

$$\cdots$$

$$a_n = [\alpha_{n-1}], \alpha_n = \frac{1}{\{\alpha_{n-1}\}} > 1 \quad (\alpha_n \text{ irrational}),$$

$$\cdots$$

Since each α_n is greater than 1, then $a_n \geq 1$ ($n = 2, 3, \cdots$). If we substitute successively, we obtain

$$\alpha = \langle a_1, \alpha_1 \rangle = \langle a_1, a_2, \alpha_2 \rangle = \langle a_1, a_2, a_3, \alpha_3 \rangle = \cdots$$

$$= \langle a_1, a_2, \cdots, a_n, \alpha_n \rangle = \cdots$$

We will now show that α is equal to $\langle a_1, a_2, \cdots \rangle$. Note that C_n, the nth convergent to $\langle a_1, a_2, \cdots \rangle$ is also the nth convergent to $\langle a_1, a_2, \cdots, a_n, \alpha_n \rangle$. If we denote the $(n+1)$st convergent to this finite continued fraction by $P'_{n+1}/Q'_{n+1} = \alpha$, then, by Theorem 5,

$$\alpha - C_n = \frac{P'_{n+1}}{Q'_{n+1}} - \frac{P_n}{Q_n} = \frac{(-1)^{n+1}}{Q'_{n+1}Q_n}$$

Since Q_n and Q'_{n+1} become infinite as $n \to \infty$, then

$$\lim_{n \to \infty} (\alpha - C_n) = \lim_{n \to \infty} \frac{(-1)^{n+1}}{Q'_{n+1}Q_n} = 0$$

and

$$\alpha = \lim_{n \to \infty} C_n = \langle a_1, a_2, \cdots \rangle$$

The uniqueness of the representation is left for the reader (Problem 2).

We have proved that each rational number can be written as a finite simple continued fraction, and each irrational number as an infinite simple continued fraction. It is conceivable that certain rational numbers can also be written as infinite simple continued fractions. The next theorem indicates that this is not the case.

■ **THEOREM 10** / If α is an infinite simple continued fraction, then α is irrational.

SKETCH OF THE PROOF: Show that if $\alpha = a/b$, then $|aQ_n - bP_n|$ is an infinite sequence of positive integers that converges to zero.

We raise one additional question in this section: Let α be a positive irrational number. Is there a relationship between the convergents to α and the convergents to $1/\alpha$? It would be natural to conjecture that they are reciprocals. A more precise statement of the relationship is stated in the following theorem. The proof is left for the reader (Problem 3).

■ **THEOREM 11** / Let α be an irrational number, greater than 1. The $(k+1)$st convergent to $1/\alpha$ is the reciprocal of the kth convergent to α ($k = 1$, $2, \cdots$).

EXERCISES

1. Evaluate
   (a) $\langle \overline{1, 2, 2} \rangle$;
   (b) $\langle 1, 2, \overline{3, 4} \rangle$.

2. Express $\sqrt{15}$ and $2 - \sqrt{15}$ as continued fractions.

3. Calculate the first six convergents to the continued fraction expansion of $\sqrt{27}$ and compare them with the decimal approximation to $\sqrt{27}$ given in a set of mathematical tables.

4. Prove that $\lim\limits_{n \to \infty} Q_n = \infty$.

PROBLEMS

1. If $\alpha = \langle a_1, a_2, \cdots \rangle$, prove that $a_1 = [\alpha]$ and

$$\alpha = a_1 + \frac{1}{\langle a_2, a_3, \cdots \rangle}$$

2. Complete the proof of Theorem 9 by proving: If

$$\alpha = \langle a_1, a_2, \cdots \rangle = \langle b_1, b_2, \cdots \rangle$$

then

$$a_n = b_n \ (n = 1, 2, 3, \cdots)$$

[*Hint:* Use Problem 1.]

3. Prove Theorem 11 by mathematical induction.

The Fibonacci Numbers. The following problem refers to the famous sequence investigated by Leonardo Pisano (Fibonacci) in the thirteenth century. The Fibonacci numbers are is defined as follows:

$$f_1 = 1$$
$$f_2 = 2$$
$$f_3 = f_1 + f_2 = 3$$
$$\cdots$$
$$f_{n+1} = f_n + f_{n-1}$$
$$\cdots$$

4. Let $\alpha = \langle \overline{1} \rangle$ and let $C_n = P_n/Q_n$ be the nth convergent to α.

   (a) Show that $P_n = f_n$. Can Q_n also be expressed in terms of the Fibonacci numbers?

   (b) *Prove:* $\lim\limits_{n \to \infty} \dfrac{f_n}{f_{n-1}} = \dfrac{1 + \sqrt{5}}{2}$.

   (c) *Prove:* $f_k = \dfrac{1}{\sqrt{5}} \left\{ \left(\dfrac{1 + \sqrt{5}}{2} \right)^{k+1} - \left(\dfrac{1 - \sqrt{5}}{2} \right)^{k+1} \right\}$.

   (d) *Prove:* If $\langle a_1, a_2, \cdots \rangle$ is an infinite simple continued fraction with nth convergent $C_n = P_n/Q_n$,

then

$$Q_n \geq f_{n-1}$$

12.6 / THE CLOSENESS OF APPROXIMATION BY CONVERGENTS

We have proved that if P_k/Q_k is the kth convergent to the irrational number α, then

$$\left| \alpha - \frac{P_n}{Q_n} \right| < \frac{1}{Q_n Q_{n+1}}$$

In this section we will prove several similar inequalities.

Note that the above inequality implies the weaker relationships

$$\left| \alpha - \frac{P_n}{Q_n} \right| < \frac{1}{Q_n^2}$$

and

$$|Q_n \alpha - P_n| < \frac{1}{Q_n}$$

This last inequality implies that if α is an irrational number, there exists an infinity of positive integers b such that $b\alpha$ is arbitrarily close to an integer. We will now prove that if $b\alpha$ is "close" to an integer, then b must be fairly large. More precisely, we will prove that of all numbers $b\alpha$, where $1 \le b \le Q_n$, $Q_n\alpha$ is the closest to an integer.

■ THEOREM 12 / If a and b are integers, $1 \le b < Q_n$, then

$$|b\alpha - a| > |Q_n \alpha - P_n|$$

PROOF: Consider the system of equations

$$P_n X + P_{n+1} Y = a$$

$$Q_n X + Q_{n+1} Y = b$$

Because the determinant of coefficients is $(-1)^n$ (by Theorem 5), the system has a unique integral solution X_0, Y_0. Since $Q_{n+1} \ge Q_n > b$, then X_0 and Y_0 must have different signs and neither can be zero. Thus,

$$
\begin{aligned}
|b\alpha - a| &= |(Q_n X_0 + Q_{n+1} Y_0)\alpha - (P_n X_0 + P_{n+1} Y_0)| \\
&= |X_0(Q_n\alpha - P_n) + Y_0(Q_{n+1}\alpha - P_{n+1})| \\
&= |X_0(Q_n\alpha - P_n)| + |Y_0(Q_{n+1}\alpha - P_{n+1})| \\
&> |X_0|\,|Q_n\alpha - P_n| \ge |Q_n\alpha - P_n|
\end{aligned}
$$

We will use Theorem 12 to show that the convergents form a sequence of "best" approximations to the irrational number α.

■ COROLLARY 12.1 / If $1 \leq b < Q_n$, then

$$\left| \alpha - \frac{a}{b} \right| > \left| \alpha - \frac{P_n}{Q_n} \right|$$

PROOF: If $\left| \alpha - \dfrac{a}{b} \right| \leq \left| \alpha - \dfrac{P_n}{Q_n} \right|$, then

$$|b\alpha - a| \leq b \cdot \left| \alpha - \frac{P_n}{Q_n} \right| < Q_n \cdot \left| \alpha - \frac{P_n}{Q_n} \right| = |Q_n \alpha - P_n|$$

which contradicts Theorem 12.

Although theorems similar to Corollary 12.1 are useful, they have the drawback that the denominator must be compared with the sequence Q_n. We will prove a similar result in which the difference between α and a/b must only be compared with a function of b. The main result is that any "close" rational approximation to α must be one of the convergents to α.

■ THEOREM 13 / Let α be an irrational number. If a/b is a rational number with positive denominator such that

$$\left| \alpha - \frac{a}{b} \right| < \frac{1}{2b^2}$$

then a/b is one of the convergents to α.

PROOF: We will only prove the theorem for the case where a and b are relatively prime. The trivial extension to the general case is left for the reader (Exercise 1).

Let $a/b - \alpha = \epsilon\theta/b^2$ where $\epsilon = \pm 1$ and $0 < \theta < \frac{1}{2}$. Expand a/b as a simple continued fraction obtaining $a/b = \langle a_1, a_2, \cdots, a_n \rangle$. By Theorem 3 we may choose n so that

$$\epsilon = (-1)^n$$

Let P_k/Q_k be the kth convergent to a/b and define β by

$$\alpha = \frac{\beta P_n + P_{n-1}}{\beta Q_n + Q_{n-1}}$$

Obviously, β is real and irrational. Since a and b are relatively prime, then, using Corollary 5.1, we find that $a = P_n$ and $b = Q_n$. Thus,

$$\frac{\epsilon\theta}{Q_n{}^2} = \frac{\epsilon\theta}{b^2} = \frac{a}{b} - \alpha = \frac{P_n}{Q_n} - \frac{\beta P_n + P_{n-1}}{\beta Q_n + Q_{n-1}} = \frac{(-1)^n}{Q_n(\beta Q_n + Q_{n-1})}$$

If we solve this equation for β, recalling that $\epsilon = (-1)^n$, we obtain

$$\beta = \frac{1}{\theta} - \frac{Q_{n-1}}{Q_n} > 1$$

the inequality holding since $1/\theta > 2$ and $Q_n \geq Q_{n-1}$. Since $\beta > 1$ we can write β as an infinite simple continued fraction

$$\beta = \langle b_1, b_2, \cdots \rangle \qquad b_1 \geq 1$$

Consider the simple continued fraction

$$\gamma = \langle a_1, a_2, \cdots, a_n, b_1, b_2, \cdots \rangle$$

Since $\gamma = \langle a_1, a_2, \cdots, a_n, \beta \rangle = \dfrac{P_n \beta + P_{n-1}}{Q_n \beta + Q_{n+1}} = \alpha$

then $a/b = P_n/Q_n$ is the nth convergent to α.

We will now show that the inequality

$$\left| \alpha - \frac{a}{b} \right| < \frac{1}{2b^2}$$

is characteristic of the convergents to α.

■ THEOREM 14 / Let α be an irrational number. Of any two consecutive convergents to α, at least one satisfies the inequality

$$\left| \alpha - \frac{a}{b} \right| < \frac{1}{2b^2}$$

PROOF: Suppose

$$\left| \alpha - \frac{P_n}{Q_n} \right| \geq \frac{1}{2Q_n{}^2} \qquad \text{and} \qquad \left| \alpha - \frac{P_{n+1}}{Q_{n+1}} \right| \geq \frac{1}{2Q_{n+1}{}^2}$$

Since the convergents are alternately less and greater than α, then

$$\frac{1}{Q_n Q_{n+1}} = \left| \frac{P_n}{Q_n} - \frac{P_{n+1}}{Q_{n+1}} \right| = \left| \frac{P_n}{Q_n} - \alpha + \alpha - \frac{P_{n+1}}{Q_{n+1}} \right|$$

$$= \left| \frac{P_n}{Q_n} - \alpha \right| + \left| \alpha - \frac{P_{n+1}}{Q_{n+1}} \right| \geq \frac{1}{2Q_n{}^2} + \frac{1}{2Q_{n+1}{}^2}$$

$$= \frac{Q_{n+1}{}^2 + Q_n{}^2}{2Q_n{}^2 Q_{n+1}{}^2}$$

From this inequality we see that

$$(Q_{n+1} - Q_n)^2 = Q_{n+1}{}^2 - 2Q_n Q_{n+1} + Q_n{}^2 \leq 0$$

which is impossible unless $n = 1$ and $a_2 = 1$. In this special case,

$$Q_1 = Q_2 = 1 \quad \text{and} \quad Q_3 = a_3 + 1 \geq 2$$

so that

$$\frac{P_2}{Q_2} - \alpha < \frac{P_2}{Q_2} - \frac{P_3}{Q_3} = \frac{1}{Q_2 Q_3} \leq \frac{1}{2}$$

which is a contradiction.

EXERCISES

1. Find three integers b_1, b_2, b_3 such that the distance from $b_i\sqrt{3}$ to the nearest integer is less than $1/20$.

2. Complete the proof of Theorem 13 by extending the proof to cover the case where a and b are not relatively prime.

PROBLEM

1. Let ϵ be a positive number. At each lattice point in the plane draw a circle of radius, ϵ, which has the lattice point as center. Prove that any straight line through the origin must intersect an infinity of these circles.

12.7* / SIMULTANEOUS APPROXIMATIONS

In the preceding section we obtain a sequence of rational approximations to a given irrational number α, satisfying

$$\left| \alpha - \frac{a}{b} \right| < \frac{1}{2b^2} \tag{12.4}$$

Suppose we are given several irrational numbers, say $\alpha_1, \alpha_2, \cdots, \alpha_n$. Is it possible to obtain rational numbers $a_1/b, a_2/b, \cdots, a_n/b$, having the same denominator, such that each satisfies an inequality of form

$$\left| \alpha_j - \frac{a_j}{b} \right| < f(b)$$

where $f(b)$ is a function similar to the right-hand side of (12.4)? It is obvious that this problem is closely related to the problem of finding an integer b such that each of the numbers

$$b\alpha_1, b\alpha_2, \cdots, b\alpha_n$$

is "close" to an integer.

In solving this problem we will not use continued fractions and, consequently, we must be satisfied with existence theorems. We will, however, be able to relax our restrictions and allow $\alpha_1, \alpha_2, \cdots, \alpha_n$ to be arbitrary real numbers.

As in Section 12.5 we let $\{X\}$ denote the fractional part of the real number X; that is, $\{X\} = X - [X]$. We also define (X) to be the undirected distance from X to the nearest integer. For example,

$$\{1\tfrac{3}{4}\} = \tfrac{3}{4}, \ (1\tfrac{1}{4}) = (1\tfrac{3}{4}) = \tfrac{1}{4}$$

■ **LEMMA** / Let N be an integer greater than 1. If $\{x\}$ and $\{y\}$ are both between k/N (inclusive) and $(k + 1)/N$ (exclusive), then $(x - y) < 1/N$.

PROOF: Since $(x - y) = (\{x\} - \{y\}) = (\{y\} - \{x\})$, we need only consider the case where $\{x\} \geq \{y\}$. In this case

$$0 \leq \{x\} - \{y\} < \frac{k + 1}{N} - \frac{k}{N} = \frac{1}{N}$$

Therefore, zero is the integer nearest to $\{x\} - \{y\}$ and

$$(x - y) = (\{x\} - \{y\}) = \{x\} - \{y\} < \frac{1}{N}$$

■ **THEOREM 15** / Let $\alpha_1, \alpha_2, \cdots, \alpha_n$ be real numbers, let N be an integer greater than 1. There exist integers $a_1, a_2, \cdots, a_n, b, 1 \leq b \leq N^n$, such that

$$|b\alpha_j - a_j| < \frac{1}{N} \qquad (j = 1, 2, \cdots, n)$$

PROOF: We define a "cube" in n-dimensional space by

$$0 \leq x_j < 1 \qquad (j = 1, 2, \cdots, n)$$

and partition it into N^n small cubes, defined by

$$\frac{k}{N} \leq x_j < \frac{k + 1}{N} \qquad (k = 0, 1, \cdots, N - 1; j = 1, 2, \cdots, n)$$

Consider the following points in n-dimensional space:

$$(0, 0, \cdots, 0),$$
$$(\{\alpha_1\}, \{\alpha_2\}, \cdots, \{\alpha_n\})$$
$$(\{2\alpha_1\}, \{2\alpha_2\}, \cdots, \{2\alpha_n\}),$$
$$\cdots$$
$$(\{N^n\alpha_1\}, \{N^n\alpha_2\}, \cdots, \{N^n\alpha_n\})$$

These $N^n + 1$ points are all contained in the large cube. Since there are N^n small cubes, at least one of them contains two or more of the points, say

$$(\{k\alpha_1\}, \{k\alpha_2\}, \cdots, \{k\alpha_n\})$$

and

$$(\{m\alpha_1\}, \{m\alpha_2\}, \cdots, \{m\alpha_n\})$$

where $m > k$. If we now let $b = m - k$, it follows from the lemma that

$$(b\alpha_j) = (m\alpha_j - k\alpha_j) < \frac{1}{N} \qquad (j = 1, 2, \cdots, n)$$

that is, there exist integers $a_1, a_2, \cdots, a_n$ such that

$$|b\alpha_j - a_j| < \frac{1}{N} \qquad (j = 1, 2, \cdots, n)$$

In the special case where N equals the larger of 2 and $[1/\epsilon] + 1$, we obtain the following corollary:

■ **COROLLARY 15.1** / Let $\alpha_1, \alpha_2, \cdots, \alpha_n$ be real numbers, let $\epsilon > 0$. There exists an integer b such that the distance from each of

$$b\alpha_1, b\alpha_2, \cdots, b\alpha_n$$

to the nearest integer is less than ϵ.

Since $0 < 1/N < 1/b^{1/n}$ we also obtain the following result which is similar in form to the statement of Theorem 14.

■ **COROLLARY 15.2** / Let $\alpha_1, \alpha_2, \cdots, \alpha_n$ be real numbers. There exists an infinity of sets of integers $a_1, a_2, \cdots, a_n, b, b > 0$, such that

$$\left| \frac{a_j}{b} - \alpha_j \right| < \frac{1}{b^{(n+1)/n}} \qquad (j = 1, 2, \cdots, n)$$

12.8 / PERIODIC CONTINUED FRACTIONS

■ **DEFINITION** / An infinite simple continued fraction is said to be *periodic* if it is of form $\langle a_1, a_2, \cdots, a_n, \overline{b_1, b_2, \cdots, b_m} \rangle$. If it is of form $\langle \overline{b_1, b_2, \cdots, b_m} \rangle$, it is said to be *purely periodic*. The smallest positive integer m satisfying the above relationship is called the *period* of the expansion.

In the examples considered so far in this chapter the infinite simple continued fractions have all been periodic and have been roots of quadratic equations with integral coefficients. In this section we will prove that this is always the case.

■ DEFINITION / A real irrational number which is the root of a quadratic equation with integral coefficients is called a *quadratic irrational.*

Observe that the above definition is equivalent to saying that a quadratic irrational is a real irrational root of a quadratic equation with rational coefficients.

■ LEMMA / Each purely periodic continued fraction is a quadratic irrational.

PROOF: Let $\alpha = \overline{\langle a_1, a_2, \cdots, a_n \rangle} = \langle a_1, a_2, \cdots, a_n, \alpha \rangle$. If P_k/Q_k is the kth convergent to α, then

$$\alpha = \frac{\alpha P_n + P_{n-1}}{\alpha Q_n + Q_{n-1}}$$

so that $\qquad Q_n \alpha^2 + (Q_{n-1} - P_n)\alpha - P_{n-1} = 0$

Thus, since α is not rational (the continued fraction expansion is infinite), α is a quadratic irrational.

In the proof of the next theorem, we use the following result from elementary algebra: If α is a quadratic irrational and a, b, c, d are rational with not both c and d zero, then

$$\frac{a + b\alpha}{c + d\alpha}$$

is either rational on a quadratic irrational (Exercise 1).

■ THEOREM 16 / Each periodic simple continued fraction is a quadratic irrational.

PROOF: Let $\alpha = \langle a_1, a_2, \cdots, a_n, \overline{b_1, b_2, \cdots, b_m} \rangle$, and let $\beta = \overline{\langle b_1, b_2, \cdots, b_m \rangle}$. From the lemma we see that β is a quadratic irrational. If P_k/Q_k is the kth convergent to α, then,

$$\alpha = \langle a_1, \cdots, a_n, \beta \rangle = \frac{\beta P_n + P_{n-1}}{\beta Q_n + Q_{n-1}}$$

It follows from the remarks preceding the statement of the theorem that α is a quadratic irrational or a rational number. Since α is an infinite simple continued fraction, then α is a quadratic irrational.

Before proving the converse of Theorem 16, we must establish some supplementary results.

■ **THEOREM 17 /** Let α be a real, irrational root of $ax^2 + bx + c = 0$, where a, b, c are integers. If

$$\alpha = \langle a_1, a_2, \cdots, a_n, \alpha_n \rangle$$

then α_n is a root of the polynomial

$$A_n x^2 + B_n x + C_n = 0$$

where
$$A_n = aP_n^2 + bP_n Q_n + cQ_n^2$$

$$B_n = 2aP_n P_{n-1} + bP_n Q_{n-1} + bP_{n-1} Q_n + 2cQ_n Q_{n-1}$$

$$C_n = aP_{n-1}^2 + bP_{n-1} Q_{n-1} + cQ_{n-1}^2$$

and where $B_n^2 - 4A_n C_n = b^2 - 4ac$

PROOF: If P_n/Q_n is the nth convergent to α, then

$$\alpha = \frac{P_n \alpha_n + P_{n-1}}{Q_n \alpha_n + Q_{n-1}}$$

If we substitute this value of α into $a\alpha^2 + b\alpha + c = 0$ and rearrange the coefficients, we obtain

$$A_n \alpha_n^2 + B_n \alpha_n + C_n = 0$$

where A_n, B_n, C_n are as given in the statement of the theorem. By direct computation we obtain

$$B_n^2 - 4A_n C_n = (b^2 - 4ac)(P_n Q_{n-1} - Q_n P_{n-1})^2 = b^2 - 4ac$$

■ **COROLLARY 17.1 /** Let α be a quadratic irrational and write

$$\alpha = \langle a_1, a_2, \cdots, a_n, \alpha_n \rangle \qquad (n = 1, 2, \cdots)$$

There exists a finite set of polynomials with integral coefficients

$$A_1 x^2 + B_1 x + C_1 = 0$$

$$A_2 x^2 + B_2 x + C_2 = 0$$

$$\cdots$$

$$A_N x^2 + B_N x + C_N = 0$$

which have all of the α_n as roots.

PROOF: Let α_n be a root of $A_n x^2 + B_n x + C_n = 0$ where the coefficients are as given in Theorem 17. Since

$$|\alpha Q_n - P_n| < \frac{1}{Q_n}$$

we can write

$$P_n = \alpha Q_n + \frac{\epsilon}{Q_n} \qquad |\epsilon| < 1$$

(where ϵ, of course, depends on n). Substituting this into the expression for A_n, we obtain

$$A_n = a\left(\alpha Q_n + \frac{\epsilon}{Q_n}\right)^2 + b\left(\alpha Q_n + \frac{\epsilon}{Q_n}\right)Q_n + cQ_n^2$$

$$= (a\alpha^2 + b\alpha + c)Q_n^2 + \left(2a\alpha + b + \frac{a\epsilon}{Q_n^2}\right) \cdot \epsilon$$

$$= \left(2a\alpha + b + \frac{a\epsilon}{Q_n^2}\right) \cdot \epsilon$$

Thus,
$$|A_n| < |2a\alpha + b| + |a|$$

which implies that all of the A_n must come from a finite set of integers. Since $C_n = A_{n-1}$, we have a similar result for the C_n. Since

$$B_n^2 - 4A_n C_n = b^2 - 4ac$$

then

$$B_n^2 = |4A_n C_n + b^2 - 4ac| < 4\{|2a\alpha + b| + |a|\}^2 + |b^2 - 4ac|$$

and B_n is also bounded. Because we have only a finite number of choices for A_n, B_n, C_n, we have only a finite number of distinct polynomials

$$A_n x^2 + B_n x + C_n = 0$$

which have all of the α_n as roots.

■ **THEOREM 18** / (Converse of Theorem 16.) Each quadratic irrational has a periodic expansion as a simple continued fraction.

PROOF: Let $\alpha = \langle a_1, \cdots, a_n, \alpha_n \rangle$ be a quadratic irrational. Since each α_n is a root of one of the quadratic equations

$$A_1 x^2 + B_1 x + C_1 = 0$$
$$A_2 x^2 + B_2 x + C_2 + 0$$
$$\cdots$$
$$A_N x^2 + B_N x + C_N = 0$$

then one of these polynomials must have at least three of the α_n as roots. Since a quadratic equation can have at most two distinct roots, then two of these α_n must be equal, say

$$\alpha_k = \alpha_{k+t}$$

By the algorithm developed in the proof of Theorem 9, it follows that

$$a_{k+1} = a_{k+t+1}$$

$$a_{k+2} = a_{k+t+2}$$

$$\cdots$$

$$a_{k+j} = a_{k+t+j}$$

$$\cdots$$

Thus,

$$\alpha = \langle a_1, a_2, \cdots, a_k, \overline{a_{k+1}, \cdots, a_{k+t}} \rangle$$

We have established that an irrational number has a periodic expression as a continued fraction if, and only if, it is a quadratic irrational. We will now investigate those quadratic irrationals that have purely periodic expansions.

■ **DEFINITION** / Let $\alpha = a + b\sqrt{D}$ where a and b are rational and $\sqrt{D}$ is irrational. The *conjugate* of α, denoted by α', is the number $a - b\sqrt{D}$.

■ **THEOREM 19** / Let α be a quadratic irrational. The simple continued fraction expansion of α is purely periodic if, and only if, $\alpha > 1$ and $-1 < \alpha' < 0$.

PROOF: (Part I) Suppose $\alpha = \langle \overline{a_1, a_2, \cdots, a_n} \rangle$. Since each of the a's is a positive integer, then $\alpha > 1$. In the lemma preceding Theorem 16 we established that α is a root of

$$f(x) = Q_n x^2 + (Q_{n-1} - P_n)x - P_{n-1} = 0$$

Since

$$f(-1) = (Q_n - Q_{n-1}) + (P_n - P_{n-1}) > 0$$

and

$$f(0) = -P_{n-1} < 0$$

then α', the other root of $f(x) = 0$, must be between -1 and 0.

(Part II) Suppose α is a quadratic irrational, $\alpha > 1$, and $-1 < \alpha' < 0$. Let $\alpha_0 = \alpha$. If we develop the continued fraction expansion of α as in the algorithm in the proof of Theorem 9, we obtain (using the fact that the conjugate of the sum equals the sum of the conjugates, etc.)

$$\alpha_0 = a_1 + \frac{1}{\alpha_1} \qquad\qquad \alpha'_0 = a_1 + \frac{1}{\alpha'_1}$$

$$\alpha_1 = a_2 + \frac{1}{\alpha_2} \qquad\qquad \alpha'_1 = a_2 + \frac{1}{\alpha'_2}$$

$$\cdots \qquad\qquad\qquad \cdots$$

$$\alpha_k = a_{k+1} + \frac{1}{\alpha_{k+1}} \qquad\qquad \alpha'_k = a_{k+1} + \frac{1}{\alpha'_{k+1}}$$

$$\cdots \qquad\qquad\qquad \cdots$$

We established in the proof of Theorem 9 that $\alpha_k > 1$ ($k = 1, 2, \cdots$) and we know from the hypothesis that $\alpha_0 > 1$. Thus, $\alpha_k > 1$ for all nonnegative k. It can be proved easily by mathematical induction that

$$-1 < \alpha'_k < 0 \ (k = 0, 1, 2, \cdots)$$

Since

$$\alpha'_k = a_{k+1} + \frac{1}{\alpha'_{k+1}}$$

then

$$0 < -\frac{1}{\alpha'_{k+1}} - a_{k+1} < 1$$

Thus,

$$\left[-\frac{1}{\alpha'_{k+1}} \right] - a_{k+1} = \left[-\frac{1}{\alpha'_{k+1}} - a_{k+1} \right] = 0$$

which implies that

$$a_{k+1} = \left[-\frac{1}{\alpha'_{k+1}} \right]$$

Since $\alpha = \langle a_1, a_2, \cdots, a_n, \alpha_n \rangle$ ($n = 1, 2, \cdots$) and α is a quadratic irrational, we know there exist positive integers k and t such that

$$\alpha_k = \alpha_{k+t}$$

Thus,

$$a_k = \left[-\frac{1}{\alpha'_k} \right] = \left[-\frac{1}{\alpha'_{k+t}} \right] = a_{k+t}$$

and

$$\alpha_{k-1} = a_k + \frac{1}{\alpha_k} = a_{k+t} + \frac{1}{\alpha_{k+t}} = \alpha_{k+t-1}$$

If we apply this process k times, we obtain

$$\alpha_k = \alpha_{k+t}$$

$$\alpha_{k-1} = \alpha_{k+t-1}$$

$$\alpha_{k-2} = \alpha_{k+t-2}$$

$$\cdots$$

$$\alpha = \alpha_0 = \alpha_t$$

Therefore, $\qquad \alpha = \langle a_1, \cdots, a_t, \alpha \rangle = \langle \overline{a_1, \cdots, a_t} \rangle$

■ **COROLLARY 19.1** / If the positive integer D is not a square, then

$$\sqrt{D} = \langle a_1, \overline{a_2, \cdots, a_n, 2a_1} \rangle$$

where $\qquad a_1 = [\sqrt{D}]$

PROOF: Let $\alpha = \sqrt{D} + [\sqrt{D}]$. Since $\alpha > 1$ and $-1 < \alpha' < 0$, the continued fraction expansion of α is purely periodic and the first term in the expansion is

$$[\alpha] = 2[\sqrt{D}]$$

Thus $\qquad \alpha = \sqrt{D} + [\sqrt{D}] = \langle \overline{2[\sqrt{D}], a_2, \cdots, a_n, 2[\sqrt{D}]} \rangle$

and $\qquad \sqrt{D} = \alpha - [\sqrt{D}] = \langle [\sqrt{D}], \overline{a_2, \cdots, a_n, 2[\sqrt{D}]} \rangle$

EXERCISES

1. Let α be a quadratic irrational. Let a, b, c, d be rational numbers, not both c and d equal to zero. Prove that

$$\frac{a + b\alpha}{c + d\alpha}$$

is either a rational number or a quadratic irrational. [*Hint:* rationalize the denominator.]

2. *Prove:* $(\alpha + \beta)' = \alpha' + \beta'$, $(\alpha\beta)' = \alpha'\beta'$, and $(\alpha/\beta)' = \alpha'/\beta'$.

3. Expand as simple continued fractions:

   (*a*) $\sqrt{33}$;
   (*b*) $\sqrt{47}$;
   (*c*) $\sqrt{94}$.

PROBLEMS

1. Let m be a positive integer, $D = m^2 + 1$. Prove that
$$\sqrt{D} = \langle m, \overline{2m} \rangle$$

2. Let m be an integer greater than 1, let $D = m^2 - 1$. Prove that
$$\sqrt{D} = \langle m - 1, \overline{1, 2(m - 1)} \rangle$$

12.9 / APPLICATION TO PELL'S EQUATION

The first result in this section shows that any solution of Pell's equation can be obtained from the convergents to $\sqrt{D}$.

■ **THEOREM 20** / Let D be a positive integer that is not a square and let n be an integer that is less that $\sqrt{D}$ in absolute value. If x_0, y_0 is a positive solution of
$$x^2 - y^2 D = n$$
then x_0/y_0 is one of the convergents to $\sqrt{D}$.

PROOF: Suppose $n > 0$. Since x_0, y_0 is a positive solution of $x^2 - y^2 D = n$, then
$$(x_0 - y_0\sqrt{D})(x_0 + y_0\sqrt{D}) = n$$
which implies that
$$x_0 > y_0\sqrt{D}$$
Therefore,
$$0 < \frac{x_0}{y_0} - \sqrt{D} = \frac{n}{y_0(x_0 + y_0\sqrt{D})} < \frac{n}{y_0(y_0\sqrt{D} + y_0\sqrt{D})}$$
$$< \frac{\sqrt{D}}{2y_0{}^2\sqrt{D}}$$

It follows from Theorem 13 that x_0/y_0 is a convergent to $\sqrt{D}$.

If $n < 0$, then by a proof similar to the above, we find that y_0/x_0 is a convergent to $1/\sqrt{D}$. Using Theorem 11, we conclude that x_0/y_0 is a convergent to $\sqrt{D}$.

■ **COROLLARY 20.1** / If x_0, y_0 is a positive solution of $x^2 - y^2 D = \pm 1$, then

$$x_0 = P_n, \; y_0 = Q_n$$

where P_n/Q_n is a convergent to $\sqrt{D}$.

PROOF: From Theorem 20 we know that $x_0/y_0 = P_n/Q_n$.

Since the fractions are reduced to lowest terms, then

$$x_0 = P_n, \; y_0 = Q_n$$

Before proving that Pell's equation has a solution, we need one additional fact about the continued fraction expansion of $\sqrt{D}$.

■ **LEMMA** / Let D be a positive integer that is not a square. Write $\sqrt{D} = \langle a_1, a_2, \cdots, a_n, \alpha_n \rangle$. There exist positive integers b_n and c_n such that

$$\alpha_n = \frac{b_n + \sqrt{D}}{c_n}$$

and

$$P_n{}^2 - DQ_n{}^2 = (-1)^n c_n$$

PROOF: Since $\sqrt{D}$ is a root of $x^2 - D = 0$, then by Theorem 17, α_n is a root of

$$A_n x^2 + B_n x + C_n = 0$$

where

$$A_n = P_n{}^2 - DQ_n{}^2$$

$$B_n = 2P_n P_{n-1} - 2DQ_n Q_{n-1}$$

$$C_n = P_{n-1}{}^2 - DQ_{n-1}{}^2$$

and

$$B_n{}^2 - 4A_n C_n = 4D$$

Note that A_n is positive if n is even, and negative if n is odd. Thus, we may write $A_n = (-1)^n c_n$ where c_n is a positive integer. Therefore,

$$P_n{}^2 - DQ_n{}^2 = A_n = (-1)^n c_n$$

as was to be proved. From the quadratic formula we obtain

$$\alpha_n = \frac{-B_n \pm 2\sqrt{D}}{2A_n} = \frac{-B_n \pm 2\sqrt{D}}{(-1)^n 2c_n}$$

We established in Corollary 19.1 that the continued fraction expansion of α_n is purely periodic. Therefore, by Theorem 19,

$$1 < \alpha_n = \frac{-B_n \pm 2\sqrt{D}}{(-1)^n 2c_n}$$

and

$$-1 < \alpha'_n = \frac{-B_n \mp 2\sqrt{D}}{(-1)^n 2c_n} < 0$$

Adding, we obtain

$$0 < \alpha_n + \alpha'_n = \frac{-B_n}{(-1^n c_n)}$$

so that B_n is positive if n is odd, and negative if n is even. From the formula for B_n we see that B_n is even. Thus, we can write

$$B_n = (-1)^{n+1} 2b_n$$

where b_n is a positive integer. If we subtract the above inequalities, we obtain

$$1 < \alpha_n - \alpha'_n = \frac{\pm 2\sqrt{D}}{(-1)^n c_n}$$

so that the sign of $\pm\sqrt{D}$ is the same as that of $(-1)^n$. Therefore,

$$\alpha_n = \frac{-B_n + (-1)^n 2\sqrt{D}}{(-1)^n 2c_n} = \frac{(-1)^{n+2} 2b_n + (-1)^n 2\sqrt{D}}{(-1)^n 2c_n} = \frac{b_n + \sqrt{D}}{c_n}$$

■ **THEOREM 21 /** Let D be a positive integer that is not a square. Let m be the period of the expansion of $\sqrt{D}$ as a simple continued fraction.
 (a) If m is even, the positive solutions of $x^2 - y^2 D = 1$ are

$$x = P_{km}, \ y = Q_{km} \qquad (k = 1, 2, 3, \cdots)$$

The diophantine equation $x^2 - y^2 D = -1$ has no solution.
 (b) If m is odd, the positive solutions of $x^2 - y^2 D = 1$ are

$$x = P_{km}, \ y = Q_{km} \qquad (k = 2, 4, 6, \cdots)$$

The positive solutions of $x^2 - y^2 D = -1$ are

$$x = P_{km}, \ y = Q_{km} \qquad (k = 1, 3, 5, \cdots)$$

PROOF: By Corollary 20.1 we know that any positive solution x_0, y_0 of $x^2 - Dy^2 = \pm 1$ is of form $x_0 = P_n, y_0 = Q_n$ where P_n/Q_n is a convergent to $\sqrt{D}$. By the lemma we know that

$$P_n^2 - DQ_n^2 = (-1)^n c_n$$

where c_n is a positive integer such that $\alpha_n = (b_n + \sqrt{D})/c_n$. Since the expansion of $\alpha = [\sqrt{D}] + \sqrt{D}$ is purely periodic with period m, we can write

$$\alpha = \overline{\langle 2a_1, a_2, \cdots, a_{km} \rangle} = \langle 2a_1, a_2, \cdots, a_{km}, \alpha \rangle$$

so that

$$\alpha_{km} = \frac{[\sqrt{D}] + \sqrt{D}}{1}$$

Thus, $c_{km} = 1$, which implies that

$$x = P_{km}, y = Q_{km}$$

is a solution of $x^2 - y^2 D = (-1)^{km}$. If m is even, then P_{km}, Q_{km} is a solution of Pell's equation for each positive integer k. If m is odd, then P_{km}, Q_{km} is a solution of Pell's equation if k is even, and is a solution of

$$x^2 - y^2 D = -1$$

if k is odd.

To prove that these are the only solutions of $x^2 - y^2 D = \pm 1$, we need only show that if $c_n = 1$, then $n \equiv 0 \pmod{m}$. Note that if $c_n = 1$, then

$$\alpha_n = b_n + \sqrt{D}$$

Because the expansion of α_n is purely periodic, then by Theorem 19,

$$-1 < \alpha'_n = b_n - \sqrt{D} < 0$$

and so

$$\sqrt{D} - 1 < b_n < \sqrt{D}$$

Because b_n is an integer, this implies that $b_n = [\sqrt{D}]$ and so

$$\alpha_n = [\sqrt{D}] + \sqrt{D}$$

which can only be the case when $n \equiv 0 \pmod{m}$.

■ COROLLARY 21.1 / Let D be a positive integer that is not a square. Let m be the period of the expansion of $\sqrt{D}$ as a simple continued fraction. The fundamental solution of Pell's equation is $x = P_m, y = Q_m$ if m is even, or $x = P_{2m}, y = Q_{2m}$ if m is odd.

EXERCISES

1. Calculate the fundamental solution of

$$x^2 - 94y^2 = 1$$

Does $x^2 - 94y^2 = -1$ have a solution?

2. For which integers, n, $0 < |n| < \sqrt{94}$, does

$$x^2 - 94y^2 = n$$

have a solution?

12.10* / THE DIOPHANTINE EQUATION $x^2 - y^2 D = n$

The diophantine equation

$$x^2 - y^2 D = n \tag{12.5}$$

was considered briefly in Theorem 20. We established that if $0 < |n| < \sqrt{D}$, any positive solution of this equation satisfies $x/y = P_k/Q_k$ for some positive integer k. Let m be the period of the expansion of $\sqrt{D}$. If (12.5) has a solution for $0 < |n| < \sqrt{D}$, it follows from the lemma preceding Theorem 21 that an infinity of solutions exist, at least one obtained from the first m convergents or from the first $2m$ convergents, accordingly as m is even or odd. Consequently, in this section we will be primarily interested in solving Equation (12.5) when $|n| > \sqrt{D}$.

▪ **DEFINITION** / A solution x_0, y_0 of $x^2 - y^2 D = n$ is said to be *primitive* if x_0 and y_0 are relatively prime.

It is obviously sufficient to obtain only primitive solutions, because if $(x_0, y_0) = d > 1$, then x_0/d, y_0/d is a primitive solution of

$$x^2 - y^2 D = \frac{n}{d^2}$$

▪ **THEOREM 22** / If x_0, y_0 is a primitive solution of $x^2 - y^2 D = n$, there exists an integer k such that

$$x_0 \equiv ky_0 \ (\text{mod } n)$$

and

$$k^2 \equiv D \ (\text{mod } n)$$

PROOF: Since x_0 and y_0 are relatively prime, then so are y_0 and n. Thus, there exists an integer k such that

$$x_0 \equiv ky_0 \ (\text{mod } n) \qquad \text{(Theorem 4 of Chapter 3)}$$

Therefore,

$$x_0^2 - Dy_0^2 \equiv k^2 y_0^2 - Dy_0^2 \equiv y_0^2(k^2 - D) \equiv 0 \ (\text{mod } n)$$

which, because $(y_0^2, n) = 1$, implies that

$$k^2 \equiv D \ (\text{mod } n)$$

■ **COROLLARY** 22.1 / If D is a quadratic nonresidue (mod n), the diophantine equation

$$x^2 - Dy^2 = n$$

has no primitive solutions.

■ **DEFINITION** / We say that the solution x_0, y_0 of Equation (12.5) *belongs to the integer k* if

$$x_0 \equiv ky_0 \pmod{n}$$

and

$$k^2 \equiv D \pmod{n}$$

It is easy to see that if (12.5) has a positive solution, then it has an infinity of such solutions. Suppose that x_0, y_0 is a solution and that s, t is a solution of the corresponding Pell's equation. If we define x_1, y_1 by

$$x_1 + y_1\sqrt{D} = (x_0 + y_0\sqrt{D})(s + t\sqrt{D})$$

it follows that x_1, y_1 is also a solution of (12.5). Because Pell's equation has an infinity of positive solutions s, t, this implies that (12.5) has an infinity of corresponding positive solutions.

■ **DEFINITION** / Two solutions x_1, y_1 and x_2, y_2 of (12.5) are said to be in the same *class* if there is a solution x_0, y_0 of (12.5) and solutions s_1, t_1 and s_2, t_2 of Pell's equation such that

$$x_1 + y_1\sqrt{D} = (x_0 + y_0\sqrt{D})(s_1 + t_1\sqrt{D})$$

and

$$x_2 + y_2\sqrt{D} = (x_0 + y_0\sqrt{D})(s_2 + t_2\sqrt{D})$$

We will now prove a fundamental theorem concerning the classes of solutions of Equation (12.5).

■ **THEOREM** 23 / Two primitive solutions of $x^2 - y^2 D = n$ are in the same class if, and only if, they belong to the same integer.

PROOF: (Part I) Suppose x_1, y_1 is a primitive solution of (12.5) and that

$$x_1 + y_1\sqrt{D} = (x_0 + y_0\sqrt{D})(s + t\sqrt{D})$$

where s, t is a solution of Pell's equation and x_0, y_0 is a solution of (12.5). Then

$$x_1 = x_0 s + y_0 t D, \qquad y_1 = x_0 t + y_0 s$$

which implies that x_0, y_0 is also a primitive solution. Thus, x_0, y_0 belongs to an integer k. Substituting, we obtain

$$y_1 k \equiv x_0 tk + y_0 sk \equiv y_0 ktk + x_0 s \equiv y_0 tD + x_0 s \equiv x_1 \pmod{n}$$

Thus, x_1, y_1 and x_0, y_0 belong to the same integer k. If x_2, y_2 is in the same class with x_1, y_1, it follows similarly that x_2, y_2 also belongs to k.

(Part II) Suppose x_1, y_1 and x_2, y_2 belong to the integer k. Then

$$\frac{x_2 + y_2\sqrt{D}}{x_1 + y_1\sqrt{D}} = \frac{(x_2 + y_2\sqrt{D})(x_1 - y_1\sqrt{D})}{(x_1 + y_1\sqrt{D})(x_1 - y_1\sqrt{D})}$$

$$= \frac{x_1 x_2 - y_1 y_2 D}{n} + \frac{x_1 y_2 - x_2 y_1}{n}\sqrt{D}$$

Since

$$x_1 \equiv y_1 k \pmod{n}, \ x_2 \equiv y_2 k \pmod{n}, \text{ and } k^2 \equiv D \pmod{n}$$

then

$$x_1 x_2 \equiv y_1 y_2 k^2 \equiv y_1 y_2 D \pmod{n}$$

and

$$x_1 y_2 \equiv y_1 y_2 k \equiv x_2 y_1 \pmod{n}$$

Thus, the two fractions in the right-hand side of (12.6) are integers, say

$$\frac{x_1 x_2 - y_1 y_2 D}{n} = s, \qquad \frac{x_1 y_2 - x_2 y_1}{n} = t$$

and so

$$\frac{x_2 + y_2\sqrt{D}}{x_1 + y_1\sqrt{D}} = s + t\sqrt{D}$$

Similarly,

$$\frac{x_2 - y_2\sqrt{D}}{x_1 - y_1\sqrt{D}} = s - t\sqrt{D}$$

Therefore,

$$s^2 - t^2 D = (s + t\sqrt{D})(s - t\sqrt{D}) = \frac{x_2 + y_2\sqrt{D}}{x_1 + y_1\sqrt{D}} \cdot \frac{x_2 - y_2\sqrt{D}}{x_1 - y_1\sqrt{D}}$$

$$= \frac{n}{n} = 1$$

which means that s, t is a solution of Pell's equation. Since

$$x_2 + y_2\sqrt{D} = (x_1 + y_1\sqrt{D})(s + t\sqrt{D})$$

then x_1, y_1 and x_2, y_2 are in the same class.

■ **COROLLARY 23.1 /** The number of classes of primitive solutions of $x^2 - y^2 D = n$ is finite.

We will now develop a method to solve (12.5) when $|n| > \sqrt{D}$. This method, a variation on one due to Lagrange, reduces the problem to that of solving a related diophantine equation

$$x^2 - y^2 D = m$$

where

$$|m| < |n|$$

▪ THEOREM 24 / Let k be an integer such that $k^2 \equiv D \pmod{n}$. Let

$$m = \frac{k^2 - D}{n}$$

The diophantine equation $x^2 - y^2 D = n$ has a positive solution belonging to the integer k if, and only if,

$$t^2 - u^2 D = m$$

has a solution t_0, u_0 (not necessarily positive) belonging to k such that

$$\frac{ku_0 - t_0}{m} > 0$$

and

$$\frac{u_0 D - kt_0}{m} > 0$$

If this is the case, then

$$x_0 = \frac{u_0 D - kt_0}{m}, \qquad y_0 = \frac{ku_0 - t_0}{m}$$

is a positive solution of $x^2 - y^2 D = n$, belonging to k.

PROOF: If x_0, y_0 is a positive solution of (12.5) which belongs to k, we can write

$$x_0 = y_0 k - u_0 n, \quad D = k^2 - mn$$

where u_0 is an integer. If we substitute these values of x_0 and D into (12.5) and simplify, we obtain

$$y_0^2 m - 2y_0 k u_0 + (u_0^2 n - 1) = 0$$

which, by the quadratic formula, implies that

$$y_0 = \frac{ku_0 \pm \sqrt{k^2 u_0^2 - mu_0^2 n + m}}{m} = \frac{ku_0 \pm \sqrt{Du_0^2 + m}}{m}$$

Because y_0 is an integer, the value of the radical $\sqrt{Du_0^2 + m}$ must be an integer, t_0, implying that t_0, u_0 is a solution of the diophantine equation

$$t^2 - u^2 D = m$$

For the same reason we must have

$$ku_0 \pm t_0 \equiv 0 \pmod{m}$$

By varying the sign of t_0 we may assume that

$$ku_0 \equiv t_0 \pmod{m}$$

so that t_0, u_0 belongs to the integer k. Thus,

$$y_0 = \frac{ku_0 - t_0}{m}$$

and

$$x_0 = y_0 k - u_0 n = \frac{k^2 u_0 - k t_0 - u_0 mn}{m} = \frac{u_0 D - k t_0}{m}$$

which implies that

$$\frac{ku_0 - t_0}{m} \quad \text{and} \quad \frac{u_0 D - k t_0}{m}$$

are positive.

To prove the converse, suppose that t_0, u_0 is a solution of $t^2 - u^2 D = m$ which belongs to k, and that

$$\frac{ku_0 - t_0}{m} > 0, \quad \frac{u_0 D - k t_0}{m} > 0$$

Define x_0 and y_0 by

$$x_0 = \frac{u_0 D - k t_0}{m}, \quad y_0 = \frac{ku_0 - t_0}{m}$$

By reversing the above steps, we find that

$$x_0 = y_0 k - u_0 n$$

so that x_0 is an integer congruent to $y_0 k \pmod{n}$, and

$$x_0^2 - y_0^2 D = n$$

In the above proof the inequalities

$$\frac{ku_0 - t_0}{m} > 0$$

and

$$\frac{u_0 D - k t_0}{m} > 0$$

are only needed to insure that x_0, y_0 is positive. If we drop the requirement that x_0, y_0 is to be positive, we obtain $|x_0|$, $|y_0|$ as a positive solution which may belong to $-k$ rather than k. By a simple modification in the above proof we obtain the following theorem:

■ THEOREM 25 / Let k and m be as in Theorem 24. The diophantine equation $x^2 - y^2 D = n$ has a positive solution belonging to $\pm k$ if, and only if, the equation

$$t^2 - u^2 D = m$$

has a positive solution t_0, u_0 belonging to $\pm k$. If this is the case,

$$x_0 = \left| \frac{u_0 D \pm k t_0}{m} \right|, \qquad y_0 = \left| \frac{t_0 \pm k u_0}{m} \right|$$

is a positive solution of $x^2 - y^2 D = n$ which belongs to $\pm k$, the sign being chosen so that $t_0 \pm k u_0 \equiv 0 \pmod{m}$.

If $|n| > \sqrt{D}$, the number m (in Theorems 24 and 25) is either less than $\sqrt{D}$ in absolute value or is less than $|n|/4$. To prove this, we note that k can obviously be picked in the range $0 \le |k| \le n/2$. If $k^2 - D > 0$, then

$$|m| = \left| \frac{k^2 - D}{n} \right| < \frac{k^2}{|n|} \le \frac{|n/2|^2}{|n|} = \frac{|n|}{4}$$

If $k^2 - D < 0$, then

$$|m| = \left| \frac{k^2 - D}{n} \right| \le \frac{D}{|n|} < \frac{D}{\sqrt{D}} = \sqrt{D}$$

By applying the method repeatedly, we eventually obtain an equation

$$t'^2 - u'^2 D = m'$$

where $|m'| < \sqrt{D}$. A word of caution: In applying the method repeatedly we must pick different values of k at each step.

Example I.

Show that $x^2 + 13y^2 = 51$ has a solution.

SOLUTION: We find that $k = \pm 8$, $s = 1$. The auxiliary equation to be solved is

$$t^2 - 13u^2 = 1$$

The fundamental solution of this equation is

$$t = P_{10} = 649, \; u = Q_{10} = 180$$

Because this solution belongs to 8 (and to -8 as well), we obtain

$$x_0 = \left| \frac{180 \cdot 13 - 8 \cdot 649}{1} \right| = 2852$$

$$y_0 = \left| \frac{649 - 8 \cdot 180}{1} \right| = 791$$

Note that this solution belongs to -8, rather than to 8.

Example 2.

Show that $x^2 - 82y^2 = 23$ has no solution.

SOLUTION: We find that $k = \pm 6$ are the only values of k in the range

$$0 \le |k| \le \frac{23}{2}$$

such that $k^2 \equiv 82 \pmod{23}$. Thus

$$m = \frac{k^2 - D}{n} = \frac{36 - 82}{23} = -2$$

Since $\sqrt{82} = \langle 9, \overline{18} \rangle$, the only equations of form

$$x^2 - 82y^2 = n \qquad (0 < |n| < \sqrt{82})$$

that have solutions are

$$x^2 - 82y^2 = \pm 1$$

Thus, $\qquad\qquad\qquad x^2 - 82y^2 = m = -2$

has no solution, and, by Theorem 24, $x^2 - 82y^2 = 23$ has no solution.

EXERCISES

1. Determine the classes of solutions for the following equations:
   (*a*) $x^2 - 23y^2 = 43$;
   (*b*) $x^2 - 23y^2 = 41$.

2. Prove that solutions x_1, y_1 and x_2, y_2 of $x^2 - y^2 D = n$ are in the same class if, and only if,

$$x_1 x_2 - y_1 y_2 D \equiv y_1 x_2 - x_1 y_2 \equiv 0 \pmod{D}$$

12.11* / LATTICE POINTS ON CONICS

The theorems in Sections 12.9 and 12.10 can be interpreted as statements about lattice points on certain hyperbolas in the XY-plane. The problem of determining the lattice points on a given conic will now be considered. We obviously may restrict our investigation to conics that have defining equations with integral coefficients.

THE ELLIPSE

An ellipse (or circle) can have at most a finite number of lattice points which can be found by trial.

THE PARABOLA

The defining equation for a parabola can be written in the form

$$(ax + by)^2 + cx + dy + e = 0 \qquad (12.7)$$

where the coefficients are integers and $D = ad - bc \neq 0$ (see Problem 1). If we let $z = ax + by$, we obtain the system of equations

$$\begin{cases} ax + by = z \\ cx + dy = -z^2 - e \end{cases}$$

that has the unique solution

$$x = \frac{bz^2 + dz + be}{D}, \; y = -\frac{az^2 + cz + ae}{D}$$

Consequently, x, y is an integral solution of (12.7) if, and only if, there is an integer z_0 which satisfies the system of congruences

$$\begin{cases} az^2 + cz + ae \equiv 0 \,(\text{mod } D) \\ bz^2 + dz + be \equiv 0 \,(\text{mod } D) \end{cases} \qquad (12.8)$$

Obviously, any solution z_0 of (12.8) will determine a class of solutions of (12.7); that is, those solutions corresponding to values of z which are congruent to z_0 (mod D). If x_0, y_0 is the solution of (12.7) corresponding to z_0, the general solution in this class can be written in parametric form as

$$x = f(k) = \frac{b(z_0 + kD)^2 + d(z_0 + kD) + be}{D}$$

$$= x_0 + (2bz_0 + d)k + bDk^2$$

$$y = g(k) = y_0 - (2az_0 + c)k - aDk^2 \qquad (k = 0, \pm 1, \pm 2, \cdots)$$

Example I.

The equation

$$(2x + 3y)^2 + x - 3y + 7 = 0$$

leads to the system of congruences

$$\begin{cases} 2z^2 + z \equiv 4 \;(\text{mod } 9) \\ 3z^2 - 3z \equiv 6 \;(\text{mod } 9) \end{cases}$$

which has no solution. Consequently, no lattice points lie on the graph of the given equation.

Example 2.

Find all lattice points on the graph of

$$(7x - y)^2 - x + y + 6 = 0$$

SOLUTION: Following the steps described above we find that z must satisfy

$$\begin{cases} 7z^2 - z + 42 \equiv 0 \ (\text{mod } 6) \\ -z^2 + z - 6 \equiv 0 \ (\text{mod } 6) \end{cases}$$

This system has four incongruent solutions (mod 6): $z_0 = 0, 1, 3, 4$. The four corresponding classes of solutions are

$$\begin{cases} x = -1 + k - 6k^2 \\ y = -7 + k - 42k^2 \end{cases} \qquad \begin{cases} x = -1 - k - 6k^2 \\ y = -8 + 13k - 42k^2 \end{cases}$$

$$\begin{cases} x = -2 - 5k - 6k^2 \\ y = -17 - 41k - 42k^2 \end{cases} \qquad \begin{cases} x = -3 - 7k - 6k^2 \\ y = -25 - 55k - 42k^2 \end{cases}$$

THE HYPERBOLA

The problem of determining all lattice points on a hyperbola is much more difficult. Consequently, we will restrict ourselves to the special case where the equation of the hyperbola can be written in the form

$$Ax^2 + Bxy + Cy^2 = D \qquad A \neq 0$$

It is obviously no restriction to assume that B is even. Thus, we may rewrite the above equation as

$$ax^2 + 2bxy + cy^2 = d \qquad a \neq 0 \tag{12.9}$$

If we multiply this equation by a and make the substitution

$$x = \frac{s - bt}{a}, \, y = t$$

it is transformed into the equation

$$s^2 - (b^2 - ac)t^2 = ad \tag{12.10}$$

It is easy to verify that any solution s_0, t_0 of (12.10) that satisfies

$$s_0 \equiv bt_0 \ (\text{mod } a)$$

will generate a solution

$$x_0 = \frac{s_0 - bt_0}{a}, \, y_0 = t_0$$

of (12.9). Thus, the problem of solving (12.9) reduces to that of solving (12.10), subject to the side condition $s \equiv bt \ (\text{mod } a)$.

Example 3.

Find all solutions of

$$2x^2 - 14xy + 13y^2 = 1$$

SOLUTION: The substitution

$$x = \frac{s + 7t}{2}, y = t$$

transforms the given equation into

$$s^2 - 23t^2 = 2 \tag{12.11}$$

which must be solved subject to the side condition

$$s + 7t \equiv s + t \equiv 0 \pmod{2}$$

The fundamental solution of Pell's equation

$$u^2 - 23v^2 = 1$$

is $u_1 = 24$, $v_1 = 5$. Equation (12.11) has only one class of solutions, in which the smallest positive solution is $s = 5$, $t = 1$. Thus, all solutions of (12.11) are of form $\pm s_n$, $\pm t_n$, where

$$s_n + t_n \sqrt{23} = (5 + \sqrt{23})(24 + 5\sqrt{23})^n$$

or

$$s_n + t_n \sqrt{23} = (-5 + \sqrt{23})(24 + 5\sqrt{23})^n$$

and these solutions generate all solution of

$$2x^2 - 14xy + 13y^2 = 1$$

For example, when $n = 1$ we obtain $s = 235$, $t = 49$ from the first equation and $s = 5$, $t = -1$ from the second. The corresponding values of x and y are

$$x = \pm 289, y = \pm 49 \qquad x = \pm 1, y = \pm 1$$

EXERCISES

Find all lattice points on the following conics.

1. $(3x + 7y)^2 + 5x - y - 12 = 0$

2. $(8x + 5y)^2 - x + 2y - 9 = 0$

3. $3x^2 + 12xy + 7y^2 = -2$

PROBLEM

1. Let $f(x)$ be an equation with integral coefficients which has a parabola as its graph. Show that the equation can be rewritten in the form

$$(ax + by)^2 + cx + dy + e = 0$$

where $ad - bc \neq 0$. [*Hint*: If $f(x) = Ax^2 + Bxy + Cy^2 + Dx + Ey + F = 0$, then $B^2 - 4AC = 0$.]

12.12* / REMARKS ON HIGHER ORDER DIOPHANTINE EQUATIONS

Let $f(x, y)$ be an integral polynomial in two variables of degree n. The problem of solving the diophantine equation $f(x, y) = 0$ has been considered for the special cases $n = 1$ and $n = 2$ (Chapters 2 and 12).

If $n = 1$, an infinity of solutions exist (if any exist at all) and they are distributed in a regular pattern. If $n = 2$, it is possible that $f(x, y) = 0$ may have an infinity of solutions, but they are no longer distributed in a simple manner. In most cases an equation of degree 3 or higher will have at most a finite number of solutions.

In 1909, A. Thue proved that a diophantine equation of form

$$a_n x^n + a_{n-1} x^{n-1} y + \cdots + a_1 xy^{n-1} + a_0 y^n = d \qquad (n \geq 3) \quad (12.12)$$

has at most a finite number of solutions unless the left-hand side is a power of a linear or quadratic polynomial with integral coefficients. If this is the case, Equation (12.12) can be written as

$$(ax + by)^m = d$$

or
$$(ax^2 + bxy + cy^2)^m = d$$

If a solution exists, then d must be the mth power of an integer d' and any solution of

$$ax + by = d'$$

or
$$ax^2 + bxy + cy^2 = d'$$

is a solution of (12.12).

In 1921, C. L. Siegel proved that if $f(x, y)$ is an irreducible polynomial[2] of degree greater than 2, then the diophantine equation $f(x, y) = 0$ can have at

---

[2] "Irreducible" means that $f(x, y)$ can not be factored as a product of two polynomials of lower degree, each with integral coefficients.

most a finite number of solutions unless the following special condition holds: There exist numbers $a_n, a_{n-1}, \cdots, a_0, a_{-1}, \cdots, a_{-n}$ and $b_n, b_{n-1}, \cdots, b_0, b_{-1}, \cdots, b_{-n}$ such that if we make the substitution

$$x = g(z) = a_n z^n + \cdots + a_1 z + a_0 + \frac{a_{-1}}{z} + \cdots + \frac{a_{-n}}{z^n}$$

$$y = h(z) = b_n z^n + \cdots + b_1 z + b_0 + \frac{b_{-1}}{z} + \cdots + \frac{b_{-n}}{z^n}$$

the expression $F(z) = f(g(z), h(z))$ is identically zero.

REFERENCES

GENERAL REFERENCES

Dickson, L. E., *History of the Theory of Numbers*. Three vols. Carnegie Institution of Washington; reprinted New York: Chelsea, 1950.

Hardy, G. H., and E. M. Wright, *An Introduction to the Theory of Numbers*, 4th edition. New York: Oxford University Press, 1960.

LeVeque, W. J., *Topics in Number Theory*. Two vols. Reading, Massachusetts: Addison-Wesley, 1956.

Nagell, T., *Introduction to Number Theory*. New York: John Wiley, 1951.

Niven, I., and H. S. Zuckerman, *An Introduction to the Theory of Numbers*. New York: John Wiley, 1960.

Ore, O., *Number Theory and Its History*. New York: McGraw-Hill, 1949.

Rademacher, H., *Lectures on Elementary Number Theory*. New York: Blaisdell, 1964.

Uspensky, J. V., and M. H. Heaslet, *Elementary Number Theory*. New York: McGraw-Hill, 1939.

Vinogradov, I. M., *Elements of Number Theory*, translation of 5th Russian edition. New York: Dover, 1954.

SPECIAL REFERENCES

Chapter 2

Colebrooke, H. T., *Algebra with Arithmetic and Mensuration from the Sanscrit of Brahmegupta and Bhaskara*. London, 1817.

Ore, Chaps. 6 and 7.

Rangacarya, M., *The Ganita-Sara-Sangraha of Mahaviracarya*, with English translation and notes. Madras, 1912.

Chapter 3

Uspensky and Heaslet, Appendices on Calendar Problems, Card Shuffling, and Magic Squares.

Chapter 6

Ore, Chap. 5.
McCarthy, P. J., "Odd Perfect Numbers," *Scripta Mathematica*, **23** (1957), 43–47.

Chapter 7

Cashwell, E. D., and C. J. Everett, "The Ring of Number-Theoretic Functions," *Pacific Journal of Mathematics*, **9** (1959), 975–985.

Chapter 9

Brauer, A., and T. L. Reynolds, "On a Theorem of Aubry-Thue," *Canadian Journal of Mathematics*, **3** (1951), 367–374.

Chapter 11

Inkeri, K., "Abschätzungen für eventuelle Lösungen der Gleichung im Fermatschen Problem," *Annales Universitatis Turkuensis*, Series A, No. 1, 1953. See also the review of this paper, *Mathematical Reviews*, **15** (1954), 401.
Ore, Chap. 8.
Scientific American, **209** (August, 1963), 114–116.
Vandiver, H. S., "Fermat's Last Theorem, Its History, and the Nature of the Known Results Concerning It," *American Mathematical Monthly*, **53** (1946), 555–578.

Chapter 12

Gelfond, A. O., *The Solution of Equations in Integers*, translated from the Russian by J. B. Roberts. San Francisco: Freeman, 1961.
Hardy and Wright, Chaps. 4, 10, and 11.
Nagell, Chaps. 6 and 7.
Niven, I., *Irrational Numbers*, Carus Monograph 11. New York: John Wiley, 1956.

Table I / *Prime Numbers less than 5000*

2	179	419	661	947	1229	1523	1823	2131
3	181	421	673	953	1231	1531	1831	2137
5	191	431	677	967	1237	1543	1847	2141
7	193	433	683	971	1249	1549	1861	2143
11	197	439	691	977	1259	1553	1867	2153
13	199	443	701	983	1277	1559	1871	2161
17	211	449	709	991	1279	1567	1873	2179
19	223	457	719	997	1283	1571	1877	2203
23	227	461	727	1009	1289	1579	1879	2207
29	229	463	733	1013	1291	1583	1889	2213
31	233	467	739	1019	1297	1597	1901	2221
37	239	479	743	1021	1301	1601	1907	2237
41	241	487	751	1031	1303	1607	1913	2239
43	251	491	757	1033	1307	1609	1931	2243
47	257	499	761	1039	1319	1613	1933	2251
53	263	503	769	1049	1321	1619	1949	2267
59	269	509	773	1051	1327	1621	1951	2269
61	271	521	787	1061	1361	1627	1973	2273
67	277	523	797	1063	1367	1637	1979	2281
71	281	541	809	1069	1373	1657	1987	2287
73	283	547	811	1087	1381	1663	1993	2293
79	293	557	821	1091	1399	1667	1997	2297
83	307	563	823	1093	1409	1669	1999	2309
89	311	569	827	1097	1423	1693	2003	2311
97	313	571	829	1103	1427	1697	2011	2333
101	317	577	839	1109	1429	1699	2017	2339
103	331	587	853	1117	1433	1709	2027	2341
107	337	593	857	1123	1439	1721	2029	2347
109	347	599	859	1129	1447	1723	2039	2351
113	349	601	863	1151	1451	1733	2053	2357
127	353	607	877	1153	1453	1741	2063	2371
131	359	613	881	1163	1459	1747	2069	2377
137	367	617	883	1171	1471	1753	2081	2381
139	373	619	887	1181	1481	1759	2083	2383
149	379	631	907	1187	1483	1777	2087	2389
151	383	641	911	1193	1487	1783	2089	2393
157	389	643	919	1201	1489	1787	2099	2399
163	397	647	929	1213	1493	1789	2111	2411
167	401	653	937	1217	1499	1801	2113	2417
173	409	659	941	1223	1511	1811	2129	2423

Table I (continued)

2437	2749	3083	3433	3733	4073	4421	4759
2441	2753	3089	3449	3739	4079	4423	4783
2447	2767	3109	3457	3761	4091	4441	4787
2459	2777	3119	3461	3767	4093	4447	4789
2467	2789	3121	3463	3769	4099	4451	4793
2473	2791	3137	3467	3779	4111	4457	4799
2477	2797	3163	3469	3793	4127	4463	4801
2503	2801	3167	3491	3797	4129	4481	4813
2521	2803	3169	3499	3803	4133	4483	4817
2531	2819	3181	3511	3821	4139	4493	4831
2539	2833	3187	3517	3823	4153	4507	4861
2543	2837	3191	3527	3833	4157	4513	4871
2549	2843	3203	3529	3847	4159	4517	4877
2551	2851	3209	3533	3851	4177	4519	4889
2557	2857	3217	3539	3853	4201	4523	4903
2579	2861	3221	3541	3863	4211	4547	4909
2591	2879	3229	3547	3877	4217	4549	4919
2593	2887	3251	3557	3881	4219	4561	4931
2609	2897	3253	3559	3889	4229	4567	4933
2617	2903	3257	3571	3907	4231	4583	4937
2621	2909	3259	3581	3911	4241	4591	4943
2633	2917	3271	3583	3917	4243	4597	4951
2647	2927	3299	3593	3919	4253	4603	4957
2657	2939	3301	3607	3923	4259	4621	4967
2659	2953	3307	3613	3929	4261	4637	4969
2663	2957	3313	3617	3931	4271	4639	4973
2671	2963	3319	3623	3943	4273	4643	4987
2677	2969	3323	3631	3947	4283	4649	4993
2683	2971	3329	3637	3967	4289	4651	4999
2687	2999	3331	3643	3989	4297	4657	
2689	3001	3343	3659	4001	4327	4663	
2693	3011	3347	3671	4003	4337	4673	
2699	3019	3359	3673	4007	4339	4679	
2707	3023	3361	3677	4013	4349	4691	
2711	3037	3371	3691	4019	4357	4703	
2713	3041	3373	3697	4021	4363	4721	
2719	3049	3389	3701	4027	4373	4723	
2729	3061	3391	3709	4049	4391	4729	
2731	3067	3407	3719	4051	4397	4733	
2741	3079	3413	3727	4057	4409	4751	

Table II / *Table of Indices for Primes <100*

Modulo 17, the index of 8 is 10. The number which has index 8 is 16

	n	1	2	3	4	5	6	7	8	9	10	11	12
3	ind n	2	1										
	anti-ind n	2	1										
5	ind n	4	1	3	2								
	anti-ind n	2	4	3	1								
7	ind n	6	2	1	4	5	3						
	anti-ind n	3	2	6	4	5	1						
11	ind n	10	1	8	2	4	9	7	3	6	5		
	anti-ind n	2	4	8	5	10	9	7	3	6	1		
13	ind n	12	1	4	2	9	5	11	3	8	10	7	6
	anti-ind n	2	4	8	3	6	12	11	9	5	10	7	1
17	ind n	16	14	1	12	5	15	11	10	2	3	7	13
	anti-ind n	3	9	10	13	5	15	11	16	14	8	7	4
19	ind n	18	1	13	2	16	14	6	3	8	17	12	15
	anti-ind n	2	4	8	16	13	7	14	9	18	17	15	11
23	ind n	22	2	16	4	1	18	19	6	10	3	9	20
	anti-ind n	5	2	10	4	20	8	17	16	11	9	22	18
29	ind n	28	1	5	2	22	6	12	3	10	23	25	7
	anti-ind n	2	4	8	16	3	6	12	24	19	9	18	7
31	ind n	30	24	1	18	20	25	28	12	2	14	23	19
	anti-ind n	3	9	27	19	26	16	17	20	29	25	13	8
37	ind n	36	1	26	2	23	27	32	3	16	24	30	28
	anti-ind n	2	4	8	16	32	27	17	34	31	25	13	26
	n	1	2	3	4	5	6	7	8	9	10	11	12

Table II (continued)

	n	1	2	3	4	5	6	7	8	9	10	11	12
41	ind n	40	26	15	12	22	1	39	38	30	8	3	27
	anti-ind n	6	36	11	25	27	39	29	10	19	32	28	4
43	ind n	42	27	1	12	25	28	35	39	2	10	30	13
	anti-ind n	3	9	27	38	28	41	37	25	32	10	30	4
47	ind n	46	18	20	36	1	38	32	8	40	19	7	10
	anti-ind n	5	25	31	14	23	21	11	8	40	12	13	18
53	ind n	52	1	17	2	47	18	14	3	34	48	6	19
	anti-ind n	2	4	8	16	32	11	22	44	35	17	34	15
59	ind n	58	1	50	2	6	51	18	3	42	7	25	52
	anti-ind n	2	4	8	16	32	5	10	20	40	21	42	25
61	ind n	60	1	6	2	22	7	49	3	12	23	15	8
	anti-ind n	2	4	8	16	32	3	6	12	24	48	35	9
67	ind n	66	1	39	2	15	40	23	3	12	16	59	41
	anti-ind n	2	4	8	16	32	64	61	55	43	19	38	9
71	ind n	70	6	26	12	28	32	1	18	52	34	31	38
	anti-ind n	7	49	59	58	51	2	14	27	47	45	31	4
73	ind n	72	8	6	16	1	14	33	24	12	9	55	22
	anti-ind n	5	25	52	41	59	3	15	2	10	50	31	9
79	ind n	78	4	1	8	62	5	53	12	2	66	68	9
	anti-ind n	3	9	27	2	6	18	54	4	12	36	29	8
83	ind n	82	1	72	2	27	73	8	3	62	28	24	74
	anti-ind n	2	4	8	16	32	64	45	7	14	28	56	29
89	ind n	88	16	1	32	70	17	81	48	2	86	84	33
	anti-ind n	3	9	27	81	65	17	51	64	14	42	37	22
97	ind n	96	34	70	68	1	8	31	6	44	35	86	42
	anti-ind n	5	25	28	43	21	8	40	6	30	53	71	64
	n	1	2	3	4	5	6	7	8	9	10	11	12

Table II (continued)

	n	13	14	15	16	17	18	19	20	21	22	23	24
17	ind n	4	9	6	8								
	anti-ind n	12	2	6	1								
19	ind n	5	7	11	4	10	9						
	anti-ind n	3	6	12	5	10	1						
23	ind n	14	21	17	8	7	12	15	5	13	11		
	anti-ind n	21	13	19	3	15	6	7	12	14	1		
29	ind n	18	13	27	4	21	11	9	24	17	26	20	8
	anti-ind n	14	28	27	25	21	13	26	23	17	5	10	20
31	ind n	11	22	21	6	7	26	4	8	29	17	27	13
	anti-ind n	24	10	30	28	22	4	12	5	15	14	11	2
37	ind n	11	33	13	4	7	17	35	25	22	31	15	29
	anti-ind n	15	30	23	9	18	36	35	33	29	21	5	10
41	ind n	31	25	37	24	33	16	9	34	14	29	36	13
	anti-ind n	24	21	3	18	26	33	34	40	35	5	30	16
43	ind n	32	20	26	24	38	29	19	37	36	15	16	40
	anti-ind n	12	36	22	23	26	35	19	14	42	40	34	16
47	ind n	11	4	21	26	16	12	45	37	6	25	5	28
	anti-ind n	43	27	41	17	38	2	10	3	15	28	46	42
53	ind n	24	15	12	4	10	35	37	49	31	7	39	20
	anti-ind n	30	7	14	28	3	6	12	24	48	43	33	13
59	ind n	45	19	56	4	40	43	38	8	10	26	15	53
	anti-ind n	50	41	23	46	33	7	14	28	56	53	47	35
61	ind n	40	50	28	4	47	13	26	24	55	16	57	9
	anti-ind n	18	36	11	22	44	27	54	47	33	5	10	20
67	ind n	19	24	54	4	64	13	10	17	62	60	28	42
	anti-ind n	18	36	5	10	20	40	13	26	52	37	7	14
	n	13	14	15	16	17	18	19	20	21	22	23	24

Table II (continued)

	n	13	14	15	16	17	18	19	20	21	22	23	24
71	ind n	39	7	54	24	49	58	16	40	27	37	15	44
	anti-ind n	28	54	23	19	62	8	56	37	46	38	53	16
73	ind n	59	41	7	32	21	20	62	17	39	63	46	30
	anti-ind n	45	6	30	4	20	27	62	18	17	12	60	8
79	ind n	34	57	63	16	21	6	32	70	54	72	26	13
	anti-ind n	24	72	58	16	48	65	37	32	17	51	74	64
83	ind n	77	9	17	4	56	63	47	29	80	25	60	75
	anti-ind n	58	33	66	49	15	30	60	37	74	65	47	11
89	ind n	23	9	71	64	6	18	35	14	82	12	57	49
	anti-ind n	66	20	60	2	6	18	54	73	41	34	13	39
97	ind n	25	65	71	40	89	78	81	69	5	24	77	76
	anti-ind n	29	48	46	36	83	27	38	93	77	94	82	22
	n	13	14	15	16	17	18	19	20	21	22	23	24

	n	25	26	27	28	29	30	31	32	33	34	35	36
29	ind n	16	19	15	14								
	anti-ind n	11	22	15	1								
31	ind n	10	5	3	16	9	15						
	anti-ind n	6	18	23	7	21	1						
37	ind n	10	12	6	34	21	14	9	5	20	8	19	18
	anti-ind n	20	3	6	12	24	11	22	7	14	28	19	1
41	ind n	4	17	5	11	7	23	28	10	18	19	21	2
	anti-ind n	14	2	12	31	22	9	13	37	17	20	38	23
	n	25	26	27	28	29	30	31	32	33	34	35	36

Table II (continued)

n	25	26	27	28	29	30	31	32	33	34	35	36
43 ind n	8	17	3	5	41	11	34	9	31	23	18	14
anti-ind n	**5**	**15**	**2**	**6**	**18**	**11**	**33**	**13**	**39**	**31**	**7**	**21**
47 ind n	2	29	14	22	35	39	3	44	27	34	33	30
anti-ind n	**22**	**16**	**33**	**24**	**26**	**36**	**39**	**7**	**35**	**34**	**29**	**4**
53 ind n	42	25	51	16	46	13	33	5	23	11	9	36
anti-ind n	**26**	**52**	**51**	**49**	**45**	**37**	**21**	**42**	**31**	**9**	**18**	**36**
59 ind n	12	46	34	20	28	57	49	5	17	41	24	44
anti-ind n	**11**	**22**	**44**	**29**	**58**	**57**	**55**	**51**	**43**	**27**	**54**	**49**
61 ind n	44	41	18	51	35	29	59	5	21	48	11	14
anti-ind n	**40**	**19**	**38**	**15**	**30**	**60**	**59**	**57**	**53**	**45**	**29**	**58**
67 ind n	30	20	51	25	44	55	47	5	32	65	38	14
anti-ind n	**28**	**56**	**45**	**23**	**46**	**25**	**50**	**33**	**66**	**65**	**63**	**59**
71 ind n	56	45	8	13	68	60	11	30	57	55	29	64
anti-ind n	**41**	**3**	**21**	**5**	**35**	**32**	**11**	**6**	**42**	**10**	**70**	**64**
73 ind n	2	67	18	49	35	15	11	40	61	29	34	28
anti-ind n	**40**	**54**	**51**	**36**	**34**	**24**	**47**	**16**	**7**	**35**	**29**	**72**
79 ind n	46	38	3	61	11	67	56	20	69	25	37	10
anti-ind n	**34**	**23**	**69**	**49**	**68**	**46**	**59**	**19**	**57**	**13**	**39**	**38**
83 ind n	54	78	52	10	12	18	38	5	14	57	35	64
anti-ind n	**22**	**44**	**5**	**10**	**20**	**40**	**80**	**77**	**71**	**59**	**35**	**70**
89 ind n	52	39	3	25	59	87	31	80	85	22	63	34
anti-ind n	**28**	**84**	**74**	**44**	**43**	**40**	**31**	**4**	**12**	**36**	**19**	**57**
97 ind n	2	59	18	3	13	9	46	74	60	27	32	16
anti-ind n	**13**	**65**	**34**	**73**	**74**	**79**	**7**	**35**	**78**	**2**	**10**	**50**
n	25	26	27	28	29	30	31	32	33	34	35	36

Table II (continued)

	n	37	38	39	40	41	42	43	44	45	46	47	48
41	ind n	32	35	6	20								
	anti-ind n	15	8	7	1								
43	ind n	7	4	33	22	6	21						
	anti-ind n	20	17	8	24	29	1						
47	ind n	42	17	31	9	15	24	13	43	41	23		
	anti-ind n	20	6	30	9	45	37	44	32	19	1		
53	ind n	30	38	41	50	45	32	22	8	29	40	44	21
	anti-ind n	19	38	23	46	39	25	50	47	41	29	5	10
59	ind n	55	39	37	9	14	11	33	27	48	16	23	54
	anti-ind n	39	19	38	17	34	9	18	36	13	26	52	45
61	ind n	39	27	46	25	54	56	43	17	34	58	20	10
	anti-ind n	55	49	37	13	26	52	43	25	50	39	17	34
67	ind n	22	11	58	18	53	63	9	61	27	29	50	43
	anti-ind n	51	35	3	6	12	24	48	29	58	49	31	62
71	ind n	20	22	65	46	25	33	48	43	10	21	9	50
	anti-ind n	22	12	13	20	69	57	44	24	26	40	67	43
73	ind n	64	70	65	25	4	47	51	71	13	54	31	38
	anti-ind n	68	48	21	32	14	70	58	71	63	23	42	64
79	ind n	19	36	35	74	75	58	49	76	64	30	59	17
	anti-ind n	35	26	78	76	70	52	77	73	61	25	75	67
83	ind n	20	48	67	30	40	81	71	26	7	61	23	76
	anti-ind n	57	31	62	41	82	81	79	75	67	51	19	38
89	ind n	11	51	24	30	21	10	29	28	72	73	54	65
	anti-ind n	82	68	26	78	56	79	59	88	86	80	62	8
97	ind n	91	19	95	7	85	39	4	58	45	15	84	14
	anti-ind n	56	86	42	16	80	12	60	9	45	31	58	96
	n	37	38	39	40	41	42	43	44	45	46	47	48

Table II (continued)

n	49	50	51	52	53	54	55	56	57	58	59	60
53 ind n	28	43	27	26								
53 anti-ind n	**20**	**40**	**27**	**1**								
59 ind n	36	13	32	47	22	35	31	21	30	29		
59 anti-ind n	**31**	**3**	**6**	**12**	**24**	**48**	**37**	**15**	**30**	**1**		
61 ind n	38	45	53	42	33	19	37	52	32	36	31	30
61 anti-ind n	**7**	**14**	**28**	**56**	**51**	**41**	**21**	**42**	**23**	**46**	**31**	**1**
67 ind n	46	31	37	21	57	52	8	26	49	45	36	56
67 anti-ind n	**57**	**47**	**27**	**54**	**41**	**15**	**30**	**60**	**53**	**39**	**11**	**22**
71 ind n	2	62	5	51	23	14	59	19	42	4	3	66
71 anti-ind n	**17**	**48**	**52**	**9**	**63**	**15**	**34**	**25**	**33**	**18**	**55**	**30**
73 ind n	66	10	27	3	53	26	56	57	68	43	5	23
73 anti-ind n	**28**	**67**	**43**	**69**	**53**	**46**	**11**	**55**	**56**	**61**	**13**	**65**
79 ind n	28	50	22	42	77	7	52	65	33	15	31	71
79 anti-ind n	**43**	**50**	**71**	**55**	**7**	**21**	**63**	**31**	**14**	**42**	**47**	**62**
83 ind n	16	55	46	79	59	53	51	11	37	13	34	19
83 anti-ind n	**76**	**69**	**55**	**27**	**54**	**25**	**50**	**17**	**34**	**68**	**53**	**23**
89 ind n	74	68	7	55	78	19	66	41	36	75	43	15
89 anti-ind n	**24**	**72**	**38**	**25**	**75**	**47**	**52**	**67**	**23**	**69**	**29**	**87**
97 ind n	62	36	63	93	10	52	87	37	55	47	67	43
97 anti-ind n	**92**	**72**	**69**	**54**	**76**	**89**	**57**	**91**	**67**	**44**	**26**	**33**
n	49	50	51	52	53	54	55	56	57	58	59	60

n	61	62	63	64	65	66	67	68	69	70	71	72
67 ind n	7	48	35	6	34	33						
67 anti-ind n	**44**	**21**	**42**	**17**	**34**	**1**						
n	61	62	63	64	65	66	67	68	69	70	71	72

Table II (continued)

n	61	62	63	64	65	66	67	68	69	70	71	72
71 ind n	69	17	53	36	67	63	47	61	41	35		
anti-ind n	**68**	**50**	**66**	**36**	**39**	**60**	**65**	**29**	**61**	**1**		
73 ind n	58	19	45	48	60	69	50	37	52	42	44	36
anti-ind n	**33**	**19**	**22**	**37**	**39**	**49**	**26**	**57**	**66**	**38**	**44**	**1**
79 ind n	45	60	55	24	18	73	48	29	27	41	51	14
anti-ind n	**28**	**5**	**15**	**45**	**56**	**10**	**30**	**11**	**33**	**20**	**60**	**22**
83 ind n	66	39	70	6	22	15	45	58	50	36	33	65
anti-ind n	**46**	**9**	**18**	**36**	**72**	**61**	**39**	**78**	**73**	**63**	**43**	**3**
89 ind n	69	47	83	8	5	13	56	38	58	79	62	50
anti-ind n	**83**	**71**	**35**	**16**	**48**	**55**	**76**	**50**	**61**	**5**	**15**	**45**
97 ind n	64	80	75	12	26	94	57	61	51	66	11	50
anti-ind n	**68**	**49**	**51**	**61**	**14**	**70**	**59**	**4**	**20**	**3**	**15**	**75**
n	61	62	63	64	65	66	67	68	69	70	71	72

n	73	74	75	76	77	78	79	80	81	82	83	84
79 ind n	44	23	47	40	43	39						
anti-ind n	**66**	**40**	**41**	**44**	**53**	**1**						
83 ind n	69	21	44	49	32	68	43	31	42	41		
anti-ind n	**6**	**12**	**24**	**48**	**13**	**26**	**52**	**21**	**42**	**1**		
89 ind n	20	27	53	67	77	40	42	46	4	37	61	26
anti-ind n	**46**	**49**	**58**	**85**	**77**	**53**	**70**	**32**	**7**	**21**	**63**	**11**
97 ind n	28	29	72	53	21	33	30	41	88	23	17	73
anti-ind n	**84**	**32**	**63**	**24**	**23**	**18**	**90**	**62**	**19**	**95**	**87**	**47**
n	73	74	75	76	77	78	79	80	81	82	83	84

Table II (continued)

		85	86	87	88	89	90	91	92	93	94	95	96
89	ind n	76	45	60	44								
	anti-ind n	**33**	**10**	**30**	**1**								
97	ind n	90	38	83	92	54	79	56	49	20	22	82	48
	anti-ind n	**41**	**11**	**55**	**81**	**17**	**85**	**37**	**88**	**52**	**66**	**39**	**1**
	n	85	86	87	88	89	90	91	92	93	94	95	96

Table III / *Continued Fraction Expansion of* $\sqrt{D}$

D	$\sqrt{D}$
2	1, $\overline{2}$
3	1, $\overline{1,\ 2}$
5	2, $\overline{4}$
6	2, $\overline{2,\ 4}$
7	2, $\overline{1,\ 1,\ 1,\ 4}$
8	2, $\overline{1,\ 4}$
10	3, $\overline{6}$
11	3, $\overline{3,\ 6}$
12	3, $\overline{2,\ 6}$
13	3, $\overline{1,\ 1,\ 1,\ 1,\ 6}$
14	3, $\overline{1,\ 2,\ 1,\ 6}$
15	3, $\overline{1,\ 6}$
17	4, $\overline{8}$
18	4, $\overline{4,\ 8}$
19	4, $\overline{2,\ 1,\ 3,\ 1,\ 2,\ 8}$
20	4, $\overline{2,\ 8}$
21	4, $\overline{1,\ 1,\ 2,\ 1,\ 1,\ 8}$
22	4, $\overline{1,\ 2,\ 4,\ 2,\ 1,\ 8}$
23	4, $\overline{1,\ 3,\ 1,\ 8}$
24	4, $\overline{1,\ 8}$
26	5, $\overline{10}$
27	5, $\overline{5,\ 10}$
28	5, $\overline{3,\ 2,\ 3,\ 10}$
29	5, $\overline{2,\ 1,\ 1,\ 2,\ 10}$
30	5, $\overline{2,\ 10}$
31	5, $\overline{1,\ 1,\ 3,\ 5,\ 3,\ 1,\ 1,\ 10}$
32	5, $\overline{1,\ 1,\ 1,\ 10}$
33	5, $\overline{1,\ 2,\ 1,\ 10}$
34	5, $\overline{1,\ 4,\ 1,\ 10}$
35	5, $\overline{1,\ 10}$

Table III (continued)

D	$\sqrt{D}$
37	6, $\overline{12}$
38	6, $\overline{6,\ 12}$
39	6, $\overline{4,\ 12}$
40	6, $\overline{3,\ 12}$
41	6, $\overline{2,\ 2,\ 12}$
42	6, $\overline{2,\ 12}$
43	6, $\overline{1,\ 1,\ 3,\ 1,\ 5,\ 1,\ 3,\ 1,\ 1,\ 12}$
44	6, $\overline{1,\ 1,\ 1,\ 2,\ 1,\ 1,\ 1,\ 12}$
45	6, $\overline{1,\ 2,\ 2,\ 2,\ 1,\ 12}$
46	6, $\overline{1,\ 3,\ 1,\ 1,\ 2,\ 6,\ 2,\ 1,\ 1,\ 3,\ 1,\ 12}$
47	6, $\overline{1,\ 5,\ 1,\ 12}$
48	6, $\overline{1,\ 12}$
50	7, $\overline{14}$
51	7, $\overline{7,\ 14}$
52	7, $\overline{4,\ 1,\ 2,\ 1,\ 4,\ 14}$
53	7, $\overline{3,\ 1,\ 1,\ 3,\ 14}$
54	7, $\overline{2,\ 1,\ 6,\ 1,\ 2,\ 14}$
55	7, $\overline{2,\ 2,\ 2,\ 14}$
56	7, $\overline{2,\ 14}$
57	7, $\overline{1,\ 1,\ 4,\ 1,\ 1,\ 14}$
58	7, $\overline{1,\ 1,\ 1,\ 1,\ 1,\ 1,\ 14}$
59	7, $\overline{1,\ 2,\ 7,\ 2,\ 1,\ 14}$
60	7, $\overline{1,\ 2,\ 1,\ 14}$
61	7, $\overline{1,\ 4,\ 3,\ 1,\ 2,\ 2,\ 1,\ 3,\ 4,\ 1,\ 14}$
62	7, $\overline{1,\ 6,\ 1,\ 14}$
63	7, $\overline{1,\ 14}$
65	8, $\overline{16}$
66	8, $\overline{8,\ 16}$
67	8, $\overline{5,\ 2,\ 1,\ 1,\ 7,\ 1,\ 1,\ 2,\ 5,\ 16}$

Table III (continued)

D	$\sqrt{D}$
68	8, $\overline{4, \ 16}$
69	8, $\overline{3, \ 3, \ 1, \ 4, \ 1, \ 3, \ 3, \ 16}$
70	8, $\overline{2, \ 1, \ 2, \ 1, \ 2, \ 16}$
71	8, $\overline{2, \ 2, \ 1, \ 7, \ 1, \ 2, \ 2, \ 16}$
72	8, $\overline{2, \ 16}$
73	8, $\overline{1, \ 1, \ 5, \ 5, \ 1, \ 1, \ 16}$
74	8, $\overline{1, \ 1, \ 1, \ 1, \ 16}$
75	8, $\overline{1, \ 1, \ 1, \ 16}$
76	8, $\overline{1, \ 2, \ 1, \ 1, \ 5, \ 4, \ 5, \ 1, \ 1, \ 2, \ 1, \ 16}$
77	8, $\overline{1, \ 3, \ 2, \ 3, \ 1, \ 16}$
78	8, $\overline{1, \ 4, \ 1, \ 16}$
79	8, $\overline{1, \ 7, \ 1, \ 16}$
80	8, $\overline{1, \ 16}$
82	9, $\overline{18}$
83	9, $\overline{9, \ 18}$
84	9, $\overline{6, \ 18}$
85	9, $\overline{4, \ 1, \ 1, \ 4, \ 18}$
86	9, $\overline{3, \ 1, \ 1, \ 1, \ 8, \ 1, \ 1, \ 1, \ 3, \ 18}$
87	9, $\overline{3, \ 18}$
88	9, $\overline{2, \ 1, \ 1, \ 1, \ 2, \ 18}$
89	9, $\overline{2, \ 3, \ 3, \ 2, \ 18}$
90	9, $\overline{2, \ 18}$
91	9, $\overline{1, \ 1, \ 5, \ 1, \ 5, \ 1, \ 1, \ 18}$
92	9, $\overline{1, \ 1, \ 2, \ 4, \ 2, \ 1, \ 1, \ 18}$
93	9, $\overline{1, \ 1, \ 1, \ 4, \ 6, \ 4, \ 1, \ 1, \ 1, \ 18}$
94	9, $\overline{1, \ 2, \ 3, \ 1, \ 1, \ 5, \ 1, \ 8, \ 1, \ 5, \ 1, \ 1, \ 3, \ 2, \ 1, \ 18}$
95	9, $\overline{1, \ 2, \ 1, \ 18}$
96	9, $\overline{1, \ 3, \ 1, \ 18}$
97	9, $\overline{1, \ 5, \ 1, \ 1, \ 1, \ 1, \ 1, \ 1, \ 5, \ 1, \ 18}$
98	9, $\overline{1, \ 8, \ 1, \ 18}$
99	9, $\overline{1, \ 18}$

SUGGESTIONS AND ANSWERS
FOR SELECTED EXERCISES

Chapter 1

1.2. Exercise 3. Let $N(m)$ be the minimum number of moves needed to shift the first m disks to one of the other posts. Show that

$$N(m + 1) = 2N(m) + 1.$$

Use this result to prove that $N(m) = 2^m - 1$.

Problem 1. If T is the set of all numbers of form $n - s$, then T must have a smallest element, t. Show that $n - t$ is the largest element of the original set.

1.3. Exercise 2(*a*). $q = -4$, $r = 3$.

Exercise 4(*a*). If $a = 2m$ and $b = 2n$, then $a + b = 2(m + n)$. Since $m + n$ is an integer, then $a + b$ is even.

Exercise 6. If $a = 4n + 1$, then $a = 16n^2 + 8n + 1 = 8(2n^2 + n) + 1$. The proof is similar if $a = 4n + 3$.

1.4. Exercise 1. 3. Exercise 3. If $d = (n, n + 1)$, then d divides 1, the difference of the two numbers. Because the only positive divisor of 1 is 1, then $d = 1$.

Problem 3. Write $1 = ma + nb$ and $1 = xa + yc$. Multiplying, we obtain $1 = (mxa + nyc + nxb)a + (ny)bc$. Because 1 is a sum of multiples of a and bc and is also the smallest positive integer, then $1 = (a, bc)$.

1.5. Exercise 1. 300. Exercise 2. Apply the theorem using the fact that $(a, b) = 1$.

Exercise 5. At least one of the factors in the product must be even and one must be divisible by 3. Since $(2, 3) = 1$, then $2 \cdot 3$ must divide the product.

Problem 3. Let $D_{n-1} = [a_1, \cdots, a_{n-1}]$, $D_n = [a_1, \cdots, a_n]$ and $D = [D_{n-1}, a_n]$. Since $D_{n-1} | D_n$ and $a_n | D_n$, then $D | D_n$. Therefore, $D \le D_n$. Since D is a common multiple of $a_1, a_2, \cdots, a_n$ and $D_n = [a_1, \cdots, a_n]$, then $D_n \le D$. Therefore, $D = D_n$.

1.6. Exercise 2(a). $(2030, 714, 2205) = ((2030, 714), 2205) = (14, 2205) = 7$.
$7 = 1 \cdot 2205 - 157 \cdot 14 = 1 \cdot 2205 - 157 \cdot (19 \cdot 2030 - 54 \cdot 714)$
$= 1 \cdot 2205 - 2983 \cdot 2030 + 8478 \cdot 714$.

1.8. Exercise 3. Write $\alpha = [\alpha] + \theta$, $0 \leq \theta < 1$. Divide $[\alpha]$ by m, obtaining $[\alpha] = qm + r$, $0 \leq r \leq m - 1$. Then

$$\left[\frac{\alpha}{m}\right] = \left[\frac{qm + r + \theta}{m}\right] = \left[q + \frac{r + \theta}{m}\right]$$

Since q is an integer and $0 \leq (r + \theta)/m < 1$, then

$$\left[\frac{\alpha}{m}\right] = q = \left[\frac{[\alpha]}{m}\right]$$

Chapter 2

2.2. Exercise 2(a). $x = 6 + 29k$, $y = 19k$.

Exercise 3(a). $x = 6 + 29k$, $y = 19k$ for all $k > 0$.

2.3. Exercise 1. $w = 27 - 10t - 2x + 6y$, $x = x$, $y = y$, $z = 3t - 2y$.

Exercise 3. 82 Type A and 13 Type B or 41 Type A and 42 Type B.

Chapter 3

3.1. Problem 1. If $m = 0$, the concept reduces to that of equality.

Exercise 3. (a) Not symmetric; (c) yes.

3.2. Exercise 4. If $a^2 \equiv 1 \pmod{p}$, then $p|(a - 1)(a + 1)$. Since p is a prime number, then $p|(a - 1)$ or $p|(a + 1)$.

Problem 3. $(g - 1)^n \equiv (-1)^n \pmod{g}$ and $(g + 1)^n \equiv 1 \pmod{g}$.

3.3. Exercise 1. (a) $x \equiv 47 \pmod{52}$; (b) $x \equiv 5, 35, 65, 95 \pmod{120}$.

3.4. Exercise 1 (b). $\mathscr{R}_{72} = \mathscr{R}_{-47}$, $\mathscr{R}_{-80} = \mathscr{R}_5$.

Exercise 2 (b). x is in $\mathscr{R}_5 \cup \mathscr{R}_{35} \cup \mathscr{R}_{65} \cup \mathscr{R}_{95} \pmod{120}$.

3.5. Exercise 1 (a). $\mathscr{R}_{2272} \pmod{3885}$.

Exercise 3. $119 + 420k$, where k is a nonnegative integer.

Exercise 4. $17 + 12k$, where k is a nonnegative integer.

Problem 2. Show that the given number is a solution and apply Corollary 6.1.

3.6. Exercise 2 (*b*). No solution; (*c*) $x \equiv \pm 9 \pmod{23}$.

Exercise 3. Let $f(x) = 2x^3 - 25x^2 + 9x + 1$. The solutions of $f(x) \equiv 0$ (mod 5) are $x \equiv 2, 4 \pmod 5$. The only solution of $f(x) \equiv 0 \pmod{11}$ is $x \equiv 3 \pmod{11}$. The solutions of $f(x) \equiv 0 \pmod{13}$ are $x \equiv 1, 2, 3 \pmod{13}$. Thus, there are six solutions of $f(x) \equiv 0 \pmod{5 \cdot 11 \cdot 13}$: $x \equiv 14, 157, 289, 432, 509, 652 \pmod{715}$.

Problem 4. Suppose that $f(k) = p$ (a prime). If $K \equiv k \pmod p$, then $f(K) \equiv 0 \pmod p$. If n is the degree of $f(x)$, there are at most n such values of K for which $f(K) = p$. For any other value of $K \equiv k \pmod p$, $f(K)$ must be composite if it is positive.

Chapter 4

4.1. Problem 2. If $a_i n + b_j m \equiv a_u n + b_v m \pmod{mn}$, then $a_i n \equiv a_u n \pmod m$, implying that $a_i \equiv a_u \pmod m$, since $(m, n) = 1$. Therefore, $i = u$. Similarly, $j = v$. Thus, the mn elements in the set are incongruent (mod mn). By Theorem 1, this implies that the set is a complete system of residues (mod mn).

4.2. Problem 1. It follows from Problem 2, Section 4.1, that the elements are incongruent (mod mn). Since $(a_i n + b_j m, m) = (a_i n, m)$ and $(a_i, m) = (n, m) = 1$, then $(a_i n + b_j m, m) = 1$. Similarly, $(a_i n + b_j m, n) = 1$. Therefore, $a_i n + b_j m$ is relatively prime to mn. Let N be relatively prime to mn. Since m and n are relatively prime, there exist integers a and b such that $N = an + bm$. Since the greatest common divisor of a and m divides N, then $(a, m) = 1$. Therefore, a is congruent (mod m) to one of the elements in the reduced system of residues (mod m), say $a = a_i + k_i m$. Similarly, $b = b_j + k_j n$. Substituting, we obtain

$$N \equiv (a_i + k_i m)n + (b_j + k_j n)m \equiv a_i n + b_j m \pmod{mn}.$$

Since each element relatively prime to mn is congruent (mod mn) to one of the elements in the set, it follows that the set is a reduced system of residues (mod mn).

4.3. Exercise 1. $\varphi(873) = \varphi(3^2)\,\varphi(97) = 6 \cdot 96 = 576$.

Exercise 2. Show that $\varphi(p^n)$ is even if p is an odd prime and $\varphi(2^n)$ is even if $n \geq 2$. Use the multiplicative property of φ.

Exercise 4. No solution.

4.4 Exercise 1. 4.

Problem 1. Use the fact that $k! | p(p-1) \cdots (p - k + 1)$ and $(k!, p) = 1$.

4.5. Exercise 2. (*a*) No; (*b*) No.

4.7. Exercise 3. 6.

Problem 1. Let *a* belong to the exponent *m* (mod p^2). Then $a^m \equiv 1$ (mod *p*) and so $k|m$, say $m = kn$. Since $(a^k - 1)^p \equiv a^{kp} - 1 \equiv 0$ (mod *p*), then $kn|kp$ and so $n|p$. Since *p* is a prime, this means that $n = 1$ or $n = p$, that is, $m = k$ or $m = kp$.

4.8. Exercise 1. $m = 7$: 3 and 5. Exercise 2. None.

App. Exercise 1(*b*).   2, 3, 8, 11, 12, 18, 25, 27, 31, 32, 44, 48, 49, 53, 65, 66, 70, 72, 79, 85, 86, 89, 94, 95.

Problem 2. Let $d = (b, p - 1)$. The congruence has a solution if, and only if, $d|(\text{ind } c - \text{ind } a)$. If this is the case, there are exactly *d* incongruent solutions (mod *p*).

Chapter 5

5.1. Exercise 1(*c*). $56.0631634450603503221 6_7$.

Problem 1. Compare the series to the geometic series

$$n + \frac{9}{10} + \frac{9}{10^2} + \frac{9}{10^3} + \cdots$$

5.4. Exercise 1(*a*). 528.

5.5. Exercise 1(*b*). 1392, third position.

Chapter 6

6.2. Exercise 1(*a*). 140, 6.

6.3. Exercise 3. a_2 and b_2, a_4 and b_4.

Chapter 7

7.2. Exercise 2(*b*). 1, 6, 6, 21, 6, 36, 6, 56, 21, 36.

Exercise 3. 6. 21.

Problem 1. Use mathematical induction to prove that $(\varphi \circ \tau)(p^n) = \sigma(p^n)$. Use the multiplicative property of $\varphi \circ \tau$.

7.3. Exercise 1. 1, -2, -3, 0, -5, 6, -7, 0, 0, 10.

Exercise 4. Consider $(\alpha \circ \beta)(1)$.

Problem 3(d). Let $\alpha(n) = n$ and define β by $\alpha * \beta = \tau$. If p and q are distinct primes, then $\beta(pq) \neq \beta(p) \cdot \beta(q)$.

Problem 4. Prove the formula for the power of a prime and use (b) of Problem 3.

Chapter 8

App. B. Exercise 1(a). $1535 \cdot 1987$.
Exercise 2. If $x - y \geq c$, then $x + y \leq N/c$. Subtracting, we obtain $y \leq (N - p^2)/2p$. Therefore,

$$x^2 = N + y^2 \leq N + \left(\frac{N - p^2}{2p}\right)^2 = \left(\frac{N + p^2}{2p}\right)^2$$

App. C. Exercise 1(a). $23 \cdot 59$.

Chapter 9

9.1. Exercise 1. Quadratic residues: 1, 2, 4, 8, 9, 13, 15, 16.

Problem 1. If $x^2 \equiv a$ and $y^2 \equiv b \pmod{m}$, then $(xy)^2 \equiv ab \pmod{m}$.

Problem 4. Use Problem 3 and Theorem 7 of Chapter 3.

9.2. Problem 2. Let a_k be the associate of b_k. Since 1 and $p - 1$ are their own associates and this is not the case for the numbers between 1 and $p - 1$, then

$$(p - 1)! \equiv 1 \cdot a_1 b_1 \cdot a_2 b_2 \cdots a_{(p - 1)/2} b_{(p - 1)/2} \cdot (p - 1) \equiv (p - 1)$$
$$\equiv -1 \pmod{p}$$

9.3. Problem 2. Obviously, the numbers $q, 2q, \cdots, (q - 1)q$ are quadratic non-residues. If one or more of these numbers is greater than p, there is a smallest such number, say kq. Since p is a prime, then

$$(k - 1)q < p < kq$$

and so $kq < p + q$. Thus, kq is congruent $\pmod{p}$ to a quadratic residue and is itself a quadratic residue—a contradiction. Therefore, each of the numbers is less than p. Since $(q - 1)q < p$, then

$$q < \frac{1 + \sqrt{1 + 4p}}{2} < \sqrt{p} + 1$$

Problem 5. Suppose that m, $m + 1$, $\cdots$, $m + k - 1$ all have the same quadratic character. It is easy to see that $m > 1$. We may thus assume that $m - 1$ has a different quadratic character than does m. Since the numbers km, $k(m + 1)$, $\cdots$, $k(m + k - 1)$ have different quadratic character than m, these numbers are incongruent (mod p) to the numbers m, $m + 1$, $\cdots$, $m + k - 1$. Thus, there exists a nonnegative integer n such that $km > np + m + k - 1$ and $k(m + k - 1) < (n + 1)p + m$. Solving the two inequalities for np, we obtain

$$km + k^2 - k - p - m < np < km - m - k + 1$$

so that $k^2 < p$.

9.5. Exercise 1(a). $+1$.

Exercise 3. $p \equiv \pm 1 \pmod{24}$.

Problem 1. $q = 5$, $p \equiv \pm 1 \pmod 5$.

9.7. Exercise 1(c). $x \equiv 1$ and $x \equiv 36 \pmod{79}$ are solutions.

Problem 2. If $x_0^2 = a + mp$ then $(x_0 + kp)^2 \equiv a + mp + 2x_0kp + k^2p^2 \equiv a + (m + 2x_0k)p \pmod{p^2}$. If k_0 is a solution of $2x_0k \equiv -m \pmod p$, then $(x_0 + k_0p)^2 \equiv a \pmod{p^2}$. Extend this result by induction.

Chapter 10

10.2. Exercise 2. (a) Yes; (b) No.

Exercise 3. Write d as a product of primes and use the unique factorization theorem.

10.3. Exercise 2, Case II. If all of the numbers are even or all are odd, then $x_0^2 + y_0^2 + z_0^2 + u_0^2 \equiv 0 \pmod 4$. If one is even and three are odd or one is odd and three are even, then $x_0^2 + y_0^2 + z_0^2 + u_0^2 \equiv \pm 1 \pmod 4$. Thus, two are even and two are odd. A similar argument holds for Case III.

Problem 1. If x, y, z are all odd, then $x^2 + y^2 + z^2 \equiv 3 \pmod 8$. If two of the numbers are odd and one is even, the sum of the squares is congruent to 2 (mod 4). Similar contradictions occur in the other cases.

Chapter 11

11.1. Problem 2(b). $x_{t+1} = x_t + 2$, $y_{t+1} = 2x_t + y_t + 2$, $z_{t+1} = y_{t+1} + 1$.

Problem 3. Use Problem 2(a) to show the existence. If x is a prime and $x = s^2 - t^2$, then $s - t = 1$ and $s + t = x$. Therefore, $s = (x + 1)/2$ and $t = (x - 1)/2$.

Problem 4. $x = |2s^2 - t^2|$, $y = 2st$, $z = 2s^2 + t^2$, where t is odd and is relatively prime to s.

11.2. Problem 1. $x = \left(\dfrac{m^2 - 1}{m^2 + 1}\right)a$, $y = \left(\dfrac{2m}{m^2 + 1}\right)a$.

11.4. Problem 1(c). Use one of the half-angle formulas from trigonometry.
$a = |s^4 + t^4 - 6s^2t^2|$, $b = 4st|s^2 - t^2|$, $c = (s^2 + t^2)^2$ where s and t are relatively prime positive integers, one even and one odd.

Chapter 12

12.3. Exercise 2. $\langle 1, 2, 2, 3, 1, 5 \rangle$.

Exercise 4(a). 31, 22.

Problem 1(a). Suppose that

$$a/b = \langle a_1, a_2, \cdots, a_n = 1 \rangle = \langle c_1, c_2, \cdots, c_m = 1 \rangle$$

where $m \le n$. Since a_1 and c_1 are integers and

$$0 < \frac{1}{a_2 + \ddots} < 1 \quad \text{and} \quad 0 < \frac{1}{c_2 + \ddots} < 1$$

then $a_1 = c_1$ and $\langle a_2, \cdots, a_n \rangle = \langle c_2, \cdots, c_m \rangle$. If we assume that $a_i = c_i$ $(i = 1, 2, \cdots, k)$ $(k < m - 1)$, it follows as above that $a_i = c_i$ $(i = 1, 2, \cdots, m - 1)$ and

$$\frac{1}{c_m} = \frac{1}{a_m + \ddots}.$$

Thus, it is impossible to have $a_m > 1$ or $n > m$.

12.5. Exercise 1(a). $(5 + \sqrt{85})/10$.

Exercise 2. $\sqrt{15} = \langle 3, \overline{1, 6} \rangle$.

Problem 1. Since $a_1 = C_1 < \alpha < C_2 = a_1 + 1/a_2 \le a_1 + 1$, then $[\alpha] = a_1$. Use the limit theorems of elementary calculus to prove that

$$\lim_{n \to \infty} \left(a_1 + \frac{1}{\langle a_1, \cdots, a_n \rangle} \right) = a_1 + \frac{1}{\langle a_2, \cdots \rangle}$$

12.8. Exercise 3(b). $\langle 6, \overline{1, 5, 1, 12} \rangle$.

Problem 1. Since

$$m + \sqrt{D} = 2m + (\sqrt{D} - m) = 2m + \frac{1}{\dfrac{\sqrt{D} + m}{D - m^2}} = 2m + \frac{1}{m + \sqrt{D}}$$

then $m + \sqrt{D} = \langle \overline{2m} \rangle$. Therefore,

$$\sqrt{D} = m + (\sqrt{D} - m) = m + \frac{1}{\sqrt{D} + m} = m + \frac{1}{\langle \overline{2m} \rangle} = \langle m, \overline{2m} \rangle$$

12.9. Exercise 1. $x = 2{,}143{,}295$, $y = 221{,}064$. No.

Exercise 2. -5, 1, 2, 3, 4, 6, 8, 9.

12.10. Exercise 1 (*a*). No solution. (*b*) $k = 8$, $x_0 = 307$, $y_0 = 64$; $k = -8$, $x_0 = 77$, $y_0 = 16$.

12.11. Exercise 1. $z_0 = -1$, $x = 2 - 15k - 266k^2$; $y = -1 + k + 114k^2$;

$z_0 = -7$, $x = -7 - 99k - 266k^2$, $y = 2 + 37k + 114k^2$;

$z_0 = 12$, $x = -24 + 167k - 266k^2$, $y = 12 - 77k + 114k^2$;

$z_0 = 18$, $x = -57 + 251k - 266k^2$, $y = 27 - 113k + 114k^2$.

INDEX OF SYMBOLS

SUBJECT INDEX

≡